Praise for *138 Dates*

'I could not put this book down. I laughed, I cried, and I was aghast at Rebekah's experiences. You will enjoy the ride, and whether you have experienced the same, you will learn what determination, persistence and a plan can do in every area of your life.'
Naomi Simson, Shark Tank, founder RedBalloon, author of *Ready to Soar*

'Rebekah paints a vulnerable and entertaining picture of loss, dating, and the struggles of being a woman building a business in a male dominated world. She cuts to the core of juggling single life, a loud biological clock, and overcoming her belief that she needs to change in order to find happiness. I laughed, learned a lot, and cried my eyes out!'
Jaquie Brown, television personality and screenwriter

'This is one of the most vivid and honest accounts of love I've read. This book will change lives — I only wish I'd read it when I was 35. I couldn't put it down for three days and it felt like saying goodbye to a great friend when I finished.'
Fleur Brown, Launch Management Group and Founding Team TEDxSydney

'I loved this book! A relatable and funny look at the realities of the online dating game as well as the not always linear journey of entrepreneurship. A fascinating read in more ways than one!'
Matilda Green, author of *The Feel Good Guide*

'Raw, relatable and real, fearless and funny. I loved *138 Dates*, a story with brains, boundless ambition and a very big heart.'
Councillor Jess Scully, Deputy Lord Mayor of Sydney

138
DATES

138 DATES

THE TRUE STORY OF ONE WOMAN'S SEARCH FOR EVERYTHING

Rebekah Campbell

ALLEN&UNWIN
SYDNEY · MELBOURNE · AUCKLAND · LONDON

For Jen
(keep going)

This book contains real people, others who have had their name and identifying features changed to protect their anonymity, and some who are composites, where the author has combined interactions with several people into a single character. The author has occasionally altered the timing of events in order to simplify the story. This book should not be considered an accurate portrayal of any single person, other than the author.

First published in 2021

Allen & Unwin
Level 2, 10 College Hill
Auckland 1011, New Zealand
Phone: (64 9) 377 3800
Email: info@allenandunwin.com
Web: www.allenandunwin.co.nz

83 Alexander Street
Crows Nest NSW 2065, Australia
Phone: (61 2) 8425 0100

A catalogue record for this book is available
from the National Library of New Zealand

ISBN 978 1 98854 784 8

Cover design by: Julia Murray
Internal design by: Megan van Staden
Set in 12/18 pt Baskerville
Printed and bound in Australia by McPhersons Printing Group

10 9 8 7 6 5 4 3 2 1

The paper in this book is FSC® certified.
FSC® promotes environmentally responsible, socially beneficial and economically viable management of the world's forests.

CONTENTS

PROLOGUE

November 2012

'I will have sex with Matthew Marino,' I decide out loud as I pace across the grass at Rushcutters Bay Park. I fold my arms across my chest. There's a chill in the early morning air and thick grey clouds gather ominously overhead.

I pace, faster, muttering like I'm making affirmations. 'It's been six weeks. He's expecting . . . I can do it. I can.' My voice shakes and I hunch my shoulders forward. Heavy droplets of water fall from the sky, wetting my loosely tied-back hair. I look up and scrunch my eyes together.

Twenty minutes ago, walking down the hill, I'd called my ex-flatmate Ainsley for advice. 'Honey, six weeks is *not* normal,' she'd said. 'Six weeks is a long time. Unless you're fresh from a convent.' I'd googled 'How long before having sex' and had found a helpful men's forum on Reddit. Six weeks is all that any man will wait.

And Matthew Marino is not *any* man. He is a forty-two-year-old senator in the New South Wales parliament. We met on that dating site RSVP — can you believe it? He is tall and distinguished and confident. He ticks every box on my ideal partner list, except, well . . .

I am a thirty-five-year-old professional woman in Sydney.

I live in a Darlinghurst apartment with high ceilings and an art-deco chandelier. On the outside, I wear makeup and high-heeled shoes, I have a small public profile as founder of the shopping app Posse.com, and I often give inspirational talks at business conferences where I encourage other women to strive for their goals.

But on the inside, I am a thousand petals shrivelling inwards. Because when I take off my makeup and high-heeled shoes and I gaze at the four walls of my nice apartment, I am alone. I shop alone, cook alone, watch TV alone and fall asleep clinging to a pillow.

Until eleven months ago, I hadn't been on a date in ten years. Then last Christmas Day something happened. An invisible dam that had been building inside me seemed to burst open all at once. I would change. I would find love, whatever it took. And I made a resolution: one date every week for an entire year.

Matthew is the forty-third man I've met so far and the only one I've been out with more than four times. Tomorrow will be our six-week anniversary, after which we will officially be boyfriend and girlfriend. We'll make holiday plans, wedding plans, we'll discuss the children's names that I've already decided on, and my pillow-clinging days will be over. But first, we *must* have sex. Because if we don't, he will think I'm frigid or not into him (I learnt this from Reddit).

I sit next to the base of a giant fig tree. Bright green leaves tremor like fingers on hands above me. *I wish I could tell him how long it's been. That I'm terrified and I won't be any good.* I stare across the grass at a dog chasing a stick and two women pushing prams as they chat and sip from takeaway coffee cups.

I stretch my arms high, clasping my fingers together. 'I can,' I whisper. 'It's natural.' I feel my stomach twist and a wash of stomach acid floods my mouth. 'I will.'

I know what you're thinking. Why didn't she date for ten years? How did a successful, intelligent woman get herself into such a pathetic ball of stuck?

If you'd asked me this back in 2012, I would have given you a list of excuses. 'I'm too busy with my career. There's no decent single men in Sydney. I still love my perfect first boyfriend and no one else will ever measure up.' I never would have admitted that, actually, I was just scared. Embarrassed to put myself on the internet. Afraid of being rejected.

I'm writing to you from July 2020. For eight years I've published blog posts and newspaper columns about startup businesses and women in tech. And every time I started penning an article about venture capital or how to nail a sales presentation, I felt my fingers quiver at the keyboard. Because I had another story to tell. Because, to me, career success seemed an inch tall compared with what really mattered.

I tell this story expecting that I'll be criticised. People might say that a woman who claims to be a feminist shouldn't admit her top priority is to find a man. I would disagree. I think women should voice what they want in life without fear of judgement. I wanted to build a business, yes. But when I lay in bed in the still of night, love is what I ached for. I wanted a partner. I wanted a family.

I am writing this book for me, age thirty-five. I would have handed it to myself, past the pile of dating advice books like *Act*

Like a Lady, Think Like a Man and *Why Men Prefer Bitches*, past the newspaper article where the male fertility doctor says 'Women over thirty-five should stop being so fussy' and past re-runs of *The Bachelorette* on Hulu. I would have handed this book to myself and said, 'Listen, this is what it's actually like. This is what it'll take to unravel yourself and let go of everything that's standing in the way.'

This isn't a tale of salacious sexual encounters or jabs at weird men from internet dating sites (although there are a few). I have written this book to be useful, to provide insights and to tell a story. And, just in case there's anyone out there who felt like I did, to show that you are not alone. You are not the only one.

As I picture that woman pacing about on the grass, deciding to have sex when she clearly isn't ready, I want to wrap her in a blanket and kiss her forehead. And I want to scream in her ear. She's about to make an awful mistake, one of a huge pile of awful mistakes on her journey of 138 dates.

I wish I could tell her she'll be okay: that Matthew will be forgiving, that the rest of this adventure will be easy and fun, and that every other man she's about to meet will be kind and genuine and safe. I wish I didn't know that she's going to get humiliated and hurt like someone squeezed her heart dry and tossed it onto a dirty railway track ready to be torn up again and again and again.

But I'd still tell her to go for it, because she has no idea what's out there at the end. Because what she'll find is so much more than she imagined. I'd tell her to go for it with two feet and a giant leap. Because what she'll find is . . .

1. CHRISTMAS DAY

Christmas is always the worst time of year to be single. You can fill the year with yoga and travel and networking events, but Christmas is the one day where you can't ignore what's missing. For me, the Christmas of 2011 was the worst of all. There wasn't a single event that ruined it: no death, no disaster. Just the beginning of a grim realisation that my life story had drifted way off-script.

I roll and a steel bar jabs my shoulder. The fold-out children's bed I'm lying on buckles under the weight of my adult body. Early glints of New Zealand sun peep through a gap between the wall and the garage door. I reach for my iPhone, face-down on the cold concrete floor. It's 5.27 a.m.

The garage I've been sleeping in belongs to Jane and Pete, who lived across the road from us when I was in primary school. Back then, this floor was jammed with mattresses and coloured sleeping bags. All those children have grown up now, scattered. I'm still here on the same fold-out bed. I cast my eyes about the stillness; my suitcase hangs open on an old wooden chair in the corner, my pale-blue Bianca Spender suit jacket drapes from a wire strung between two hooks.

I pull on a T-shirt and shorts and creep down the corridor, past Pete's rattling snore and the guest bedroom where Mum and Dad must still be asleep. Outside, the air is sweet like daisy syrup and tūī and bellbirds chirp to the early morning sun.

Jane and Pete live on Mill View Road, a narrow street winding around the side of a stark brown hill overlooking the oil refinery in Whangārei. Simple square houses line the ridge like boxes placed spaced evenly apart. In the distance, a tall pipe on the refinery pumps steam and the lights of Whangārei glow under a crisp silver sky.

I cross at the corner and I'm standing opposite our old house. It's small and white like it always was, with a slab of concrete out front. I swivel my hips, looking back across the road, and I'm eight years old again, rollerskating in circles. I remember standing here watching Jane and Pete's family: the four kids squealing on the trampoline, their black cocker spaniel barking at the sprinkler. Jane, with her cakes and juice in the garden. It all seemed so alive over there on the other side of the road. They were so happy, so carefree, so *normal*. I'd stood straight-legged, all awkward and quiet with bright red hair and scrawny knees.

I turn to pace further up Mill View Road. It's not yet 6 a.m. and thick mist rises from the asphalt. A green Ford Laser packed with teenagers tears around the corner and slows as it approaches. The stereo bass rattles, and one side of the steel back bumper scrapes along the road. A boy with long black hair rolls down his window. 'Merry Christmas,' he shouts, gesturing cheers with a stubbie of Steinlager. I smile and wave a thumbs-up.

I usually dread the approach of Christmas. I know I'll be a tagalong, the third wheel in a get-together of my parents' friends. But there's something about Christmas morning that always feels different. I notice a spring in my step as I continue up the street.

The lights in the houses begin to flick on. I stop to watch one house through their half-open curtains. It's square and wooden, painted light yellow. A patch of overgrown garden climbs the steps and a rusted tricycle lies overturned in the driveway.

A woman with shoulder-length hair appears in the front room. There's a young boy running and another one, probably three years old. The Christmas tree lights up. Two sharp squeals of delight and a thump as the older boy leaps towards a stack of presents. The woman bends, she's cuddling the smaller boy, whispering something into his ear, pointing to the tree. A heavy-set man steps into the room carrying two mugs of steaming drink.

I feel the corners of my mouth curve into a smile. This is what I love about Christmas. The joy it brings other people, like this family. I love Christmas for them, and I love it because one day it'll be me.

Ever since I can remember, I've wanted to be a mother. As a kid, I'd look at my dolls and my books and our neighbours and I formed a fuzzy vision of the future. I'd be tall and thin (like Barbie), find a tall husband with dark hair (like Ken), marry in a white dress (like Cinderella) and have lots of children, a trampoline, a sprinkler and a dog (like Pete and Jane across the road).

But now, at thirty-four, my urge is deeper. I want a home full of love and belonging. I want to nurture. I want to create new little people and care for them and help them to learn and grow. I want to show them all of the wonder in our world. I am a mother. Every cell in my being is sure.

The woman steps up to the window and I shuffle back out of view. I can see her skin more clearly now as she presses her forehead against the glass. Her cheeks are firm, eyes bright. *She must be twenty-something.* I crunch my eyes together and I start to calculate. If I meet a partner by next Christmas, it'll probably take six months of dating to move in, another year or two before he'd agree to start trying for kids. By then, I'll be approaching thirty-eight.

I crouch on the curb hugging my knees in tight and I count back the years since I last kissed a man. *Shit.* Wasn't it just yesterday that I was thirty-three, with so much time?

'Champers, anyone?' Mum pops open a bottle of sparkling. We're seated around a wide wooden table with salmon in the middle and broccoli and a potato casserole on the side. Pete is still in his yellow work singlet, just home from delivering a truck of strawberries to the supermarket; Jane is bleary-eyed from her overnight cleaning job at the hospital. Mum wears bright red lipstick and a black lace top, which, if she'd asked my opinion, I would've said is way too see-through for a woman of her age. Dad's look is classic physics teacher — goofy smile at the front, shiny bald patch at the back and wire glasses resting crooked across his nose. I'm in my Bianca Spender suit, of course.

Our family has always been what I will generously describe as different. We emigrated from Scotland when I was three years old. There were three of us — Mum, Dad and me. 'My chosen only,' my mother would tell people when they asked if I had siblings, stressing the word *chosen* to make it clear that I was special. I'd cringe every time.

My early memories of Mum are of her bright clothes and loud voice. She didn't bake or sew or do shifts at the school canteen. She worked in an office where she clip-clopped down a vinyl corridor in high-heeled shoes.

Dad and I were always close. He'd take me swimming after school, take me running through streams and read me Roald Dahl at night. But he was also odd. He didn't drink beer or play sports or man the barbecue at parties. He'd spend Saturday afternoons alone in a tiny room with a screwdriver, some wires and a box of broken computers.

'So, Becky.' Pete leans across the dining table, his big Kiwi face glowing with affection. 'If there's someone else you'd like to bring for Christmas, he's always welcome. Or sh—'

'There isn't,' I cut in. 'I've just been so busy building the business. I haven't had time.'

'Rebekah's a career woman,' Mum chimes in. 'She's prioritising.'

'It's not that,' I say. 'This has been a big year for me. I started a tech company, a mobile phone app. Next year I'm going to get some investors.' I pause, waiting for follow-up questions. *Oh wow, impressive. What does the app do? How will you raise money?*

'Who was that young bloke,' continues Pete, 'with the long hair? Years ago.' Mum spins, her worried eyes meeting mine. Pete leans forward with his arms on the table. 'We love you, Becky, and family is — you know . . .'

I wake on my garage bed just after 11 p.m. I'd taken a nap after lunch, hoping the hours would pass. There's a shriek from the kitchen, followed by cackles and the low rumble of voices who've had too many glasses of sparkling.

I peel off my suit and my shirt and I'm standing naked in front of a propped-up mirror. I turn to examine my back: my skin is dry and flaky, there's cellulite on my thighs and a varicose vein behind one knee. I grab at a butt cheek with one hand. *Is anyone going to want this?*

I pull on pyjamas and climb back into bed. The steel beam still presses against my shoulder and I curl into myself. I remember the day. Eight years old in rollerskates, watching other people have fun; thirty-four watching a family Christmas through half-open curtains. *When is it my turn?* I picture myself age eighty, rocking in a chair in the lounge of some old people's home, all alone. Watching happy couples and grown-up kids coming to visit.

I squirm awkwardly in the tiny bed. It's as if a giant knife is carving a line down my chest. I'm going to explode. Tears pour the wrong way across my face, sideways to my ears and into my hair. I must change. I will unstick myself. Whatever it takes.

2. STEVE

1995

'What happened to Oasis?' I moaned as 'Champagne Supernova' cut off mid-chorus. Mum and Dad were out late, and I'd invited some school friends over to hang out in our basement. Kristy, my best friend Liz and a couple of others. We'd listen to music, skim the top from some bottles of my parents' spirits, swallow, dance, vomit, that kind of thing. Just a regular Friday night.

Two peculiar-looking boys huddled over a CD next to the stereo. One had long wavy blond hair and a brown-patterned shirt open over an enormous belt buckle, the other wore tight flared jeans and a chain round his neck.

'Hi,' said the long-haired boy, spinning with an eager grin. 'I'm Steve.' He gestured to his friend. 'We're here with Kristy.'

Kristy bounded through the room with a cigarette between her fingers.

'Hey, smoke that outside,' I ordered. 'My parents will have a fit.'

'You met my friends,' she said, stepping into the garden.

Steve was still smiling, his eyes following my steps. 'Come and listen to this,' he said, and beckoned for me to sit down. 'It's Robert Plant from Led Zeppelin. His other band.' It turned out that Steve met Kristy at a party last weekend after she'd had a fight with her mum. 'She had nowhere to go.' He shrugged. 'She seemed like a nice kid, just a bit lost.'

'And so do you have a flat or something?' I asked.

He laughed. 'I live around the corner, with Mum and Dad.'

'Seriously? In Tawa?'

On the outskirts of Wellington, Tawa must be one of the most boring suburbs on earth, up on a hill with eerily quiet tree-lined streets. *No one interesting lives in Tawa.*

We arranged to meet the following Tuesday after school. I waited on a row of benches overlooking Lyndhurst Park. Steve sauntered down the hill like a seventies movie star: blond hair, stripy shirt, tight black pants, pointed leather boots and eyes so bright they could've started a fire. 'Hiya,' he called, reaching to hug.

We sat and talked as new friends do. I learned that he was two years older than me, studying English and women's studies at Victoria University in town.

'What are you reading?' he asked, pulling the thick paperback from my schoolbag and examining the tattered cover of *Pride and Prejudice*.

'We're studying it in class,' I said. 'To be honest, I'm struggling. The language is so old.'

'What? This is a classic.' He stood, opening the first page. '"It is a truth universally acknowledged, that a single man in possession of a good fortune, must be in want of a wife."'

He flashed the grin I'd noticed on Friday. 'Who says it's a universal truth? She's being satirical, of course, the author. The whole book is like that — genius.'

'Satirical? I know I should know what that means. But tell me.'

'Satirical, like satire.' He paused to construct an explanation. 'It means to criticise but in a way that's funny.'

I nodded, repeating the word to code it into my brain. *'Satirical.'*

Steve opened his bag and held up a leather notebook he'd bound with string. 'This is what I'm reading.'

'For uni?'

'It's poetry. All my favourites. Some of my own stuff too.'

'Can I read?' I reached out for the book. 'Your poems, the ones you wrote.'

He tipped his head to one side. 'Sure.'

I flicked through the pages: perfectly formed sonnets with language so stunning it felt like leaping into cold water. 'You wrote these?'

He nodded.

'Are they published anywhere? I mean, I'm not an expert or anything, but I'd buy this. You should publish.'

'Nah.' He smiled. 'Maybe one day. We'll see.'

We sat on that bench for hours and our conversation was like nothing I'd experienced in my seventeen years on the planet. I felt empty plots of land in my brain spring to life for the first time, each cell blossoming to the music of Steve's passion for words, for meaning, for romanticism. 'I don't mean romantic like boy meets girl,' he said. 'I mean romantic as a way of looking at things: it's like noticing beauty in nature, in people, in everything really.'

The first time we kissed was a few years later under a boat club in the city. We'd driven in with my friend Fiona and had spotted a cluster of smokers outside the building. There was loud music, coloured lights and what looked like an open bar.

'Let's sneak in by carrying this table,' I'd said. The three of us picked up a coffee table and snuck through the door. Inside, we dropped it in a corner and merged with the crowd. We clinked beer bottles with strangers and whooped and cheered while a group danced to Gaelic folk music.

When it was time for speeches Steve raised his hand. 'I'd just like to thank the Victoria University Scottish Football Club for hosting such a wonderful night. It's great to see so many familiar faces.' Quizzical eyes stared. Steve was half the age of the other men and the only one not wearing a kilt. I knew if I made eye contact with my tight-panted, long-haired friend that I'd explode. We just made it outside before our laughter erupted. We climbed under the steps of the boat house and laughed and laughed until I couldn't breathe. Steve pulled me towards him, and we kissed. I was shocked at first and pulled away. *He's my best friend.*

Fiona dropped us both off at my house and Steve insisted that he stay over. 'If we sleep in different houses then we'll have to meet tomorrow and it might be awkward,' he said. 'If I stay, then I'll just be here the whole time.' I gave him a blanket and he curled up on the carpet like a pet. In the morning there wasn't an inkling of awkwardness and, in the afternoon, he left flowers that he'd picked from the side of the road in the letterbox.

It took weeks for our relationship to become physical.

'I really like your shirt,' he'd said one night at a party, admiring my fitted green cotton blouse.

I felt hot blood in my eighteen-year-old veins. 'I hope you're going to take it off.'

A nervous smile crept up the side of his mouth. 'Ye— ye— yes. If you'd like me to.'

'I would.' I nodded commandingly.

In the morning I held his face between my palms. 'Why do you have your hair so long? I could cut it.'

'No way,' he said, pulling his head back. 'You've seen my dad, my grandad. Every Pengelly man is bald. I'll go like that one day. Until then —' he tugged his hair into a side ponytail '— I'm making the most of it.'

From that day on, I spent almost every night in Steve's single bed. I could tell that Dad especially found this hard. He wasn't big on sharing his feelings, but it was clear that if he stacked up every experience of his life in a pile, the hours we spent together during my childhood would rank at the top. And all of a sudden, he'd been gazumped.

Steve's parents cautiously accepted our arrangement. His mum, Chris worked in a bank and each night she'd quietly set the table for four, expecting me to be there. Sometimes I'd come home to find a new camisole on the edge of Steve's bed, or a lipstick or skirt. There'd be a note: 'I saw this in town and thought you'd like it, love Chris.' His dad, Mike, was practical and straightforward. He was a mechanical engineer and spent the evenings refining new products he'd invented. 'Feet on the floor,' he'd call in the morning as we slept in late.

The sensation I remember of this time is one of falling. Steve's face was permanently imprinted in the front of my mind. I missed him every second we were apart, and when I saw him after classes it was like being drawn together chest-first.

It was a blissful two years before our first argument. We were camping under a tree next to Lake Taupō when Steve spotted a gaggle of siblings in head-to-toe orange Lycra suits.

'Our kids are going to need togs like that,' he said, pointing to the family.

'No way,' I groaned. 'My parents made me wear those stupid suits. My kids are going to be normal.'

We bickered back and forth about our hypothetical children for an hour. We lay back on the pebbles outside our tent, foreheads touching, and my entire future seemed to catch in his eyes. He smiled, draping his arm over my shoulder, gaze fixed. *I'm his girl. He'll love me forever.*

For the next seventeen years I'd dream myself back to that moment, and try to squash the question that entered my mind next. *Are we actually going to have children? Is my one boyfriend going to be my only boyfriend? Is Steve it?*

A few days later we spotted a marriage registry office in town and joked about getting hitched right then and there.

'Let's do it,' implored Steve.

The registrar of births, deaths and marriages was inside probably the oldest building in Taupō: tall and stone, with cream pillars marking the entrance.

Steve bounded up to the counter. 'One marriage please.'

'You're not serious, are you?' I started to worry that he actually was.

'Just joking,' he said, handing back the form.

The question that had entered my mind on the beach had started to grow. *Steve is lovely, but* . . . I started to notice all the ways that he wasn't perfect. Sometimes he drank too much red wine and it crusted around the outside of his lips. He wasn't into the same bands as me. 'Why do you only listen to seventies music? Can't we put on something, I don't know, modern?' And I'd always imagined myself marrying someone tall with dark hair. Or would it be Steve, with his long hair and pointed shoes?

And without consciously making any decision, I began to push him sideways. I didn't have the courage to initiate a proper breakup conversation. Looking back, I wonder if it was because I was confused. I knew Steve was special, but something stopped me from committing. I couldn't say 'You're it', not when there was a whole world to see. I started going to parties and not inviting him. He'd call and I'd pretend to be busy. And our love drifted like a neglected spirit, above the parks and buildings, into the clouds and so high I couldn't see it anymore.

Months later I spotted his red leather jacket walking down the main road of Tawa and I pulled over the car. 'I'm sorry,' I said, empty of an explanation.

His eyes were red as he turned to continue up the street. 'I'm just disappointed, that's all. I thought we were something. I thought you were different. I dunno, forget it.' He swatted his hand down like I'd just wasted his time.

3. SOMETHING BETTER

27 December 2011

I board a speedboat to Gili Trawangan and within minutes we're hooning across the blue open sea. I gaze at my fellow travellers: groups in their twenties and thirties, a family with two blond children, three Balinese men probably hitching a ride home. It seems bizarre that just yesterday I was waking up in a Whangārei garage.

A few weeks ago at our office Christmas lunch, my colleagues had shared their plans for the holiday. '*We*'re going to visit family.' '*We*'re off to Queensland.' '*We*'re going skiing in Japan.' I changed the subject before anyone asked me.

The boat spins and a splash of water catches my face. Ahead, an oval island with a single tree on a hill and white sandy beaches glistens in the afternoon sun. On shore, a jam of small horses and bright yellow carts awaits.

Gili T is the largest of three sister islands, about three hours by boat from Bali, Indonesia. It's famous for no motorised transport, no police force, and wild parties. But I'm not here to party. I like to spend this time of year thinking and planning the year ahead. It feels good to use the time productively.

We pull into a beach and I'm ushered along a plank of wood to a lady with a clipboard and a rusted megaphone. After a rollcall there's just me and a short man with a pink sunburnt face. 'Going to Vila Ombak?' the woman asks, leading us to a horse.

We help the driver heave our suitcases onto the back carriage while a skinny grey horse with a sweaty mane stares at the ground. It looks much too small to pull the weight of us all. 'Are you sure, this is okay?' I ask.

The pink-faced man snorts, slapping the horse twice on its neck. 'You're good, aren't you buddy?' We're facing each other now. Pink-face is probably early forties; he's wearing a brown T-shirt with a matchbox car on the front. I've already decided I don't like him. *Uncaring. Sunburnt.* But I hate the awkwardness of silence. 'Have you been here before?' I ask.

'No, first time. You?'

I shake my head.

'You here for New Year's? There's a full moon party on the other side of the island. My mate went last year.' He hands me a scrunched flier. 'Come with us if you want.'

I picture myself surrounded by backpackers and thumping techno. 'Thanks, I'll let you know.'

Gili T is a new world. Walkers, horses and tourists on bikes amble on a path that circles the island. Three goats look up as we pass. Young tourists laze in hammocks drinking Coronas and an array of shack enterprises promote everything from fish pedicures to magic mushrooms. Green grass fields stretch on as our carriage trundles towards the resort.

The Vila Ombak is a grand collection of gazebos and villas sprawling over the side of the hill with a giant blue pool in the centre. I lug my suitcase towards reception and a young woman with a long dark ponytail hands me a scented wet facecloth and sweet iced tea.

'Would you like two keys or just one?'

'Just one.'

She smiles, eyes twinkling. 'Would you like another, just in case?'

Just in case what? Just in case I lose it or just in case I meet a man and invite him to move in? I picture myself knocking back premixed spirits and dancing on a table at that full-moon party. A tall English man walks me back. 'Sure, thanks.' I take the second key. 'Just in case.'

She leads me along a newly cobbled path and the smell of sweet frangipani flowers floats in the tropical heat. My villa stands at the foot of the hill in cream stone with a heavy steel door. Inside, fresh yellow petals rest on the covers of a huge king bed.

A few hours later I venture out for dinner. I feel a pinch of nerves. What if I bump into the man from the cart? *What would we talk about? There'd be silences. He'll think I'm weird. Or what if he likes me? How would I tell him I'm not interested?* I creep around the back, avoiding the common areas where he might be lurking.

Back on the path, ground lights glow in the twilight; it'll take at least five minutes to reach the first shop. The odd backpacker bikes past, shouting a friendly 'hello' as they wave and ring their bells. The Vila Ombak must be the most isolated spot on the island. The only people on this stretch of the path would be hotel guests or cyclists. Later, I'll have to walk home in the dark.

I reach a bar with an open front and the name, Sama Sama, painted in red, yellow and green Rastafarian stripes. A three-piece reggae band fills the air with beats. I feel my knees jive in time as I examine the menu out front. I peer into the kitchen:

a fresh fish burger dripping in tartare sauce and vegetarian nachos. *Yum.* I take two steps back outside and gaze at the row of buzzing and bright establishments that I haven't checked out yet. *Something better might be just around the corner.*

Back on the strip, there's a line of clothing boutiques with racks of sarongs, bikinis and tie-dyed dresses. Locals perch on shopping crates along the dirt path. There are cafés and pizza bars and kebab shops, but none of them as appealing as Sama-Sama. *Now I have a benchmark, I have to beat it.* Otherwise I'll be a loser for leaving the first place.

At 9 p.m. my toes are covered in dust and my stomach groans. I spot a place called Kayu, with steel windows and a blue sandwich board out front reading 'Cold pressed juices & healthy smoothies'. *Fine.*

A boy who can't be more than twelve hands me a giant menu covered in Post-It notes. My eyes scan for a fresh fish burger or vegetarian nachos. *Should I go back?* No, too far. *Loser.* 'Fish and chips please,' I say, handing the menu back to the boy. 'And a vodka lemonade.'

I pull a black Moleskine notebook from my bag and scribble on the inside cover: 'Rebekah Campbell: 2012'. As far back as school, I've set goals each year. I used to just write them at the front of a diary, but more recently I've chosen to keep a journal. A place where I keep a detailed record of my objectives and make notes on my progress. My 2009–2011 book is full of to-do lists, ticks and detailed lessons that I mark down every time there's something I want to remember.

I open the front page and write a heading: 'Goals'. *What was I going to do this next year?* I tap the pen on my cheek.

1. Raise $1M for Posse
2. Hire a lead software engineer to build the app
3. Get 10,000 users

I look up. Yes, this is a good list. On the wall behind the counter rests a chalkboard with pretty pink calligraphy: 'Be the best version of you.' I check my goals again, feeling the weight of something I've forgotten.

That annoying affirmation is making me think. *What is the best version of me? Is it here, pale legs drinking vodka alone on this random island?* I gaze at the tightly thatched roof of the café and file back through the years in my mind. Not long after Steve and I had drifted, I'd started to feel anxious. Now, from my vantage point in Gili T, it's clear that pushing Steve out was the moment I took a colossal step off my predestined life path. I must have disrupted some universal alignment of the planets.

Just a few weeks after Steve had swatted his hand at me on the road in Tawa, I'd sat in a lecture theatre with five hundred students, feeling sure that I was about to have an epileptic fit. I gripped the table. My chest surged with panic. I'd seen a friend have a seizure once and, even though I hadn't been diagnosed as epileptic, I was convinced it was going to happen to me. I imagined losing control of my body right there in my seat, dropping to the ground, shaking and dribbling, smashing my head on the stairs. *How embarrassing.*

I ran for the lecture theatre door, dived for the ground outside and scooped in deep breaths until the fear subsided. Then it happened again and again. I went to the GP, who put me on medication. I stopped getting what he called 'panic attacks' and the tense feeling numbed a little.

Two years later I moved to Sydney and got a job as a management assistant for Bardot, the girl group from the first *Popstars* series. I made new friends; I started to joke, to laugh, to dance and notice beauty in the world again. I went hiking in thick green bush and felt the joy of cold water against my skin when I dived into the ocean. I stopped taking the medication. I went to a bookshop, looked up Byron and Shelley (Steve's favourites), and let my brain dance at the music in the words.

Then there was a phone call. It was 2 p.m. on a Tuesday in October. I was sitting at my computer in the groundfloor office of the music management company looking out to the concrete Surry Hills street. Mum's number appeared on my screen.

'Rebekah, I've got the newspaper.' She hesitated. 'There's been an accident on the road. It's Steve. I'm sorry, Rebekah, he's dead.'

'What?' I said. 'Steve who?'

'Steve Pengelly. Your Steve.'

Mum can be stupid sometimes. Steve wasn't dead. She must have read it wrong or it must be a different Steve Pengelly.

'Come on, Mum, that can't be right. Steve lives in Auckland now.'

'It's definitely the same Steve. It happened on Saturday night driving to Wellington. His new partner was in the car too. They hit gravel and spun into the path of an oncoming car. They were both killed instantly.'

There was a long pause as I processed the information. 'I know that stretch of the road,' she continues. 'Terrible for crashes.'

'Mum, stop. I have to go.' I sat in my chair staring blankly at the window. I imagined Steve grinning at me on that park bench in Tawa. I remembered us dancing at the boat club and touching foreheads outside our tent next to the lake. *People like Steve don't die. He's only twenty-six years old, he's full of life.* The newspaper must have made a mistake.

I keyed 'Steve Pengelly car crash' into Google and my heart collapsed through my chair as a picture of his mangled car appeared on the screen. The headline read 'Travellers take the slow road home: Motorists returning to Auckland after the long weekend had a miserable drive home due to a spate of accidents, long queues and pelting rain.' And there it was. 'Steve Colin Chamberlain-Pengelly, age 26, from Auckland.' My Steve. He was dead.

I grabbed my handbag and stumbled towards the door. Outside, the cobbled streets moved beneath my feet as I floated without direction. My vision tunnelled like I was watching everything through the narrow lens of a camera. The only sound was my breath: in, out, in, out. Everything else: frozen.

Where was Steve? I felt my brain squint inside my head. *People don't just go.* Steve has a whole future to live. He's going to be a famous poet. He must be out there, but where? I pictured his mum, Chris, with her brown wavy hair and quiet voice. She'd be kneeling on the floor, her arms in her hands.

I called my friend Justin and asked him to meet me for a drink, now. I couldn't be alone. We met at the Paddington Inn on Oxford Street and I drank and drank and drank until my brain stopped. A few hours later I woke alone, howling. I'd been drop-kicked by the biggest boot.

'You'll feel better in time,' people would say. *How should I be feeling?* I told myself that I didn't deserve to be so upset because I'd pushed him away. Why was it again, that we broke up?

The following May, I travelled back to New Zealand to spend time with his parents. I wanted to be with Chris on her first Mother's Day without her son. It took me forever to select a gift: something personal that wouldn't remind her of anything. I chose a cling-wrapped basket of hand creams and shower gels from The Body Shop.

We met at an Indian restaurant near their house. They were there when I arrived and stood to greet me. Chris smiled, stretching out her arms. 'It's so good to see you, Rebekah. We're really happy that you came.'

It struck me how small they looked, like they'd both shrunk. It hadn't been long since I'd seen them, but they'd aged twenty years. They were the same kind, open faces I'd known, but the cheery Mike and Chris had vanished. Their shattered shells stood before me.

'It's lovely to see you too,' I said.

The three of us embraced like a rugby scrum and I felt their warm breath on my face. They *were* happy to see me. We drank wine and ate curry and spoke, about Steve of course, and other things too. I asked Mike how his inventions were going, and he gave a long description about a leak in the roof of their house.

'It's all over the news here,' he said. 'People have been building with this dodgy cladding and now they're all leaking.' He leaned forward and I spotted a flicker of the old Mike. 'I've got something that fixes it.'

The sharp arch of Mike's nose connected with his deep hazel eyes. They were Steve's eyes, and I imagined him sitting across from me as an older man. I could look into those eyes every day. I could have made children and grown old with those eyes. There would never be anyone as perfect.

Mike and Chris wanted to know everything I was up to. I told them about my work back in Sydney, how I planned to start my own company managing bands. It all seemed so fickle and pointless — I felt embarrassed. Here I was, still alive when Steve was gone. Surely I should be doing something more useful with my time?

I dreaded the inevitable question that I knew Chris wanted to ask. She steadied herself: 'Are you seeing anybody, Rebekah? Is there anyone special?'

I shook my head. 'I haven't since—' I hesitated. The truth was that I'd been out with a few men in Sydney. But I had a benchmark. I'd be a loser to settle for anyone less. 'You know, he was just so different. I don't know. I'm not ready.' I wanted desperately to tell them how much I loved their son. How extraordinary he was. He'd seen something in me, he'd brought me to life. I couldn't find the words.

Chris took my hand. It was as if her arm reached into my jaw, down my throat and held my bloody beating heart between her fingers. 'We really hope you meet someone, Rebekah.'

Tears streamed down my face and hers as we clasped each other across the table.

Mike settled the bill and I gave Chris the gift from The Body Shop. 'Happy Mother's Day,' I said with another hug.

Later that night I lay in my childhood bed. The wind howled outside, rain pelted the windows and the wooden beams creaked and groaned. *Where is Steve? Was he with us at the table? Is he with me now?* An eerie warmth blanketed my shoulders. 'Is that you?' I asked out loud. 'Steve,' I said again. 'I'm not scared, you can come out.' I willed to see his ghost at the end of the bed. 'Please come out.' I strained my eyes for his outline.

There was nothing. 'Look, I know I messed up. I'm sorry for hurting you.' An electric wave sped up my back. I shivered. 'I was young and stupid. I didn't know what I wanted. Please forgive me: please, please, please.'

I climbed onto the floor and knelt, gripping my hands together like I'd seen at church. I closed my eyes so tight that my cheeks hurt. *Could I erase the past few years and land back outside that tent in Taupō?* It seemed like it should be possible. It was a real event; I had been there. Somewhere in time and space it must still exist. Why not go back?

On my knees, I prayed and pleaded to God. 'Please take me back there. I'll do anything, anything.' I imagined opening my eyes to see Steve sitting by our tent in his swimming trunks, hair floating in the breeze, smiling as he lit a Marlboro cigarette. I kept kneeling next to the bed, waiting and praying. After a while everything seemed to still, and I opened my eyes. I couldn't change what had happened. I couldn't go back.

My mind levelled. *What would he want me to do?* He'd be grateful I'd seen his mum on Mother's Day. But what else? I imagined his spirit surrounding me, drifting and lost. What of all his big dreams, the places he'd wanted to see, the poetry he'd publish? I sat up and began to rationalise. I must stop him from dying. I must compensate for the terrible person that I was when we were together.

And an idea landed as if by magic. *Could I share my body with him? Could he ride along and see the future through my eyes?* I clutched at my chest, my hips, my shoulders. *There's enough space in here.* 'Steve,' I whispered. 'I think you should live with me. You've lost your body and I've still got one.' The warmth seemed to flood my back. 'It's you, isn't it. I know it is.' Every cell in my body seemed to loosen. 'You'll be with me.' I could keep him alive *and* make him like me again. I'd become that person he'd seen under all my horridness. *If Steve is with me, he'll see everything. I'll be good. I won't make any mistakes. Life is serious now. I'm responsible for both of us.* 'I'll make you proud,' I said decisively.

I gaze back at the walls of the Kayu Café as the young waiter reaches for my plate. 'Everything okay?' he asks. I knock back the rest of my drink and pull back my seat. 'It was great, thanks.'

The path outside is alive with reggae music, lit-up stalls and the early rumblings of beach parties. Girls who'd worn bikinis a few hours earlier have changed into short skirts and makeup. Boys march in groups looking for adventure. I make my way through the crowd in the direction of my hotel. As I walk, the crowd thins, the music quietens and the path narrows.

After a while, the music fades to nothing and all I can hear is waves lapping at the shore next to me. The fields on the other side of the path have become black caverns. I'd seen unhappy-looking animals in those fields earlier. Anything could be there now. I walk faster, then break into a trot. The ground lights are too far apart, leaving holes of darkness between them. I don't remember the hotel being so far. I widen my stride and speed to a sprint.

Finally, I reach the glow of the resort and my panic dissolves. Back in my room I collapse into bed. *Enough of being alone.*

4. SMART, TALL, FUN

I wake in the luxurious king bed, crisp sheets folded tight around me like an envelope. I roll twice to reach my iPhone, miles away on the bedside table: 5.40 a.m. I've been in Gili T for a few days now and have established a daily routine.

I leap out of bed, pull on my swimsuit, a shift dress and running shoes. Out on the path, the air is cool and still. It's dark and I flinch at rustles in the trees, but the longer I walk, the brighter it'll get. This morning I'll circle the island in an anticlockwise direction, so I'll reach the eastern side in time to watch the sun rise for the last time in 2011.

For forty minutes, I say hello to the same fields of goats, horses and tin shacks that I pass every morning on this walk. But today there's a bustle of organisation. Tonight, it'll be New Year's Eve. Three young boys scuttle past carrying white plastic chairs. I turn a corner and the path opens to reveal a huge construction zone: clusters of men stand hammering poles into the ground and hoisting up marquee tents. I continue and some of the workers look up, waving. 'Come back later!' one of them shouts.

A few hundred metres further is a tiny tin shed called The Coffee Hut. A skinny twenty-something man stands behind a rough wooden counter. He has sparkling eyes, teeth that look like missing dominoes, and he's wearing a grey singlet with

'I ♥ Dublin' on the front. I order a green tea and wonder if he has actually been to Dublin or in fact anywhere outside Bali. *Unlikely*. I can't decide if I feel sad, guilty or jealous.

I climb down to the beach and carve out a seat on pebbles. There's a goat chewing grass and birds pecking at something in the sand. I open my Moleskine book and re-read the list of goals. I imagine myself at the end of the year with ticks on every line, like I'm an athlete being handed a medal on TV. I wait to feel a surge of excitement at the tasks ahead but there's just a dull tone of stress thinking how much work I'll have to do. I look back to the man in the coffee hut. *Definitely jealous.*

Ever since I'd made my commitment to Steve's ghost *(you're responsible, be good, no mistakes)*, I've stuck to my goals like the bible. After telling Chris that I planned to start a music company, I did it. Within weeks I'd signed my first client, a group of teenage brothers I met on that same New Zealand trip calling themselves Evermore. I organised the recording of their first single and hand-delivered it to the Triple J radio station. I signed more artists: Lisa Mitchell, Van She, Matt Corby. Each year, I'd set new goals and do 'whatever it takes' (my motto) to achieve them.

But somewhere in the middle of all that striving and achieving, I noticed the tense feeling return. This time it was darker, like I was being followed by my own little rain cloud. I couldn't sleep, I ate too many cakes from the Turkish bakery, and I'd stamp my foot when someone said something I didn't like. I spoke to my GP and she recommended I try therapy.

Ruth's clinic was above a nail salon in Bondi Junction. The first time I arrived, a receptionist handed me a clipboard with a pen tied to string. A few minutes later, a chirpy high-pitched voice screeched towards me. 'You must be Rebekah,' she said. 'Come through.' I took a seat in a square brown leather chair. I poured myself a cup of water and noted the tissue box on the coffee table.

Ruth would have been nearing sixty, with thick-rimmed mahogany glasses. She sat leaning forward, creasing her floral shawl, and her deep eyes wrinkled inquisitively. A large white clock hung on the wall behind her left shoulder.

Ruth asked why I'd come to see her. I explained that I was unhappy, I had few friends and I didn't know how to connect with people. It was terrifying at first, to pull apart shields of flesh and leave my insides exposed to a stranger. But Ruth just nodded, unphased by the sprawl of guts and heart and mess on her floor. It was as if she'd seen it all before. And then the long hand on the clock reached the top, our time was up. I remember driving away feeling lighter, like my rain cloud had lifted a little.

I continued seeing Ruth every week. In some sessions we'd work on practical challenges like when I had to attend the MTV Music Awards. I hated these events. I didn't know how to approach people and often found myself wandering aimlessly between the bathroom and the door, trying to look like I had somewhere to go. Ruth and I roleplayed the conversations I'd have. She suggested asking people questions, simple things like, 'What are you planning to do in the holidays?' And then follow-ups to indicate interest in their story.

At the end of the year I gave Ruth a huge hug and thanked her for everything. 'It's my pleasure,' she said. I folded into the layers of her silk shawl and her chest smelt of Yves Saint Laurent perfume. As our eyes met, a tear trickled across her cheek. *I'd moved her. By allowing her to help me, I'd also given her something.* I reached for the tissue box. We agreed that, going forward, I'd just call when I wanted to see her. She'd always be there if I needed help.

I glance again at my goal list for 2012. 'What did I say to myself as I sprinted back in the dark the other night? On Christmas Day, as I lay on that fold-out bed?' I click down my pen, turn to page four and write a new headline: 'Personal Goals'. I run my pen back and forth under the words. I shuffle back in my beach cradle of stones, sip my green tea and gaze out to the ocean. 'I want a partner,' I declare out loud to the birds and goat on the beach. Not just someone to make babies with, I want a best friend. Someone who inspires me, who'll entertain me, and who'll keep me safe in the dark. I want a great love. My personal goal for the year is to 'Find a husband'.

My pen hovers. The goal doesn't feel right. *What if I don't find the right person? I'm not going to settle for the wrong guy just to meet a deadline.*

In business, there are two types of goals: output and input. I always set output goals — what would I *achieve* by the end of the year, like raise $1 million for Posse. An input goal would be how many pitch presentations I'd plan to give. The output is what's important; it doesn't matter what I do to achieve the goal, so long as it's done. But for personal goals, my 'whatever it takes' approach might not work. The output I want (to find a husband) might not even be possible. *What if no one finds me attractive? What if I can't find someone interesting enough? If I do find someone, how will I stop myself from stuffing it up?*

I conclude that personal goals should be input-based. I'll set myself a list of tasks and a schedule, and stick to it with the same ruthless tenacity I apply to my work. Yes, I'll devise a plan that'll challenge me to take every step imaginable towards finding a partner. I'll be responsible for maximising my chances, then God or Steve or the Universe or whoever's in charge will decide the outcome. I run my tongue across my top lip and put my pen to the page.

Personal Goals 2012

1. One date every week for the entire year (52 total): Join eHarmony and RSVP. If travel, then should keep dating in new cities. If miss a week because sick or travelling, then need to make up with extra dates.
2. Appearance: Get haircuts every 8 weeks, eyebrows every 6 weeks, do makeup course, yoga 3x per week, buy dating clothes, try Botox. Get new photos done for dating profile.
3. Psychologist: See Ruth again and tell her the plan. Ask for dating advice, find out what men want.

I read the goals over and over: *fifty-two dates in fifty-two weeks.* A rush of terror freezes my chest, my arms and my legs. *I'll have to list myself on dating websites like a cow for sale at a market. What if someone who knows me sees my profile? People will think I'm desperate.* I wonder what kind of men list themselves online. Surely all the best guys are married already? Isn't online just full of leftovers and freaks? *What if I meet a psycho-murderer?*

But under the fear and the dread, I feel a glimmer of something else: hope. *If I go on fifty-two dates, then I might find someone. Surely, one out of fifty-two has to be good enough.* The optimism engine in my chest begins to rumble. *Maybe next Christmas, I won't be holidaying alone.*

I imagine my future husband right here on the beach. *What does he look like? What are the characteristics of my perfect man?* I make another list. I'll give myself three attributes, any more is too picky.

My ideal partner

1. Smart: Be able to have good conversations, someone inspiring I can learn from.
2. Tall: At least as tall as me in heels.
3. Funny/fun: Makes me laugh, do fun things together.

I debate for a while as to whether being fun is more important than being tall and decide that 'tall' is non-negotiable. *I have to feel attracted to the guy.* I know height is superficial but wanting it doesn't make *me* superficial. A superficial woman would care about looks or money — not me. It's natural for a woman to want a bigger man; it's evolution. I don't want to tower over him like King Kong, clomping giant arms and legs against his delicate little limbs.

I put 'smart' at the top because I loved this quality in Steve. When I was with him, I lived in the front part of my brain all the time. *Learning is, for me, key to sexual attraction.* I want a husband for life, so he'll need to be clever enough to still make good conversation when we're both in rocking chairs.

And third, 'funny/fun'. I know that, despite the photos on my Facebook page, easy-going wouldn't be the first word people would pick to describe me. But I do like to laugh, and I don't laugh nearly enough.

I glance back through my list and try to visualise this man: smart, tall, fun. *Is he out there? And will he like me?* I imagine myself on New Year's morning of 2013, looking back on 2012. I'll have completed fifty-two dates, met fifty-two different men. I feel like a character at the start of a novel. Who knows where the plot will take her?

I flick through the pages of my 2012 plan: my work goals then personal goals. I narrow one eye and I take out my pen again. I point the nib halfway down the P in 'Personal Goals' and draw a line left, straight across the top of the page to the edge then across the top of the next page to the edge again. On the front page, I continue the line until it crosses over the top of the heading 'Business Goals'. I draw an arrow and an asterisk to show that 'Personal Goals' are top priority.

'You coming back for the party tonight?' shouts the coffee hut man as I brush the pebbles from my dress. 'It's big, big party. Very famous in Bali. My band is playing 10 o'clock.'

'I'll try,' I shout back. 'Good luck if I don't see you, and thanks.' I step back onto the path and the giant marquee is already up. White sand and teal blue water sparkles in the background. I tip my head back in the breeze, holding my phone up to snap a shot for Facebook: 'Getting ready for New Year's Eve in Gili T.'

5. THE PREPARATION

P *ound. Pound. Pound.* I stride across the wharf at Woolloomooloo
and up the steps towards the Botanic Garden. A giant naval
ship is sailing towards the harbour, the Sydney sky is blue and
perfect as always. I run faster around the rocky point, stepping
to avoid the hordes of tourists who've stopped to take pictures.

I didn't go to that Full Moon Party in Gili T. I got dressed,
had a drink in the hotel bar. The path around the island
had been packed with revellers stumbling towards the giant
marquee. I'd pictured myself there alone, with no one to talk
to. *Maybe I'll go later.* Back in my room I'd read *One Click: Jeff
Bezos and the Rise of Amazon*, watched the fireworks on television
and fallen asleep.

But that was 2011, and 2012 is a brand new year. Back in
Darlinghurst, I sprint back past the shops and climb the steps
to my apartment. Inside, my suitcase lies half unpacked in the
middle of the lounge. *No one is going to see.* And the silence. That's
the thing about living alone. There's just so much silence, as if
it's going to ring on forever.

I pull out my laptop and station it on the dining table, ready
to begin. I key in eharmony.com. It's the only platform I know of
where my profile won't be seen by the general public, only men
who are matched with me. *Ha ha, have you seen Rebekah Campbell is
looking for a date!* My fingers tremble as the website flashes up. A thin

woman in a tight purple singlet with long chestnut hair smiles back. 'On average, every 14 minutes someone finds love on eHarmony.'

The first question is easy: I am a woman seeking a man. Then comes 'email address'. I've only got my work account, which our developers have access to. *The risk of people at work finding out. The shame.* I set up a Gmail account and click 'Let's go'.

I stop: 'Date of birth'. I grimace, biting the side of my cheek. I think back to my twenty-fifth birthday. I remember feeling that I hadn't achieved enough. 'Twenty-five,' I'd said out loud. 'A quarter of a century.' No, it didn't seem right. A twenty-five-year-old should have done so much more than me. *But what if I could be twenty-four again? Delete a year. Who would know?* 'Twenty-four today,' I'd said again. Much better, like slipping into the perfect shoe. From then on, every form I filled in (with the exception of medical and taxes) made me one year younger. Every birthday celebration would be for one year less than my actual age. Somehow getting old didn't feel so bad. I'd worked out how to cheat the system.

A series of reasonable and simple questions follow: ethnicity, education, profession, personal income, height, how often do you drink, smoke, exercise, et cetera. And then the compatibility quiz. I recognise the format as like the psych test my business coach gave me. 'How well does the following describe you: Warm, Clever, Dominant, Outgoing, Quarrelsome, Stable, Predictable, Affectionate, Intelligent, Energetic, Attractive, Compassionate, Patient, Caring, Ambitious, Passionate, Vivacious, Wise, Bossy, Leader, Irritable . . . I rank each on a scale between 'Not at all' to 'Very well'.

The next part is more confronting: empty text boxes. The first is 'Share what you're passionate about'. A prompt suggests to 'Be yourself and have fun'. I list:

I like to travel to interesting places, meet new people and experience different cultures and perspectives.

I love to run, swim in the ocean and do yoga.

I enjoy reading, especially non-fiction, and I'm currently obsessed with *The West Wing* TV series.

And I'm in! 'Congratulations, you've got 24 matches!' Smiling, colourful faces fill my screen, four columns across, six rows down. There's Stuart, 35, from Wollstonecraft; Alan, 33 from St Leonards; Ad, 34, Rooty Hill; Tyson, 35, Bondi; Thomas, 30, Surry Hills; Jazz, 39, North Sydney; Dan, 35, Crows Nest; Ali, 29, Gosford; Lakshan, 36, Pymble; and on and on and on. I softly punch my fist in the air. *I'm doing this!*

I explore the candidates. Stuart from Wollstonecraft is a 'caring, loving, honest and hard-working guy looking for a genuine and humble girl to start a relationship with'. Alan from St Leonards 'likes being active and checking out everything this great world has to offer'. There are options to 'Send a smile' or 'Send a message'. I spend the afternoon reading profiles and sending smiles to friendly-looking men.

Later at night I lie in bed staring at the space between me and the roof. 'Steve, I'm doing good, right?' I whisper. 'Or, happier at least. Next life I'll find you again.' I roll, knowing he is next to me. I picture us meeting again at that basement party in Tawa. 'Next time it's going to be so different. I won't . . .' I close my eyes.

The next morning, I wake just after 4 a.m. I know I should sleep more but there's too much anticipation. I slip through to the lounge where eHarmony is still open on my browser. I hit refresh. Two messages! No new matches yet, but there are *two messages.*

Ad, 34, Rooty Hill

Hi Rebekah,

How are u today? I'm just hanging out. Do u want to chat?

Ali, 29, Gosford

Hi Rebekah,

Thanks for the smile. I like your profile. I've just come back from a couple of days fishing with my brother. What are you up to this weekend?

Look forward to hearing more from you.

Ali

I draft a one-page letter in Microsoft Word then cut and paste it back into eHarmony. As I sign off, I ask if they'd like to meet in person. My first dates!

Two days later, there's no reply from Ad or Ali. *Did I say something wrong?*

There are three new messages in my inbox, this time from Thomas, 30, Surry Hills; Dan, 35, Crows Nest; and Jazz, 39, North Sydney. I rest my chin on my fingers to think. I should change my reply. Make it shorter, more like theirs. Don't ask to meet.

Hi Jazz,

Thanks for your message. Sounds like you had a fun weekend. I've just come home from a week in Gili T (an island off Bali). What did you get up to over summer?

Rebekah

When I check again at lunchtime, Jazz and Dan have both replied. We fire back and forth short, informational and mildly flirtatious messages. Finally, sometime after six, a fish bites.

> Dan, 35, Crows Nest
> Do you want to meet up in person?

'Rebekah. So lovely to see you,' says Ruth, stretching out her floral-sleeved arms. She takes her seat opposite me in the consultation room. 'Gosh, how long has it been, four years?' Ruth's pale skin is crinklier than the last time I saw her, dark hair perhaps not quite as natural. 'Is there something in particular you'd like to talk about?'

'Well.' I shuffle in the chair. 'I've decided it's time to find a husband. I still haven't seen anyone since, you know, Steve.'

Ruth jumps to her feet, clapping in joyous applause.

'I've set a goal for the year to go on one date every week. The first is on Thursday and I want your advice.'

Ruth exhales, beaming through her teeth. 'Oh Rebekah, I'm so happy to hear this. How old are you now, thirty-three?'

'Thirty-four.' She *is* a medical professional, after all.

'Well yes, you want to get on with it then — if you want a family.'

I know this of course, but it still stings.

'Tell me about your date. Who is he? How did you meet?'

'His name is Dan, we met on eHarmony.' I gaze out the window to the carpark. 'He works at Vodafone and just seems normal and nice. Anyway, I wanted to get your advice because I've never done this before.'

'Done what?'

'Been on a date — well, a proper one like this. It's been ten years. I don't know the protocol.'

Ruth peers over her mahogany glasses which have slipped to the tip of her nose. 'For a start, there isn't a protocol. A date is just two people meeting to see if they connect, if they're attracted to each other. If they want to see each other again. Think about it like you're meeting a friend.'

I pour myself a water from the coffee table and take big sips as the January heat seeps in from outside. 'What do you think is going to be hard for me? Where do you see me getting stuck?'

Ruth squints a little. 'You're going to need to be tolerant. Don't be quick to judge. Remember you're not the only nervous person there. Men get just as anxious on a first date as women, often more so.'

Hmm. This is new information. 'I'd always thought of men as the hunters,' I say.

Ruth nods. 'It's a problem. Women think they're the only ones who fear rejection. I see lots of men in my practice in the same position as you. They worry that they're too shy, too overweight or something else, especially if they're looking for an emotional relationship. They go to a first date with hope, just like you. So be compassionate.'

She reaches behind her desk and pulls out a beige manila folder with my name on it. 'Remember, the secret to being interesting is to be interested. Ask open questions, smile, help him to feel comfortable. If you spend your time looking for what's wrong, then he'll sense rejection and pull away. You won't get to see the good in him.' She looks straight into my eyes with clear command. 'But don't give him the third degree. If you ask if he's ready to get married and have children right away, then he'll think you're desperate and probably run a mile. Just relax, be present and give the relationship space to develop.'

'But I kind of *am* desperate,' I remind her. 'I'm thirty-four. I can't waste time with guys who don't want a family.'

'Well, you don't need to wait for months, but you can't ask on the first date. Wait till the third or fourth.'

I pause, trying to make sense of her advice. *What's wrong with being direct? Isn't it more efficient to be upfront?*

I steady myself for more direction. 'What do you think I should ask? You must see lots of couples who end up splitting. What makes a man long-term partner material?'

Ruth scratches her neck. 'Try to find out about his relationship with his mother.' She pauses. 'Most of us look for the relationship we had with our opposite-gender parent. How he treats his mother is a good guide for how he'll treat you. When he describes his family, you want him to say that his mum is great. They clash occasionally, but they work out their differences.'

'What about me?' I ask. 'Will I look for the relationship I have with Dad?'

Ruth glances at her notes and up to me. 'Yes, and you need to be aware of it. I see this all the time with women of your age, especially in the Eastern Suburbs. Your father treats you like a princess, and this is the model you have for how a man should treat you.'

I think about Steve and my dad. *They are actually quite similar.* If I close my eyes and picture each of them and who they are to me, the image is identical: Socratic figures preaching from an ancient Athenian square; voracious readers with brains like encyclopedias and values as solid and unmoveable as the stone pillars of the Parthenon. *It's true, I am looking for a man like Dad.*

'Be realistic,' Ruth continues. 'You're not going to find another version of your father and you're not going to find another Steve. If you find yourself thinking "he's not this or that", then ask yourself if there's actually something wrong or is he just different to what you're used to.' She scribbles something with a biro pen. 'Have you thought about what you want in a partner?'

'Yes,' I say. 'Actually, I've made a list and ordered it by priority'.

Ruth tips forward, spluttering a mouthful of water in a spontaneous laugh. 'Of course you have.' She smiles, beckoning with both hands. 'Let me hear it then. What's on the list?'

'I'm looking for someone clever who challenges me —' I open one finger to count the attributes '— someone tall —' two fingers '— and someone to do fun things with —' three fingers.

She leans back and her swivel chair creaks with the movement. She's thinking. Her forehead crinkles like a wise monk. 'Come and see me again soon. I'm curious to know how many dates it'll take before you rethink that list.'

She doesn't like my list. Ruth stares, straight and silent. *But I'm happy with my list.* The monk doesn't want to give me the answers. I'll have to work it out myself.

Watson Brown is a glass-walled clinic in Darling Harbour. There's a sign on the window: 'Specialists in Non-surgical Cosmetic Treatments: Lasers, Botox, Microdermabrasion, Peels, Lip augmentation and Leg vein treatments'. *Will anyone I know see me enter?* I dart towards the door and tug on the metal handle. Tug again. It sticks. I grimace, imagining myself being spotted by someone from work.

'Okay love, hang on,' an Irish accent calls. She opens the door. 'Sorry, it does that sometimes.'

Inside, there are posters of happy, shiny-faced people and advertisements for treatments and creams. 'You must be Rebekah,' the woman says. 'Fill out this form and Michelle will be right with you.'

I perch myself on a golden velvet seat and read. 'I have requested that Michelle Cummings attempts to improve my facial lines with Botulinum Toxin Type A.' The form lists common side-effects which include 'headache, respiratory infection, flu symptoms, temporary eyelid drop, nausea' and so many others that I stop reading and sign the bottom. Over the page there's a sketched outline of a woman's face and instructions to 'Mark the areas that concern you.'

One Saturday night a few months ago I walked down Darlinghurst Road en route to the supermarket wearing tracksuit pants and sneakers. A couple holding hands had approached from the other direction, clearly on their way to a party. One was an older man in a bowtie and waistcoat. The younger man wore sparkling orange fairy wings behind his waxed pink chest and black Lycra shorts that could have been undies.

I smiled as they came closer. 'Smile, honey, smile!' shouted the man in fairy wings. *But I am smiling.* I waved and stretched my face to reveal the biggest smile my cheeks could muster. 'Why so glum, darling?' called the man in the bowtie. 'It's Saturday night!' He stopped to jiggle like a belly-dancer.

What? I am smiling. It must be the line between my fucking eyebrows: it makes me look permanently pissed off. I need Botox, I need plastic surgery. I must fix my miserable face!

On the form, I make a big cross on the face between the

eyes and draw an arrow marking 'frown line'. I also circle: the outside of both eyes, which wrinkle like parched bedsheets; my entire forehead area, which looks like ripples on a still lake; both eyelids with their sagging hoods; under both eyes with their tired circles; my cheeks, which aren't as full and pert as they were in my twenties; and my chin, with its acne scars that remind me of the surface of the moon. Finally, I stab the page adding dots to mark freckles, moles and other imperfections.

'Rebekah Campbell.' A blonde ponytailed woman with sandpapered skin stands in the doorway. 'Hi, I'm Michelle. Follow me.'

We sit in a small consultation room and I hand her my drawing. She looks at the form then up at me. 'There's quite a lot here,' she says. 'What is it that you're most unhappy with?'

'Definitely the frown line,' I say, wondering if I've put too much on the form. *Is she assessing my mental health? Is the drawing some kind of test?* She steps close, examining my skin. I feel naked, exposed. She can see everything: every line, scar, freckle and fault I work hard to cover with makeup. I wait. *Maybe she'll tell me I'm beautiful. Maybe she'll tell me I don't need Botox.* I fear that I am ugly, that I'm unusual. All I want is for her to say something reassuring.

She places two sets of three fingers on each eyebrow and stands back, cocking her head. She draws a line with her thumb across my forehead. 'Did you know, one of your eyebrows is —'

'Ah, no. I don't know.'

'Your right eyebrow droops a little.' She takes a small mirror and holds it up. 'See, the left one is higher.' Inside I feel my little ego wince, tumble and fall through the floor.

'I can try to fix them with Botox if you like. If I put a few units into this muscle, it'll force these ones to work harder. And if we get it right —' she pinches the skin above brow '— yes, I think we can get this one to lift.

I'm defeated. 'Okay, if you think it'll look better. But I don't want to look, you know, like I'm surprised all the time. Like those celebrities.'

She laughs. 'It's a tiny amount. We just want your eyebrows to look like twins. Symmetrical.'

She pulls out a blue marker and draws lines across my forehead, above my nose and on my chin. She holds up the mirror again and I look a bit like the sketched face on the form. 'This is what we can do.'

'But is it going to be too much?' My voice quivers. 'Like I said, I don't want . . .'

Michelle places one hand on her hip and the other on the desk. Light streams in through a window in the roof, illuminating her face more clearly. She'd be late forties; she's beautiful in a way, symmetrical. But she also looks slightly strange. Her skin is pulled tight like clingwrap, her pink lips bulge like a monkey's anus, and her eyes dart up, down and to the side — everywhere except to meet my gaze directly.

She lets out a huff. 'What if we just start with your frown and eyebrows today, and you can see how it feels? We can add more next time.'

'That sounds good,' I reply.

Michelle holds a frozen yellow rubber glove up to my face. 'Hold this for ten seconds.' For the next four or five minutes she numbs and pricks spots along the lines on my forehead. I imagine the needle deep in my skin, poison escaping from the syringe to paralyse my eyebrow muscles. It feels like a cold water pistol and I squeeze my fist with every jab.

'If you're okay then I'd like to do two more on your chin. Let's try to soften those dimples.'

I knew it. My chin is hideous. I am hideous. 'Sure, go for it.'

I pay the Irish receptionist $650 and step outside. Darling Harbour glistens in the late afternoon sun. Three women laugh confidently to each other as they step past me on the paving next to the mall. They look so perfect. They belong in this city.

I continue walking sensing a swell of uneasiness inside. *Was that bad, what I just did to myself?* Two voices in my brain seem to argue in reply.

Left: *Yes, it was bad. You just injected your perfectly healthy body with poison.*

Right: *It's safe. The poison just stays in the . . .*

Left: *Did you read that form? What about the future? They're bound to discover . . .*

Right: *It's for dating, to look better. Overall, I'll be healthier if I'm happy and I'll increase my chances . . .*

Left: *Women shouldn't have to poison themselves to look attractive. What century are we in?*

Right: *But it's what everyone does. Isn't it?*

6. DAN

I wake at 5.30 a.m. and clench my fists under the sheets. This is it. I crawl out of bed and log into eHarmony. Today there are messages from Orin, 38, Pennant Hills; Sunny, 34, Marrickville; Lakshan, 36, Pymble; and Dan, 35, Crows Nest. My heart skips a step.

> Hi Rebekah,
> Good morning! Hope you had a good sleep. I stayed up watching Lleyton Hewitt in the tennis. It was a late one! Looking forward to meeting you tonight. I'll be wearing a dark blue shirt and black pants. Off to the gym now. See you at 7.
> Dan x

My mind darts between excitement — *Dan sounds nice; he sent me an 'x'* — to despair — *What if he thinks I'm ugly or weird? What if he walks out as soon as he sees me?*

Excitement: *It'll be fun to dress up, go out to a restaurant, meet someone new.*

Despair: *What if we can't find anything to talk about? What if there are awkward pauses as we stare blankly across the table?*

Excitement: *He might be the one!*

I shower, wash my hair and shave my legs. I pull on the black-and-white leopard-print dress I bought last Saturday at

David Jones. New clothes for dating, tick. I lean in and scrunch my eyebrows to make a frown. Try Botox, tick. And I remember those perfect-looking women at Darling Harbour. This *is* what everyone does. *It must be.*

It's eight minutes before 7 and my legs clam together with sweat under my office desk. My stomach is tense and queasy. I haven't eaten since breakfast, but I've been to the bathroom six times. *Hope I don't have a stomach bug.* It'll take five minutes to exit the office and walk next door to The Winery. *Am I supposed to be late or on time?* I decide ten minutes late is the optimal time to arrive. *There should be some anticipation. I want to look busy, like I haven't been waiting all day around for the date. But I don't want to be rude.*

At seven exactly my phone buzzes.

> Dan: Just arrived. I've got a table outside.
> Me: Sorry, 10 mins away.

I slip off sandals and pull on strapped cream shoes with tall steel heels. My red-painted toenails sparkle. I am a wrapped Christmas gift with neatly tucked paper and a ribbon like it's been done at the shop. Shoes, tick, nails, tick, leg blemish concealer, tick, new dress, tick, makeup and hair, tick tick, teeth brushed, tick.

I stop at the bathroom on my way out to apply another coat of lipstick and check my appearance one final time. Michelle's wonky eyebrow assessment stares back like a raw wound. *What's he going to think of this face?* And down the stairs I walk.

Are you proud of me, Steve? Here I am sitting across the table from a nice, normal man. I'm on a date, Steve. A real date like other people, like normal people.

I face Dan at the end of a row of tables on the deck. Plants wrap around railings and lanterns line the walls. Young waitstaff buzz around us in blue denim shirts and black aprons. The orange afternoon sun sits on the horizon, waiting to be replaced by the moon and stars.

Dan's cheeks are plump and dimpled on the right. He smiles when he talks and the dimple bounces like a yoyo on a string.

'You won't believe what happened this morning,' he says, his voice higher and scratchier than I'd imagined. 'I went to the gym at 5. When I got back to my apartment, I smelt smoke in the stairs. I knocked on my neighbour's door. She's an old Italian woman, Rosa. She lives by herself and I thought there must be a fire in her kitchen. I called from the stairwell, "Rosa, are you okay?" and I banged and banged to wake her up.' He speaks fast, racing to catch a breath. 'She came out in her nightgown, hair everywhere. I looked inside and everything was fine. Then I opened the door to *my* apartment and realised the smoke was coming from my stove! I'd started boiling an egg when I got up and I must have forgotten about it. Anyway, my whole living room was just thick smoke. The pot was still on the stove, completely black. Burnt right through. But it wasn't on fire. That's the incredible bit. It was just black and smoking. Can you believe that? It must have been burning for an hour.'

I watch Dan recount his story with such animation. His eyebrows rise and fall with each amazing fact. He waves his hand across his nose to show how he fought through the smoke as he traversed his living room to find the pot. And it strikes me: Dan has rehearsed this story. He's been thinking about it all day, planning a witty tale of his morning fire fiasco so he'll have something to talk about on the date. *He must be nervous too, just like Ruth said.* Dan pauses, his eyes wide like a puppy waiting for me to throw him a stick.

'And what did you do next?' I lean forward and cock one ear, as if this story of the boiled egg and burnt pot is the most thrilling tale ever told.

'Well,' he says, shrugging his shoulders. 'I just turned off the stove and opened the window. I had to throw out the pot, of course. But isn't it amazing that there wasn't a fire?'

'Yes.' I nod enthusiastically. 'Amazing.'

The restaurant is loud, chattering voices are pierced by squeals of laughter and the clomp of heeled shoes on wooden panels. Music blares from the bar.

'I love this song,' says Dan. 'Do you know it?'

'Um.' I pause to concentrate. It's energetic indie guitar. There's a boy singing, then a girl. 'No, I haven't heard it before. I like it though.'

'It's San Cisco, they're from Perth. This song is all over Triple J at the moment.'

'Ah, I used to listen to Triple J. I used to manage bands, actually.' I purse my lips. 'It's part of getting old, isn't it? Losing touch with what's on the radio.'

'You're not old. You're thirty-three, right? Rebekah, 33, from Darlinghurst.'

Hang on. My chest thuds. *Should I tell him?* I feel like I should. It's got to be bad luck to lie on a first date.

'Yeah, thirty-three.' I avoid eye contact and cross my fingers between my legs.

Dan looks at the menu. When the waiter comes, I order the salmon and a glass of New Zealand sauvignon blanc; he orders the duck and an Asahi beer. We clink glasses. I talk about growing up in New Zealand. Dan talks about his family, how his parents and brother emigrated from Malaysia before he was born. 'Dad worked as an engineer at the airport, so we lived out in Sutherland,' he says. 'It was a nice place but very white. We were the only Asian kids at school.'

'And do your family still live out that way?' I ask.

'Yeah. But we lost my brother in a car accident when he was twenty-one. In New Zealand actually, up north. He was on a surfing holiday with some mates.' Our eyes meet. 'We're really close now, the three of us. Especially me and Mum. I'm her only kid, you know.'

The muscle in my heart softens and spreads throughout my chest. *Should I tell him about you, Steve? He's being so honest. Should I share that I too lost someone on those harsh New Zealand roads?* But an ex-boyfriend is different to a brother. And Steve is still here, sitting in the invisible third chair. Not yet.

'I have to tell you, this is the first time I've been on a proper date,' he says, biting his bottom lip.

'Really? Me too. You seem so confident.'

He laughs. '*You* seem confident. I'm kind of shitting myself.'

We order dessert, and the wine mixes with my relief that the date is going well. My mind starts to wander. *Our children would be cute. Aren't mixed-race kids supposed to get the best genes?*

'Can you believe it's almost 11?' he says, signalling to the waiter.

'What? We can't have been here for four hours.' I look behind me and the bar has emptied to a small group. We're the only ones still on the deck.

The waiter hands the bill to Dan on a small plate. 'Let me get half,' I offer.

Dan rolls his eyes and holds up his hand like he's stopping traffic.

'No way.' He hands the waiter his credit card. 'Come on, let me be the guy. I'm getting this.'

We walk out to the street and Dan flags for a taxi. 'Do you want a ride home?' he asks as the taxi stops at his feet. 'I have to go through Darlinghurst anyway.'

'No thanks. I think I'll walk. It's such a nice night.'

'Okay.' Dan places a warm hand on my left shoulder.

I flinch. Don't look inside. There's so much you don't know . . .

'It's been really nice to meet you, Rebekah, 33, from Darlinghurst.'

I smile, twirling a lock of hair around my finger. 'It's been nice to meet you too, Dan, 35, from Crows Nest.'

The moon is high in the sky as I stroll across Oxford Street. Thursday night drinkers blend with street buskers and corporate folks walking home late from the office. I'm swinging my hips to the music in my head.

Three large men who look like they're straight off a building site are walking in my direction. One of them has noticed me. He's got thick dark hair and a moustache, and his belly hangs out of the bottom of his green Victoria Bitter beer singlet.

He waves both hands like he's bouncing a giant pumpkin.

'Beautiful, beauuuutiful!' he shouts, elbowing his two mates.

I smile, holding my skirt in a mock curtsey as I swing past. The music in my head is louder now. The moon glows in the sky and my heart glows in my chest.

My phone buzzes, it's Dan:

Great night! Let's do it again soon.

7. MUUUUUM

There's a layer of fog on my windscreen this morning as I pull out of the carpark and crank up the warm air conditioning. It's 7.28 a.m., on the radio Kyle and Jackie O are making jokes with Prime Minister Julia Gillard.

My phone buzzes:

> Mum: I'm here! I'll be at the meeting point in 5 minutes. How far are you?
> Me: OK. Will be there in 20.

Mum had asked me to pick her up at 7.30 but she's usually the last off the plane. It's hard to imagine what takes her so long.

I pull into the parking zone at Sydney Airport and make my way towards the terminal. Crowds of tourists push trolleys stacked with suitcases, and the taxi rank is lined with four rows or more. The cool morning air smells like jet fuel and cigarette smoke.

Under a sign marked 'The Meeting Point' sits Mum. She's wearing a tight black T-shirt with 'NICE' written in sequins across her breasts. She's deep in conversation with a young couple. I wave and Mum jumps. She clutches her chest in one hand and pumps the air like she's trying to flag down a rescue boat.

'Rebekah! Rebekah!' she shouts.

I walk closer. *Be calm, it's only a week.* 'Yes, I can see you, Mum.'

She leaps from her seat and throws her arms around me. Her head is only as high as my shoulders, but her grip is ferocious. She places an open wet kiss on my cheek. I smile and grimace at the same time.

She motions at the couple still sitting down. 'These are my new friends, Deepa and Anil.' The woman smiles. She has a long black ponytail and looks tired from travelling. Anil is wearing a white T-shirt with the outline of New Zealand on it.

'I sat next to these two on the plane,' continues Mum. 'We had a lovely chat, didn't we?' The woman nods.

'I'm sorry,' I mouth at her.

'I thought Deepa might know my Indian friend in Wellington,' says Mum.

'We're actually from Pakistan, and we were just visiting, on holiday.'

I hear myself thinking the same embarrassed plea I used to make as a teenager: *Muuuuuuuuuuuuum.*

'We've heard a lot about you,' says Deepa. 'You've got a new boyfriend?'

Oh god. I've been on three dates with Dan and Mum is already telling strangers on an aeroplane.

'Now Jacqui, please do stay in touch.' Deepa pulls a pad and a pen from her handbag. 'Here's my email address and phone number. We'd love to see you if you're ever visiting Karachi.' Mum hands her a card, and they clasp hands looking at each other with the glow of new friendship. I shake my head.

'Can you take this bag?' Mum passes me a giant purple

suitcase on wheels. 'And I'll push this.' Next to her is an airport trolley stacked with even more bags. *One week.*

We make our way through the carpark and I flip the boot of my BMW as we approach.

'You've still got this car,' she says. 'It must be very expensive.'

I scowl inside trying not to remember the hire-purchase payments. *Can't she just enjoy the car?*

'I was hoping you'd buy an apartment soon. I can help look while I'm here, if you like.'

'Mum, I can't afford property right now. I'm starting this company.'

She *tsk tsks.* 'It's not too early to start thinking about the future. You know, you're not getting . . .' She stops.

I take two deep breaths and we drive towards the gate. 'What are you going to do while you're here?' I ask.

She rubs her hands together. 'There's so much on. I've got lunch with Penelope, dinner with my friend Ian, Rotary with Clover — that nice woman I met at the Bondi Junction bus stop. And some research meetings at Sydney Uni.'

I roll my eyes thinking about Mum's *research.* She's been studying for a Master's in HR for years, always using it as an excuse to interview people as though she's important.

'And on Friday I've lined up a special project.' I glance over and her eyes are bright with mischief.

'What kind of special project?'

She smiles. 'You'll see.'

8. ONE MILLION DOLLARS

I'm on the fifteenth floor of a building owned by the accounting firm PwC. The room hums with chatter. I don't recognise anyone here, but my name is printed on one of the plastic tags at the front table in a set marked 'Speakers'. The event is for Launchpad Angels, a group that invests in tech startup companies.

'Rebekah, hi. You ready for this?' Cameron walks towards me, his hand outstretched, sandy hair bouncing.

'I guess.' I clutch my laptop bag, feeling nauseous like I'm car sick. 'Who's in the audience again?'

Cameron casts his eyes about the room. Men in suits cluster in circles, a few women in silk jackets chat and nod. 'I'd say half the room are active investors, people looking for good founders, good ideas to back. And the rest are interested onlookers. Sometimes we get the tech media too.'

I want to vomit. 'How many?'

'We're hoping for two hundred.'

'Right.'

'Look, I'm sure this seems a bit intimidating, but . . .'

Intimidating! The last time I spoke in public was Year 10 English class. I try to force a smile.

We look across the audience and he rests a hand on my upper back. 'Everyone here wants you to do well. Just relax. Describe what you're doing, the same as when we met in my office.'

I'd decided to start a tech company after watching that Facebook movie in 2010. *With a good idea and a lot of work maybe I could build a billion-dollar business.* My first attempt was a website for concert tickets. I used my own money and hired some developers in India to write the code. The result was a disaster of broken links and endless invoices that ate almost half of my savings.

My new idea is an app to help customers find and recommend cafés and restaurants. This time, I'll hire engineers I can work with in Sydney. And this time, I'll find investors who know how to build tech businesses, who can give me advice and share the financial risk.

I met Cameron at a networking drinks run by a group called Silicon Beach. It was a Friday afternoon in a dingy hotel bar, and young men dressed in anoraks and thick-rimmed glasses milled about drinking beer and talking to each other with jerky enthusiasm. I stood on the sideline trying to spot an outlier.

At the bar stood a tall man with a sharp nose who was much older, probably fifty. I must have looked different too in my red blouse because he peered across the heads and waved. I walked over. 'Hi,' he said, holding out his hand. 'I'm Cameron.'

I learned that Cameron was an investor. 'I started three tech companies. Now I invest in other people's businesses where I think I can help. Add value, more than just money.'

A week later, I visited Cameron at his office in a high-rise at Circular Quay. Ceiling-to-floor windows looked out to the sparkling harbour, with yellow ferry boats and the giant bridge. I tried to imagine how much it would cost to rent. Then stopped.

'Rebekah, hi. Come in.' Cameron gestured towards a low

black leather couch next to a glass coffee table and poured me a tumbler of water.

'Hang on a minute,' he said, walking towards his door. He waved to his colleague in the next office. 'Gary, come and meet Rebekah.' A short man with floppy grey hair sprang into the room carrying a notebook.

Cameron listed some companies he and Gary had invested in together. I nodded like I recognised the names.

'We back people,' he said. 'Most startup companies will change strategy. They'll learn that whatever they thought was going to work probably won't. But if they're smart, they'll still figure out how to make money.'

Cameron rubbed his hands together. 'Okay, hit us with it.'

I unfold my laptop and open PowerPoint. 'I used to work as a band manager, and I started this website to get fans to promote tickets to events.' My first slide showed the webpage with its overlapping fonts and uneven spacing. 'It was hard to get the coders to build the right thing. But it did work. We sold a lot of gig tickets.'

Cameron and Gary leaned forward in unison.

'Ultimately it wasn't profitable, because our commissions were too small. But I learnt a ton. Now I want to make a similar app for cafés and restaurants. It'll be like Yelp or TripAdvisor, except the recommendations you'll see will be from friends.'

Cameron nodded. 'Got it.'

Gary looked up from his notebook. 'How many software engineers will you need to hire? How are you going to sign up cafés and restaurants? How much will that cost you?'

I flicked open my budget. 'If every startup changes business plan, then why is all this important?' I asked.

'Ha,' said Cameron. 'We don't believe these numbers mean anything. But we want to know that you've thought about it'.

After an hour of questions, they leaned back in their chairs and looked at each other. 'How much are you raising?' asked Cameron.

'One million dollars.' *I can't believe I said that.* I sound like the extortionist in *Austin Powers*. *It's ridiculous, I'm ridiculous.*

'And what commitments do you have?' asked Gary.

'Commitments?'

'What other investors do you have? Who else has said yes?'

'Well, I'm just starting. You're the first people I've seen.'

Cameron stopped tapping his chin and straightened his posture. 'Okay,' he said. 'I like your idea and I like you. I want to be part of this. You can put me down for 100K.'

What? Did he just say . . . Can't he see I don't know anything?

'I'm in for fifty,' said Gary. 'But only if you can get together the rest of the round.'

'Round?' Now they'll definitely know I'm a fraud.

'You want to raise a million, right?' said Cameron.

'Yes'

'So, you need to put together a group of people who'll each invest a bit of money. I've said I'm in for a hundred, Gary's in for fifty. You need to find another 850K. Then you'll have a round.'

'Oh. Right, of course.'

'We're part of Launchpad Angels,' said Cameron. 'It's a group of investors who work together on deals. We've got a meeting next month. I'll see if I can get you a spot to pitch.'

And here we are, on the fifteenth floor of PwC. Cameron positions himself behind the microphone. 'Welcome everyone, we're about to start.'

I scan the room, the seats are almost all full. Everyone is in neutral colours, pressed shirts and neat jackets. Everyone is on time. I sit in the front row, next to Cameron's bag. I close my eyes and breathe.

'Bex.' I'm being elbowed from my right. 'Bex, sorry I'm late. Have I missed your talk?'

Mum appears next to me wearing a red mesh top, her breasts presented out front like cupcakes.

'*Shhh!*' I point to the microphone.

Cameron introduces the first company, and two guys present something about data and agriculture. There are graphs and PowerPoint slides with lots of words and numbers. One of the presenters is very tall, wearing a neat polo shirt over new jeans and a leather belt. The other is older, with grey hair. I don't understand what they're talking about, but they look impressive. *Much more Mark Zuckerberg than me.*

Cameron gets up again. 'Next up, I'd like to introduce Rebekah Campbell from Posse.com. This is her third company and her second tech company.' I flinch. I want to melt into a puddle and disappear into the carpet. *They weren't real companies. Just managing bands and a website disaster.* He nods to me, proud and expectant. *He thinks I can do this.*

My title slide flashes up: Posse.com in rainbow colours. I get up and look out to the crowd, at row upon row of men and the occasional woman with nice hair and smart makeup. *I don't belong here.* I might look tidy right now but actually I'm a mess. My stomach squeezes. And there in the front row, in bright red see-through clothing, is Mum.

Hang on, she's signalling something. *What's she trying to say?*

She's waving her hands from under her mouth, up, like she's

starting to conduct an orchestra. I try to ignore her, but her waving is getting more aggressive. I lean forward around the microphone and hiss '*What?*'

She runs her hands up from her mouth again. 'Smile'. She's drawing a half-circle with her hand. *She's drawing a smile.*

I want to shout, '*Muuuuuum!*' I scan the faces in the room again. I need to make a start. The sensible voice in my brain tells me to breathe.

I smile at my mother, who grins back like a satisfied cat. *Just focus, don't look at her again.*

9. VALENTINE'S DAY

Zzzzzzz goes the office intercom.

'I've got a delivery for Rebekah Campbell.'

'Sure, come on up,' says Josh, my young assistant. 'Turn right at the top of the steps and we're at the end of the corridor.'

I'd rented the office in anticipation of raising investment. It's a huge open room with a polished concrete floor, twenty-two empty desks and a huddle in the corner where my very small team work on the app. There's Glen, our impossibly quiet software engineer; Jen, our impossibly loud salesperson; and Josh, who covers everything administrative.

A minute later a courier in sunglasses wanders through the glass door carrying a bouquet of red and pink flowers.

'Rebekah?' he asks.

Every year on Valentine's Day, I'd notice couriers carrying flowers. I'd monitor them as they scouted about the office building. *Anything for me?* I'd think back through the men I'd exchanged glances with in meetings.

Left brain: *Maybe I've got a secret admirer?*

Right: *Don't be stupid. No one likes you.*

For ten years I'd had these thoughts, and every year the hopeful voice from my left dwindled a little. The flowers were always for someone else, someone with long shiny hair, who'd blush and giggle as she read the card.

Josh jumps towards the door, lifting the bouquet in his hands. He turns to me and sings, 'This is for you!'

I take the flowers and check the three faces in the room. Glen smirks and continues tapping at his keyboard. Jen marches towards me.

'Ooh, who's it from, who's it from?' she says in her cheerful Irish voice.

I breathe in the sweet smell of roses. Jen and I pull open the card like eager schoolgirls.

> Happy Valentine's Day, Rebekah!
> Can't wait to see you tonight,
> Dan xx

Jen wiggles her hips. 'He sounds so nice, Rebekah. When do we get to meet him?'

I try to calibrate what I'm feeling right now. There's warmth across my chest, and pride. That's it: pride. Almost like when I achieve something at work. I search for butterflies, the ones that start in your tummy and flitter up to your heart like magic. I *do* like Dan and we've been dating for a month. He reliably calls me every night at 7.

But right now, my feeling is pride. Someone sent *me* flowers for Valentine's Day. *I can do this. My strategy is working.*

Later that night, Dan leans over the table towards me. 'What are you thinking? I'm thinking the pork belly.'

The dark blue water glistens at Finger Wharf in Woolloomooloo. A few metres away from us, people on their giant boats laugh and pop champagne bottles.

'This place is beautiful,' I say. 'Everything is so perfect. Like someone dreamed it up in a painting, even the little yellow flower beds on the walkway there.'

The restaurant Dan picked is called China Doll, which I googled earlier today. *Wow, fancy. I'll wear my suit.* Dan is wearing a pink open-collared shirt and dark pants.

'We're lucky to get a table here on Valentine's Day. I booked it two weeks ago. They said we got the last one.'

Two weeks? I can't remember planning anything two weeks out.

'I brought my team here for Christmas last year, the food is amazing.' Dan flashes a smile and his cheeks pop. 'Do you want to share a starter? A prawn san choy bow?'

'Yeah, great.'

A waitress appears at our table and unfolds crisp white napkins across our knees. I feel 'posh', as my mother would say. I'm out on a Valentine's Day date.

'Would you like to start with drinks?' she asks.

'Sure.' Dan's eyes twinkle over the black leather drinks menu. 'Shall we get a bottle of bubbly?'

I'd only allowed myself two drinks on our dates so far. The Millionaire Matchmaker says two drinks is the rule. But I feel tense. I need to loosen up. *This is a really nice guy. Maybe champagne will help me feel more of what I'm supposed to be feeling.*

'Sounds great,' I reply.

'We'll get the Stefano from Tasmania,' he says, handing the menu back to the waitress.

I look across the table at Dan. His chestnut brown eyes glimmer in the candlelight. He smiles again. He's looking at me with such affection. *What is it that you see in me? What is it that you like?*

'How's work going?' I ask.

'Yeah, good,' he says. 'My team's killing it at the moment. We're on track to beat our target this quarter by thirty per cent. How about you? Did you get your investment sorted?'

'Ah, yeah.' I puff out my breath. 'We signed the forms yesterday.'

'Congratulations!'

The waitress appears with the bottle in an ice-bucket and pours two glasses. Dan raises his flute. 'Cheers to you.'

I lift mine reluctantly.

'What's up?' he asks. 'Aren't you thrilled? I mean, it's what you've been working on, right?'

My talk at the Launchpad Angels event must have gone well because a lot of people wanted to meet me afterwards. I stood around chatting and collecting business cards for what seemed like hours. Cameron followed everyone up, working out how much each person would invest. Then there was a meeting with lawyers where I agreed to everything they asked for: a board of directors would oversee our budget, our business plan and my performance as CEO.

And yesterday morning I signed the shareholder certificates: 'Christopher Johns: 50,000 shares', 'Mark Milton: 50,000 shares', 'Adrian Robertson: 25,000 shares' and so on. I felt a shudder of dread at each name. *Twenty-three intelligent, good, hard-working people trust me. They're relying on me to pull this off.*

I look out to the water again. The people on those boats seem so carefree. Money does that, I guess. But not for me. Because the $1 million in the company's bank account isn't mine. I'm just in charge of it. I have to spend it, carefully. I have to hire the right people, make the right decisions and turn this company into something worth more than one million dollars so everyone can get their investment back.

'It's just scary,' I tell Dan. 'Being responsible for all that money. I'm not that organised, you know.'

'You seem organised to me.' He reaches over to pat my shoulder. 'You're gonna do this. It's going to be great.'

I notice his eyes again, all bright and impressed by the woman he thinks I am. He doesn't know that when I got home from our first date, the power in my apartment had been cut because I'd forgotten to pay the bill. He looks at me now in my ironed shirt and tidy heels and doesn't know that I ate four servings of cheesecake on Sunday afternoon. *I don't have the self-discipline to hold this together.*

But I know who he is. I can picture him in his corner office at Vodafone, a view over North Sydney and a plaque sign on the door: 'Sales Manager'. Inside there are charts to track the progress of every employee. His desk is clear except for neat folders in trays that are lined up straight and labelled with colour-coordinated stickers.

I imagine peeking inside his ear. His brain is neat too, just like his office, with folders for this and that in rows — everything just in its place. My brain is a clutter of papers and meetings and anxieties about not being enough.

Our food arrives and Dan reaches across the table to stroke my cheek with the back of his fingers: our first real touch. But that question, I can't stop asking myself. *What is it that he sees in me?*

No one has actually *seen* me since Steve. I miss that the most — being completely known by someone. He saw my talents, my flaws, my insecurities; and he still liked me. Dan — it's like he's a different species.

'Do you want to come to church this weekend? Mum really wants to meet you,' he says.

'Oh, sure,' I reply. But think, *Are you ready to meet his mother? She must love him so much, especially after losing his brother.* I visualise a petite woman standing in a church pew, smiling. Dan introduces us and she wraps me under her arm like a new member of her flock.

'It's in Alexandria,' he says. 'We go to the 10 o'clock service. I'll pick you up before and we can get breakfast in Surry Hills.'

'Okay.' Shit. What if I decide that Dan isn't the one? The woman in the church pew kicks me. *'Don't mess around my son. Can't you see we've been through enough?'*

The bubbly is starting to reach my brain and the pills of doubt I felt earlier are dissolving. Dan's fingers, on my cheeks just a few moments ago. I want to stuff them into my bra. I want them to cup my flesh, to circle my nipples and pinch my skin.

'Shall we go?' I ask after our meal. 'For a walk or something.'

Dan signals for the cheque.

'Let me get it this time,' I say. 'You always pay.'

He shuffles awkwardly in his seat and pulls out a thin leather wallet. 'I like paying, and we're celebrating.'

I raise one hand for him to stop and reach for my handbag with the other.

'Okay,' he says. 'We can go halves. I ordered the wine, remember.'

He places his American Express on top of the bill.

'Hang on a sec.' I rummage in my handbag. *Where's my purse?* There are dirty tissues, receipts I keep meaning to tally, some Mentos wrappers, a lipstick whose lid has come off, sand and dust that's getting stuck to the open lipstick, my diary, my phone, tampons, a makeup bag. I rummage deeper. 'I know it's in here.' *Why can't I be neat and organised? Why can't I carry a small wallet with everything in its place?* Dan waits patiently. *Do you see me now?* My head feels like the contents of my bag: tangled, frustrated, chaos. And under everything I hit the top of my purse.

'Here it is,' I beam, pulling out my tattered Visa card like I've found a lost ring in the ocean.

A few minutes later we're strolling across the old wooden wharf. The boats are quieter now. There are steps down to a ledge and a fuel pump which must be for the boats. It's dark and empty and the calm water laps against the planks.

'Shall we take a look down here?' I say.

We climb down onto the ledge where no one can see us. I wrap my arms around Dan's neck, and he lunges forward to kiss me. His tongue enters my mouth like paddle boat going directly straight: in and out in perfect rhythm. I want to grab his hands and slap them onto my breasts, under my skirt. The wine has made everything loose and slippery.

But Dan isn't loose or slippery, he's tight and steady. He's respectful. So we stand, orderly, like two thirty-something professionals, kissing like they'd show in a textbook.

10. GUIDELINES FOR DATING

The jangle of keys at my door interrupts season three of *The West Wing*.

'Are you there, Rebekah?'

'Yes, Mum. I'm here.' I hit pause on the remote.

Mum opens the front door. She's holding what looks like a giant statue covered in plastic. She's grinning so wide that her teeth match the sparkles on her stretchy 'PARIS' T-shirt.

'What's that?' I ask.

'My project!' she exclaims.

She places the statue on the coffee table, next to the flowers from Dan, and begins to unravel the layers of wrapping. The object is big, around half a metre high and heavy.

'Should I be afraid?'

'Of course not,' she tuts, peeling back more and more plastic. 'It's . . . it's . . .'

It's a bronze women's torso. There are two large breasts with pointed nipples. It looks like a sculpture you'd see in a museum in Florence, except new and shiny and the shape bulges.

'It's me!' Mum's eyes glint with delight.

'What do you mean, you? What is it?'

'It's my breasts cast in bronze. I had it done last week.'

'What do you mean *your* breasts? I don't understand.' Is there an actual statue of my mother's breasts on the table?

'There's a man out in Cronulla who does them. He made a plaster cast, then he tips the bronze in. I picked it up today.' She's proud, she's organised this herself and she's proud.

'But, but . . .' I'm searching for words. 'But why?'

'I've got great breasts, Rebekah. Don't you think?' She squeezes her chest with both hands. 'They're fabulous! I want to remember them. Not everyone has breasts like these.'

I let out the cry I've been holding in since we met at the airport. '*Muuuuuum*. Argh. You're crazy. Do you realise that? This isn't normal.'

'What's wrong with loving your body, Rebekah? Aren't you proud of your body?' Her eyes scan me up and down. 'Your breasts are good too — firm, not as big as mine.' She reaches at my chest and I swipe her hand.

'Mum, please don't talk about my breasts.' I head for the kitchen and open the fridge for wine.

'Why are you so uptight, Rebekah? You didn't get it from me.' I hand her a glass. 'You know, your father and I have joined a naturist club.'

'A what?'

'A naturist club, where we don't wear clothes. We've bought a caravan and we go out there at weekends.'

I'm trying very hard not to think about my mother and father walking around together unclothed. With other people. The harder I try, the stronger the image. The stronger the image, the greater my distress.

'But it's cold in Wellington,' I protest.

She laughs. 'We don't go nude when it's cold, only when it's sunny. There's a tennis court and a pool.'

'Mum, I really don't want to know.'

'Why not?' She's halfway through her wine already. 'It's natural. It feels divine to have the breeze on your body. It's the way we were made.' She shimmies her shoulders to watch her cleavage jiggle. 'You should come along with us sometime. You'd love it. They're very nice people.'

I gulp a giant breath of air, puff out my cheeks and exhale slowly. 'There is no way on earth that I would come to a nudist camp with you. Please don't ask me again. Don't tell me about it again.'

'Okay, but the invitation is there.'

'*Muuuuuum*, stop.'

I pace back and forth across the lounge, clutching my glass of wine. The breasts and the bright flowers hover in the foreground as symbols of two mammoth obstacles that I have to shift. As much as I find my mother's behaviour disturbing, there's a tiny part of me that's jealous. *Why do I feel so icky about my body?* I'd never go naked in public — that's too far — but I know I'm more grossed out than I should be.

And what about Dan? He's so sweet, but it just isn't right. I can't go to church on Sunday.

'You haven't told me about your date,' says Mum.

I sit. I need to talk this through, to clarify things in my head. I'm sure Mum will be biased: she's too impressed by the flowers, too eager to tell her friends about my new man, too desperate for grandchildren.

'The date was nice. He's really nice. But I don't know. Something isn't right.'

Mum's gets up to pour another glass. 'What is it that you don't like?'

I think. 'We're just quite different people. I want to find

more of a match. Dan's got everything together and I'm still, well you know, a bit of a shambles. He's so organised. I don't know what I want.' I wait for the comment. The judgement is coming, I'm sure of it.

'When he looks at me, I feel like he's looking at someone else. This woman in his life plan.' Pause again. 'It's like he doesn't see *me*. Almost like we're two people talking, but we're in different places psychologically. Does that sound stupid?'

Mum clasps her hands together. 'How many times have you been out? Four?'

'Yes, four.'

'Well if you don't feel it's right by now, then you'd be best to call it off.' She cocks her head. 'Like you said, you're probably not right for each other. There are plenty of other men out there and you'll know when you meet the right one.'

Hang on, did Mum just agree with me? Did she listen? And say something sensible?

'It's not fair to keep going on dates if you don't think there's a future,' she continues. 'There'll be a woman out there who's perfect for him too, and you don't want to get in the way.'

'But how do I tell him? He's so nice. He sent me these flowers.'

'Just be honest. He'll be okay. People appreciate honesty.' She points to my phone and signals for me to go into the bedroom. I sit on my bed and prepare my words.

Hi Dan, you're a wonderful person and I've loved hanging out with you but:

~~I just don't feel we have chemistry~~ *TOO MEAN*
~~This isn't the right time for me~~ *NOT TRUE AND HE KNOWS IT*
~~I'm just not over my ex~~ *IT'S BEEN TEN YEARS! TOO PATHETIC*

I think we're too different GOOD BUT LEAVES OPEN FOR DEBATE

I dial.

'Hey, I was just thinking about you.' Dan sounds soft and nurturing. *I'll miss this voice.*

'Hi, me too.'

'How was your day?' he asks.

'Oh, okay. Nothing spectacular. How about you?' *Procrastinate.* 'Team still firing?'

He laughs. 'Yeah, we landed a big deal today actually.'

Silence. One, two, three seconds: 'Listen, Dan. There's something I have to say.'

'Yes.'

'I'm just . . . I'm just not sure this is going to work. I mean, you're lovely and I really like hanging out. But —'

'It's okay,' he cuts in. 'I got a sense last night.'

'Really?' How could he have known? Last night was perfect.

'You were a little distant. Your body language or something.' He sniffs, and I hear him exhale slowly though his lips. 'It's okay, really. I mean I'm disappointed, but I understand.'

This man is so lovely. I'm so cold for hurting him.

There's silence again and I have to break it. 'I don't know what to say. I've had so much fun getting to know you.'

He laughs. 'Thanks.'

'And thanks so much for the flowers.' I'm guilt-ridden now too. 'They're just beautiful and I know you spent all that money.' My voice is cracking.

'Hey. It's okay, really. I enjoyed buying them. It was nice to have someone to get something for on Valentine's Day.'

Silence again and this time he's the one who breaks it.

'Listen, Rebekah, it's been great. I feel a lot better about dating after meeting you.'

'Me too. I couldn't have imagined finding a nicer person for my first online date.'

He's still making long exhales. 'Yeah.' Another breath. 'So back to eHarmony, hey.'

I let out a groan. 'I suppose so.'

'I'm sure you'll find your perfect man,' he says. 'I'm sure he's just around the corner. So you keep at it, okay.'

Arrrrrrgh he's so nice. What if there's no one as nice as Dan?

'You too.' *I hope I've made the right decision.* 'You're an amazing catch, you know.'

He laughs again. 'Goodnight Rebekah, 33, from Darlinghurst.'

'Goodnight Dan, 35, from Crows Nest. Sleep well.'

Click.

Back in the lounge I sit at the dining table and open my goals book. Under the list of what I'm looking for in a man, I add a new heading: 'Guidelines for Dating'. I'll add notes when I discover an important lesson.

1. If I feel like something isn't working or I'm not excited to see the person, then call it off straight away. Don't waste his time or create unnecessary emotional stress. I'll know when I meet the right person.
2. For ending a relationship: Always break up by phone conversation, not text message.
3. For ending a relationship: Be honest AND compassionate. Don't make up excuses that aren't true.

I flop back onto the couch and open my laptop. Mum is in the bathroom brushing her teeth. I key in eharmony.com. I have five messages from men called Julian, Gene, Orin, Anuj and Henry. I'll reply tomorrow, but there's one thing that can't wait.

I click on 'Profile' and hit the 'Edit' button. There's a pop-up box that allows you to change your name, but age is uneditable. I scroll to the bottom of the page. 'Contact customer care'.

> Hi,
> When I created my profile, I accidentally entered the wrong birth year, so my age is showing 33 when it should be 34. How can I correct this?
> Thanks,
> Rebekah

It's late now and Mum is asleep. She's on one side of my queen bed, next to the window. The sheet is crooked and the lower parts of her legs and feet lie bare. I climb in the other side and pull the blanket up to my neck. Mum is snoring, a soft open-mouthed suction noise. She's smiling, content with her day and her bronze breasts. I lean over to adjust the sheet so her legs are fully covered. She grunts and there's dribble on her pillow. I kiss her hair and turn out the light.

11. JULIAN

I've picked a Jamaican restaurant called Queenies for my date with Julian. We've messaged each other just twice on eHarmony and all I know is that he's a computer-game programmer with long brown hair and freckles. His profile picture reminds me of a school photograph where the kid sits up straight on a stool, hair tied back grinning for the camera.

It's cooler today so I'm wearing fitted jeans, a long-sleeved shirt and black heeled boots. Queenies is a ten-minute walk so if I leave now, I'll be perfectly late for our 6 p.m. arrangement.

Mum flew home to Wellington yesterday. I dropped her at the airport and helped lug her three suitcases and a giant tote bag containing the bronze breasts. I imagined her carrying it through security screening. *'It's me,'* she'd say, holding open the bag to a guard with a moustache who'd blush, not knowing where to look.

I approach the top of Foveaux Street and feel a blister on my heel. *Why do women have to wear such uncomfortable shoes?* Only a couple of blocks left. I'm not nearly as nervous as my first date with Dan. *Maybe Julian is the one. He's a computer programmer so he must be smart.*

On the footpath I spot someone who looks like a tall ten-year-old with stubble. He's wearing an oversize black T-shirt with 'StarCraft' printed on it in fluorescent purple letters, baggy jeans and frayed white running shoes that would definitely smell if he took them off.

'Rebekah?' he says like he's asking a question.

I grit my teeth into a smile. 'Hi, you must be Julian.'

We climb the stairs to the restaurant. Inside, I examine Julian more closely. His eyes are bloodshot like he hasn't been outside in days, and he walks with the stoop of someone who needs a stick. *Don't judge.* Ruth's advice rings in my ear.

'What did you get up to today?' I ask as we wait in line for a table.

'Just played games, you know. And kicked about the house.'

'What do you mean? Did you work?'

'It's what I do — I'm a *gamer.*'

'Oh, sorry. I thought you wrote games. Like a computer programmer.'

He looks at me like I'm an idiot. 'No, I *play* games and broadcast them online.'

'And people pay you for that?' Whoops, that fell out of my mouth.

'Yeah, kind of. I've got some followers on YouTube and this new platform, Twitch.'

'Right.'

Queenies is packed and the guy at the front says there's an hour wait for a table. We'd agreed to get dinner. *Think, somewhere that's quick.*

'There's a sushi place just around the corner,' I suggest. Zushi back on Crown Street has pre-made rolls. I can shave half an hour from this date by getting food that doesn't have to be cooked.

He shrugs. 'Cool.'

Crown Street is alight with creative types and the odd fast-paced self-talker. Friends call out to greet each other and taxis blare their horns. My heels clop along as we walk among the bustle. *What to ask next?*

'Here it is,' I say, gesturing to the glass door.

Inside, a young woman picks up two menus and directs us to a table.

'I think I'll just get one of these,' I say, pointing to the made-up rolls and edamame under the counter. 'Can we order now?'

I scoot to the seat closest to the door and Julian sits opposite. The waitress plops our food on the table. The restaurant is dimly lit with orange Japanese lanterns. I wait. Silence.

'So, you played games at home today.' *Try not to sound patronising.* 'Where do you live?'

'Out at Bexley,' he says, looking apprehensively at the food. I hand him chopsticks, a plate and a serviette.

'That's south, right?'

'Yeah,' he says. 'Do you know it?' He looks nervous and I feel a pang of guilt in my chest. *Be kind, be compassionate.*

'I haven't been there, but I've driven through it.' I take a chilli-salted green bean and suck.

Julian examines a pod from both ends. 'What's this?'

'It's called edamame.' I pick up another pod. 'You just kind of suck it and bite with your teeth at the same time. Don't eat the outside — just the beans.'

He sucks and a giant slurp escapes his mouth. He shoots an embarrassed glance and we giggle.

'Do you live with flatmates out at Bexley, or friends?'

'Nah, just with Mum and my step-dad. I want to move out, but you know.'

'I think you're really lucky,' I cut in.

'How?'

'To live at home,' I say. 'I wish I could live with my parents.' *Okay, a white lie.* 'Rent in Sydney is crazy.'

His face relaxes. 'And what about you?' he asks. 'Where do you live?'

'Just around the corner actually. In Darlinghurst.'

There's silence again and Julian assesses the sushi rolls. I pour soy sauce into my side plate and mix in the wasabi. Julian follows as if I'm leading an arts and craft lesson on *Play School*.

'Hang on, not too much of that —' I reach across for the wasabi packet.

He licks his fingers. 'Shit.' I twist my face sympathetically. 'Shit, shit, shit.' He reaches for the water.

'You only need a little, little bit of that.'

We munch at the sushi rolls and I search my brain for questions. I'm looking for something we have in common, anything. I only manage one. 'Have you done any other eHarmony dates?'

'No.' He sniffs. 'I've messaged a few but you're the first one I've met in real life.'

'Oh.'

'How about you?'

'Just one other, you're the second.'

We both look to the ceiling in search of a follow-up.

'So, how do you think this is going?' I ask.

'Good,' he says quickly. 'Well, okay so far. You seem nice.'

I smile again, already feeling guilty that I'm going to reject him. 'You seem very nice too, Julian.' I fold my serviette on the table. 'It's getting a bit late for me. I have some work to do before bed.'

We get up to pay. 'I'll get it,' he says. 'Isn't that what you're supposed to do, the guy pays.'

'No way.' I pull out my credit card and hand it to the waitress. 'We'll go halves.'

Outside we hug goodnight and I notice the curved bones in his thin shoulders. 'Do you want to catch up again?' he asks, with high-pitched awkwardness.

'Look. It was really lovely to meet you.' *What's a nice way to say this?* 'Let me think about where I'm at. I'll come back to you.'

I check my phone on the walk home: 6.52 p.m. *Less than an hour, including dinner!* I contemplate the lessons I can take from this experience. If I'd done better research on Julian, I could have saved an uncomfortable night for both of us. And I feel bad for making him rush through dinner. At home, I add new guidelines in my journal.

4. Planning dates: Don't do dinner on a first date. Organise to meet for a drink somewhere we can stay for dinner if the date is going well – or escape quickly if it's not! Stick to venues where this is easy.

5. Planning dates: Always do a screening phone call. Don't meet anyone in person that I haven't had a good connection with on the phone.

6. On paying: Always offer to split the bill. But only insist on paying half if I know I'm not going to see the guy again. It's only fine to let them pay if I can pay for the second date, so it's equal.

12. HENRY

Tonight, I have a knot in my stomach. Like before that first date with Dan, I've been rushing to the toilet all afternoon. In half an hour I'll meet Henry, a six-foot-two blond who works in the city as a lawyer.

This morning I woke to discover a pimple emerging next to my left nostril. It started out as an innocuous bump, but it's been growing all day and now there's a white ball of pus on the top. I've examined it ten times or more and can't decide if I should pop the puss ball or leave it to heal. *If I pop it, I might be able to hide it with makeup.* I decide against the minor surgery. *It might bleed during the date. Yuck.*

I'm wearing the same print dress and patent leather heels as the night I met Dan. *This outfit worked the first time.*

I haven't had a phone call with Henry because we arranged the date before I came up with the screening idea. His profile picture is the face of a model — the kind who'd be photographed wearing a Rolex watch or promoting fancy luggage at an airport. Blue eyes, tall, clean-cut, handsome.

My phone buzzes.

> Henry: I'm here sitting outside on the table next to the street.
> Me: OK 5 mins.

Henry: Can I order you a drink?

Panic. What should I ask for? Something alcoholic but not too alcoholic. Sophisticated but not like a princess. I stare at my phone.

Me: Sure. Whatever you're having.

I remember that TED Talk — 'Your Body Language May Shape Who You Are'. I pull back my shoulders and pace towards the restaurant. I do feel stronger, but there's still a quiver deep inside.

Emmilou Tapas Bar at 413 Bourke Street is a tall terrace house with a wrought-iron fence against the footpath. The wide glass doors are open and inside there's a collage of art and photographs. Gotye's 'Somebody That I Used to Know' blasts from behind the bar.

My eyes scan the seats outside. There, right in corner, sits Henry. His pale blue eyes match his ironed short-sleeved shirt and a lick of blond hair falls across his forehead. He brushes it back when he spots me.

'Rebekah, hi.' He stands and reaches around my back to place a kiss on my left cheek.

He doesn't look disappointed, but he hasn't noticed my pimple yet. I choose the seat next to him rather than straight across, so he'll only see the clear side of my face.

Henry pushes a salt-rimmed cocktail glass towards me. 'Margarita. It's what I'm having.' He lifts his glass and we clink.

This guy is so good-looking. He can't be interested in me. But here I am, so all I can do is try. I remember a fact from *How to Win*

Friends and Influence People. People like the sound of their own name: 'So, Henry. How was your day?'

We talk for a while about his work and order tapas to share. He's on the mergers and acquisitions team at Wiles & Williams, one of the biggest law firms in Sydney.

'It's okay,' he says, taking a sip from his margarita. 'The hours are crazy though. I always thought I wanted to make partner, but now I don't know.'

'Why not?'

'I'd like to have a family one day, and I see how hard these guys work. They're never at home.'

Aww, he's wants children. I imagine the two of us arriving arm in arm at Christmas lunch, how impressed everyone would be.

'Did you always want to be a lawyer?'

He mulls the question. 'I suppose so. All the boys at my school did finance or law. I hated maths, so, you know.' He shrugs. 'I'm actually really jealous of what you're doing. I'd love to start a company.'

'Ha,' I laugh. 'It's not as fun as it looks.'

'Really?' he narrows one eye like a charming actor from a spy movie. 'What's it's like then? What did you do today?'

He's actually interested. I tip my head back and give an exaggerated sigh. 'You really want to know?'

He nods.

'Okay. This morning I had breakfast with my friend Mel. She's also a startup founder. But much better than me.'

He gestures like he wants me to continue.

'My team is in an office just around the corner.' I wave in the direction of our building. 'And a few weeks ago, I raised a round of capital.'

'Well, that's big.'

'Hmmm, kind of. I suppose.' Our eyes meet. *How much should I say?* The voices in my head screech into the spotlight.

Left: *Stop bragging. Men aren't interested in powerful women.*

Right: *Bragging? Seriously, Rebekah. Who do you think you are? You're not powerful. Your company is tiny, it's nothing.*

'This one investor helped me put the deal together, so it wasn't really me.'

What I won't tell him is that after we signed the investment papers, Cameron picked some guys to join the board. We met in a glass room with a long wooden table, just down the hall from Cameron's office. Six men in dark suits swivelled in my direction.

'Why haven't you hired a chief engineer?'

'Is that woman you've got doing business development really qualified?'

'I think we should focus on the States. Have you lined up any partners there?'

I left that meeting with my head spinning on its axis.

The next day, Cameron called. 'One of the guys thinks you need a COO.'

'A what?'

'A Chief Operating Officer. Someone to work alongside you, like a partner. Terry reckons he knows someone — this guy Don he used to work with.'

They don't think I can do this.

'It'll be good,' said Cameron. 'You'll still be in charge.'

'I guess it *would* help to have someone more experienced around.'

A waiter arrives with a plate of zucchini fritters, some potato tostadas and two more margaritas. The restaurant is packed now. There's a long table next to us celebrating a birthday. A waiter carries a cake topped with sparklers and a woman blushes as they sing. The margaritas have untangled my nerves and I watch Henry watch the group. Those dreamy blue eyes, square football-player shoulders. *He can't be interested in me.* It just seems so, so . . .

'So, Rebekah.' Henry places his hand over mine and I jolt. 'What's your plan?'

'My plan right now?'

'No.' He shakes his head. 'Your life plan. Where do you want to be in five years?'

I listen for the voices in my head. *Come on, what should I say here?*

Right: *Not too much, he'll think you're up yourself. He'll be intimidated. Talk yourself down, be a lady.*

Left: *But he's obviously interested. Just be yourself, be confident.*

Wait, is that the sensible voice or is that the margaritas?

'I'd like to build up the business and sell in around three years. I'd like to have kids, two or maybe three. I'd like to buy a house at Bondi Beach because there's great schools around there and I'd love for my kids to grow up at the beach.' I feel my voice gallop as I repeat out loud the same goals that I say in my head several times a day. 'After I sell the business I want to go into politics.' I pause. *Does he like my plan? Should I stop?* 'And then, one day I'll retire, I guess. And go on cruises. I've always thought it would be cool to travel when I'm old.'

He leans back in his seat. 'Two to three kids. That's a lot.'

'I know,' I say awkwardly.

Right: *You're an idiot, Rebekah. You've blown this now.*

Left: *Didn't you hear? He likes the plan. It's good to have direction.*

'I'm an only child and I was lonely a lot, growing up. I'd like my kids to have friends.' I pause. *Do I sound deluded? Inject some realism perhaps?* 'I don't know, I'm thirty-four. We'll see.' *Not that realistic.* 'I'm easy really.'

'It's sounds like you've got it all figured out.'

I've almost finished my second cocktail and Henry signals again to the waiter.

'I'm okay.' I hold my hand over my glass. I feel perfectly lubricated, happy and in control, but probably on the edge of saying something stupid. Or maybe I already have? I can't tell.

Henry's hand rests across mine and I slip my fingers around his wrist. 'What about you?' I ask. 'What's your five-year plan?'

Henry's shoulders are still, but his eyes flit side to side. 'I don't know. I don't have a plan like you do.'

I try to catch his gaze, but his look is vacant. It's like he's a different person under his polished inner-city lawyer skin. He taps the table with a teaspoon.

'Maybe I should hitch along with your plan: two kids, house by the beach. Sounds good. Not sure about being married to a politician though.'

We both chortle. 'I'm not set on that one.'

The birthday group has dissipated and the porch is much quieter now. 'It's getting late,' he says, checking the time on his phone. 'I've got soccer in the morning.'

We stand and Henry approaches the counter. 'Can I get half?' I reach into my bag. He waves. 'No way.'

Outside, Henry says he wants to walk me home. He puts his arm around my shoulder as we criss-cross streets on our way to Darlinghurst. Taylor Square is still painted in rainbows from Mardi Gras last Saturday. We talk about his weekend plans: soccer, a mate's birthday tomorrow night, and visiting his grandma on Sunday. 'She's always hassling me to bring a girlfriend,' he says, his left hand brushing my ear. 'She's going to love you. She likes strong women.'

Right now, I don't feel like a strong woman. I feel like a little girl, all mushy under the arm of my handsome date. Just like when I was ten years old, asking a boy to our Year Five dance.

Colin had been much shorter than me, with blond hair that looked like it had been cut using the outline of a bowl. It was customary, in our class, for boys to ask girls to the dance. The popular kids had already paired off. I chose Colin because he was the only boy who played four-square with us at lunchtime. He was quiet and kind and I knew he'd never have the courage to ask anyone. I'd have to ask him.

One day after school, I sprinted across the field to catch him alone so that none of our friends would see. 'Colin.' He spun around. I didn't wait to catch my breath. 'Do you want to go to the dance with me?'

He stood still, staring at me like a stunned animal. 'Um, okay.'

'Okay,' I replied. Without another word I turned to run back towards the classroom, leaping so high in the air that my little legs splayed out to the side like loose pins. I couldn't name the feeling at the time, but I can now. It's the feeling of '*Yes*': the cute boy will be my partner at the dance. The tall handsome lawyer is walking me home. He's interested in me. I can't be such a freak after all.

Henry's jaw is sharp in the light of my apartment building. 'This is me,' I say. *Is he expecting me to invite him in? Not on a first date.* Nerves pluck at my chest.

He smiles. 'I'll leave you here, now I know you're safely delivered home.' Like a movie star, he confidently takes my waist and kisses my lips. He kisses once, twice: soft, slow, wet kisses, then his tongue enters my mouth and my tongue meets his. His lips taste sweet and salty like margaritas. His breath puffs gently against my face and his warm body presses against mine. After a minute we stop and embrace in a long hug.

'It's been really lovely to meet you, Rebekah.' He steps back, taking my hand, his eyes darting between me, my apartment building and the ground. *He's shy, how sweet.*

'I'd love to do this again. To hang out more, if you want to?' he says.

I feel my mouth stretch into a smile so wide that I think my cheeks might crack. 'Yes, of course. This has been, like —' I shake my head like I'm dreaming '— the best date ever.'

He lets go of my hand and turns towards the taxi rank. 'I'll call you tomorrow, okay?'

He blows a kiss and I blow one back. 'Good night Henry, see you soon.'

13. THE NEXT DAY

11 a.m.

Jen and I link arms as we exit the lecture theatre at the University of New South Wales. We've just finished the final class of a ten-week Toastmasters course that we'd taken together to improve our public speaking skills.

'So, tell me,' Jen pleads, her voice high in anticipation. 'How was it, last night? What's his name again?'

'Henry,' I reply.

'Oh yes, Henry. Or should I say Daniel Craig.'

We giggle. Jen is the only person, other than Ruth, that I've told about my dating plan. After Dan sent the Valentine's Day flowers, I spilled the whole thing over lunch.

'He was nice.' I bite my lip. I want to appear in control, but I'm about to burst. 'He was *so* nice, Jen. It was just amazing.'

We pass a row of jacaranda trees in the university grounds, their golden leaves fluttering in the autumn sky.

'I'm so happy for you!' Jen hugs me and I feel tears forming in the corners of my eyes. She takes my shoulders in both hands. 'You deserve it.'

2 p.m.

Those nerves I felt when Henry was at my door, they're still ringing in my chest. *On our next date, he'll definitely expect sex.* I picture him — tall, confident, lawyer. And me — nervous, awkward, fraud. I imagine us having the conversation. Me admitting how long it's been. Him chuckling into his hands, slipping out the door.

4.10 p.m.

I check my recent calls to make sure I haven't missed one from Henry. *Maybe, while I browsed the internet? The reception might have* . . . There's nothing. I place my phone on the coffee table and stare at it. Waiting. *It's still early.*

9 p.m.

I've been to the Turkish cake shop across the road twice. The first time for a cinnamon scroll and then for a slice of cheesecake. My phone is still on the table. Waiting.

9.17 p.m.

Bzzzzzzz

My heart takes two giant bounds forward to grab the phone.

> Hi Rebekah. Great to meet you the other night. Catch up again soon?

I take a deep breath. 'Thank you, God!' I click into the message. 'Fuck!' I want to throw the miserable piece of glass and metal at the window. *Julian!*

10 a.m. Sunday

> Me: Hi Julian. I had a great time meeting you but I don't feel like we have a strong enough connection to go out again.

Julian: OK. Thanks for letting me know. All the best.

I pull out my journal and add an * next to rule number two:

2. For ending relationship: Always break up by phone conversation, not by text message. *It's OK to use text message if I've only been on one or two dates. Three or more dates should be done by conversation.

9 p.m. Sunday

Still nothing from Henry. Maybe he lost his mobile phone? Maybe he's getting a new phone today and he won't have my number?

Should I text him? I imagine tall, handsome Henry pleading to a man behind the counter at the Telstra shop. *'Can't you find my old phone numbers anywhere? I just met this girl.'*

I can't bear it any longer.

Me: Hi Henry. Hope you had a great weekend.

I delete 'great'. Sounds too formal.

Me: Hi Henry, Hope you had a fun weekend. Let me know if you want to catch up again.

No, that sounds like I'm sitting around waiting. Think again. Be mysterious.

Me: Hi Henry, Hope you had as much fun this weekend as I did . . .

No, too provocative, too weird.

> Me: Hi Henry, I had fun on Friday. Been thinking about you.

No, too desperate.

> Me: Hi Henry, I had fun on Friday. See you soon.

Send.

14. RIPE

On Wednesday afternoon I park my car outside Ruth's office at Bondi Junction. I've texted Henry twice more, once on Monday after work and again last night. No reply. I make my way up the lift, past the nail salon and slump onto the waiting-room couch. There's a documentary about cryogenics on the television and I feel just like one of those macabre-looking bodies where they've drained out the blood for freezing.

Colin had been a faithful partner at that Year Five dance. It was a Thursday afternoon, and our mums and dads watched from wooden benches along the sides of the draughty school hall as we attempted the foxtrot, the cha cha and the waltz. Colin's head had only reached the top of my shoulders, so I'd bend for him to manage the twirls.

After the dance we sat on the steps outside and agreed to 'go around together', which meant we'd be known at school as boyfriend and girlfriend. From that day on, Colin stopped playing with us at lunch. His face turned red whenever he saw me, and we never spoke. A few months later one of his friends ran up to me outside class. He had short hair with a scraggly rattail out back and his yellow uniform shirt hung untucked over his little brown shorts. 'I've got a message from Colin.' He pushed his chin forward like he was about to spit. 'You're dumped!'

It felt like a kick in the chest. I walked home that day in a fog of rejection, the lyrics to 'Total Eclipse of the Heart' running circles around my head.

For the very first time, I understood what singers were on about. This *love* thing. *The angst, the rejection, it's awful.* But now looking back, at least Colin didn't leave me hanging. Even if he did send his scraggly-haired friend to deliver the message.

Ruth welcomes me with her familiar warmth. I fold into her arms before taking my position in the leather armchair. I can tell she's noticed my glumness. She leans forward, over her mahogany glasses. 'How's the dating going?'

'Not good,' I reply, puffing out my cheeks.

'How many have you done so far?'

'Three. Well, three different men, but I went out a few times with the first one.'

She shuffles in her chair and waits for me to continue.

'I met this lovely guy on Friday night. Henry.' Ruth nods. 'We had such a great date. The conversation was easy, the chemistry was . . .' I feel myself blush. 'We kissed.' I let out a huff. 'He said he'd call me on Saturday. And now it's Wednesday.' I hold out my phone like it's a schoolyard bully who's been taunting me all week.

Ruth sits forward, calm in my anguish. 'Tell me about Henry. And tell me about the date.'

'He's a lawyer, although he said he'd rather be a startup entrepreneur.'

'Like you,' she adds.

'Yes, I suppose.' She waves for me to keep talking.

'He's *very* good-looking.'

Ruth scrunches her lips suspiciously.

'What? What's wrong with good-looking?'

She shakes her head. 'How did the conversation go? What did you talk about?'

'Just normal stuff. Like work, family. It seemed to go well, there weren't any silences or anything.'

I gaze out the window and comb my memory for what happened. 'There was one thing that kind of felt weird,' I continue. 'Where I might have stuffed up.'

'Okay.'

'He asked about my plan, where I want to be in five years' time.'

'And what did you say?'

'I told him the truth. Two or three kids, live at Bondi Beach, sell the business. You know, the stuff I've always said.' Ruth sucks air through her teeth like I've just slipped over a cliff. 'Did I say something wrong?'

Ruth closes her notebook and crosses her legs. 'It's important to be yourself, of course. And confident.' She pauses, like she's considering how to put the words together. 'Men still want to be needed. They want to know that you need what they've got. If you brag about how fabulous your life is, that you're successful and financially independent, then you rattle off a five-year plan — well, it might be hard for him to see where he fits.'

'Do you think I should hold back?'

'I'm not saying don't be honest. Just, maybe don't put it all on the table on the first date. It might be overwhelming.' Ruth smiles. 'I know this sounds silly, but underneath, men still think they're here to look after us.'

I stretch my face in disbelief. 'Men still think like that? But

I want an equal. I don't want to be looked after.'

'I know, and you will find an equal. I'm sure. It's a balance. Relationships are about balance. You've got a great career, you're confident, attractive. But there has to be vulnerability. Men like an opening, some area of your life where they can help you. If he feels like you don't need him, then he might come away with a sense that you don't make him feel special.' Her eyes twinkle. 'Perhaps it's in the bedroom?'

Gulp. Don't go there.

I lean back in the chair, remembering that first year that I'd seen Ruth. At the end, how she teared up with pride at my progress. By allowing her to help me, I'd given her something. *Maybe it's not just men.* Maybe letting people in, letting people help, is how we make connections.

'Have you tried contacting Henry?' she says. 'I mean, it's possible he lost his phone.'

'Yes, I thought that.' I turn my phone over on the table. No missed calls. *Maybe if I stop looking at it . . .* 'But I texted on Sunday, and Monday and Tuesday.'

'Oh.' She's writing something in her book. 'Don't do that.'

'What?'

'Keep texting.'

'It was only three times.'

'Think about it.' She's looking up now, eyes fixed. 'You're chasing him. If someone started chasing you down the street, what would you do?'

I imagine a shadow speeding towards me. My heart pounds. 'I'd run away, I guess.'

'Exactly. As soon as you start chasing someone, they'll run. It's human nature.'

'Okay, I'll remember that.'

'And be wary of the good-looking ones.'

'What?'

'You said Henry was good-looking: tall, well-groomed, muscular.'

'Does that mean something?'

Ruth taps a finger across her lips. 'Appearance can be a sign of values. It's not that hard to be a ten these days with plastic surgery, the gym. If you really value appearance, then you'll do whatever it takes. If you care a bit — you want to be healthy, but it's not your whole life — then you probably won't be a ten. You might be a seven or eight.'

'Right,' I say.

'When you meet a man who's incredibly handsome, or muscular, it can be a flag for shallow. There's exceptions, of course. But it's something to watch.'

She turns to check the clock, and hands the Medicare form.

'Don't let this experience get to you. There's plenty of men out there. You've just got to find one who's buying what you're selling.'

'What do you mean, buying and selling?'

'Well, just because you're not what Henry is looking for right now, doesn't mean there's anything wrong with you. It just means he's looking for something else, or maybe he's not shopping to buy. Maybe he's just browsing.'

'He said he wanted a relationship.'

'Everyone says that. How old is he?'

'Thirty-five.'

She snorts. 'That's still young for a man. He's a lawyer in the city, he's single and he's thirty-five. He probably isn't ripe yet.'

'Ripe?'

'Yes, like you are right now. You're ready to partner up, have a family. You're ripe.' She pauses like she's waiting for me to show I understand. 'Men will drift through dating and relationships, but their focus is on themselves, their friends, their careers. Then, usually for a short period of time, they'll soften and look about for the right person. You need one like this. Ripe, ready to be picked.'

Outside, I notice children skipping across the footpath behind the mall. A man piles shopping bags into his car and a woman carries a cat in the direction of the vet. I picture myself as a product on a shelf. There's someone out there shopping for me. There's a strange comfort in imagining myself as a unique object with special features. *Maybe the product isn't faulty. I just need the right buyer.*

15. THE MEN OF SYDNEY, PART 1

Tony wears dark jeans and a black leather belt around his swollen waistline. His hair is brown, almost black against his pale skin. 'How's the online dating going? Have you done many yet?' he asks.

'Just three.'

'You're a baby then. Fresh.'

I examine his face. *His profile said thirty-eight.* His forehead and cheeks are smooth but in the corners of his eyes are clusters of tiny wrinkles. *Botox?*

'Why, how many have you done?'

'Fifty.' He shrugs. 'Maybe a hundred.'

Tonight, I'm trying out a place called The Victoria Room, just around the corner from my apartment. From the road there's just a door and a straight set of stairs. At the top, the room opens into a high-ceiling loft of velvet couches, gold-trimmed lightshades and a jumble of décor that looks like it's lifted from the set of the Moulin Rouge. There's a bar to the left and a restaurant on the right.

After a friendly phone call on Sunday, I'd agreed to meet Tony for a drink. He has his own company that lends finance to people borrowing cars. 'I wouldn't say it's my passion or anything. But it makes good money.'

'What is your passion?' I ask.

He shrugs again. 'I don't know. Meeting girls like you I guess.'

It's clear that Tony is a pro at dating. He asks lots of questions and makes quips that I'm sure I'm not the first woman to hear. He lives alone in a Paddington terrace with his dog Thumper. 'He's a greyhound rescue, he used to be a racer.' Tony pulls out his phone and flashes a photo of himself cheek-to-cheek with a brown-haired dog, tongues out like they're both smiling.

'He's beautiful. You look like friends,' I say.

'He's my best mate. He was in a pretty bad state when I got him, only had half a tail. That's why I call him Thumper, cause the stump of his tail thumps on the ground when he's lying down.'

Tony suggests we relocate to the restaurant for dinner and I can't help but notice the chunky heels on his thick leather shoes. *Male platforms? His profile said five-ten.* We take a seat on high-backed wooden armchairs under a glowing chandelier. Across the table Tony's face looks warm in the dim orange light.

A waitress with a thick black fringe and a sleeve of tattoos approaches our table. 'Have you dined with us before?' she asks.

We shake our heads.

'It's a tapas-style menu. Everything's designed to share.' She hands us menus in leather folders. 'For two people I'd suggest three dishes, or four if you're hungry.'

We talk and laugh and eat. Tony is confident and polished. He tells me about his family, who've lived in Sydney for three generations. He sails on the weekend with a bunch of friends who share a small yacht, he skis at Thredbo in the winter. I look into his eyes and those wrinkles still bug me. *He can't be thirty-eight.* And his hair is too dark for his face, even the sideburns.

My head is a jumble as we walk back down the stairs to

street level, and I search inside for feelings. I imagine myself slipping into Tony's life. I'd move into his terrace house, cuddle Thumper at night, sail on the weekend.

'I had a lovely time, Rebekah.' He holds my hand and leans in to kiss my cheek. 'Listen, you text me if you want to meet up again. I know you haven't done many dates yet.'

I search his eyes. His comment suggests that dating is just like shopping for a car: assess the market, then decide. He knows he's one of the first models I've seen. Ruth said to think of myself as a product but I'm not ready to be so clinical. *There should still be magic.*

I want to say 'That was fun' or 'Let's do it again' but my mouth remains closed. I can tell he's waiting for something. We stand in awkwardness.

He smiles again. 'Good night.' And there's a meeting of our eyes to acknowledge that our paths on this planet just crossed for a few hours this Thursday evening at a restaurant in Darlinghurst and from here on will continue different directions. He walks away, up the street towards Paddington, suit jacket swung over his shoulder and dyed hair bouncing in the moonlight.

Paul is thin and carries a black leather briefcase. Tonight, I've arrived at The Victoria Room first and have taken a seat at the far end of the bar next to the grand piano. Paul's mousey-blond hair is parted in the middle and his knees poke through his grey suit pants like tent poles as he walks cautiously across the room.

'Rebekah?'

'Hi.' I stretch out my arm to shake hands.

Paul perches on the stool next to mine, his eyes cast down.

A bartender in a tight mesh T-shirt approaches. 'Can I get you anything?'

I ask for a vodka lemonade and Paul orders a gin and tonic. His eyes seem set on the coasters under our drinks and I notice his bottom lip is shaking. *I'll need to lead this one.*

'So Paul, you're an accountant, right?' He looks up and, finally, eye contact. 'What have you been up to today?'

He twists his mouth apologetically. 'Nothing much, I'm afraid. Just the same old.' There's a long pause and I take a sip of my vodka lemonade to fill the void. *Think of another question. Give him an opening to say something interesting.*

'What kind of accounting are you in? Any famous clients?'

He laughs out through his nose. 'I mainly do tax. I work with some names you might know, but I can't say. It's confidential.'

'Oh.' I sip my drink again, once then twice.

Now that I can see up close, it's clear that his bottom lip is shaking harder and his fingers tremble as he wraps them around his glass. I'm lost. The 'accountant' exchange is at a dead end. I need a new line of questioning.

'Have you done this before, met someone online?' *This must be his first time.*

He flashes a brief shy smile. 'Yeah,' he says. 'Maybe ten, but over a couple of years.'

Okay, I can work with this.

'How have you found it? Any funny stories?'

There's a sincerity to his face that draws me in. 'Honestly, everyone I've met has been really nice. I just haven't . . .' He looks down at his drink again. 'I just haven't met the right person yet, you know?'

We chat back and forth for a bit. The music is loud and

Paul's voice is soft, so I lean in to hear. 'Mum and Dad just had their fortieth wedding anniversary and we had a big party. My two brothers were there with their wives and kids. They were all running around, screaming in the garden.' His face brightens. 'Charlotte is two. She kept spraying everyone with the hose.' He shrugs his shoulders and stretches back on his stool. 'I guess I just want that. A family, you know, some crazy kids.'

'Yeah.' I look at Paul like we're two travellers searching for the same destination. 'Me too.'

Another pause in conversation. Paul is sweet but this is hard work. I decide to let the silence hang. Let's see if *he* can conjure up a question.

'Tell me about your work. You're an entrepreneur?'

I describe Posse with enthusiasm, assuming he'll be interested in the capital-raising part. 'I managed to get twenty-three investors into the same deal.'

Paul looks impressed. 'You know, our firm runs the Entrepreneur of the Year awards. You should enter.'

My mind has started to process the date. Paul is friendly and genuine about his search. He's got a good job, he's tall enough with nice eyes, his family sound lovely. I picture myself sitting in a floral print dress sipping wine cooler at his family party. I like the image, but it isn't me. It's a woman who's softly spoken, reserved, courteous.

'It's been really nice to meet you, Paul.' I'm thankful for my strategy to meet for a drink without the expectation of dinner. It's not that I don't want to spend more time with Paul, but that the more time we invest, the worse I'll feel when I text him 'no thanks' tomorrow.

'You too.' Paul makes that shy smile again and I wonder

what's running through his brain. *Does he like me? Was he impressed by my capital-raising story or was it too much? What's more attractive: confidence or humility?*

The bartender lifts our glasses and I notice Paul has shredded his cardboard coaster into a pile of tiny fragments. He walks me to the door and the waitress with the dark fringe and tattooed sleeve smiles at us, raising her eyebrows.

Hang on. My eyes fix on Paul's shoes. *He's wearing platforms too!*

On the street we knock shoulders in an awkward hug. 'Do you want to go out again?' he asks.

Shit. I'm conflicted: honest or nice? 'Sure.'

'I'll text you tomorrow,' he says, holding up his phone like it's a promise.

Three days later I look at my phone on the table and wrinkle my nose. There's been no message from Paul; he disappeared just like Henry. *Is this a thing? Why didn't he want to go out again?* I file through my memory of Thursday night. I smiled, asked questions. I said I'd go out again.

I consider calling and asking for honest feedback. Then I could iterate and improve myself, just like we use customer feedback to improve our app. I decide it would be too weird and he might not be honest, so I lie in bed staring at the ceiling.

My mind burns hot with anger and fear.

Anger: *I'm a great catch for Paul. He should feel grateful that I showed interest in him. I worked so hard to make him comfortable.*

Fear: *How attractive am I? I can't be horrendous, or Dan wouldn't have liked me and Henry wouldn't have kissed me. But what if I am ugly?*

Anger: *He must have been intimidated by my work or my confidence. I should have played it down, been coy. Make him feel like the impressive one.*

Anger: *I don't want to talk myself down and I shouldn't have to.*

Fear: *What if no one wants me? Are my expectations too high?*

The left side of my bed is empty. I take the unused pillow, cuddle it like a body between my arms. 'Steve,' I whisper, 'lie next to me.' I pull back the blanket and imagine him jumping in, wide grin, flowing hair. *I'm so lucky I found you, even if it was just for a while. Some people go their whole lives and never find true love.*

Roger has rosy cheeks and dangles his legs over the wooden boardwalk at Manly Wharf. It's Sunday afternoon and the outdoor beer garden is alive with throngs of colourfully dressed patrons making the most of the late March sun. Roger and I have just walked along the beach. We've decided to sit for a beer and a chat at the end of our second date.

Our first date at The Victoria Room had been a blast. I spent most of the night folded in half, clutching my stomach with laughter. Roger is an investment banker and his passion is a hobby farm in the Hunter Valley that he bought last winter. He'd grown up in the country town of Tamworth and is the youngest of seven.

'I'm Mum's favourite cause I'm the baby,' he said, tugging his cheeks with his fingers. He didn't ask about my family, but I jumped in anyway.

'I'm the only,' I said. 'I would have loved siblings.'

'Ah, a first born,' he said. 'No one to break in the parents.'

I came away from our date feeling as if I'd been part of a magic show. His charisma seemed to fill the restaurant and I took on the role of his eager assistant. But there were glimpses of behaviour that worried me. After dessert, he raised an arm and clicked his fingers twice. 'Could you get me another beer, sweetheart.' The tattoo-sleeved waitress rolled her eyes and

I winced in embarrassment. He spoke about a deal he'd just closed: 'It took giant balls, you know, to hold out like we did.' I couldn't help but picture the lack of balls between my own legs. *Is he saying I couldn't be an investment banker, do deals like him?*

But at the end of the night my net feeling was of enchantment. I was probably being over-sensitive. Roger was loud, cheerful and intoxicatingly funny. We embraced in a warm country hug and he said we should catch up on Sunday.

I gaze out across Manly Harbour and back to Roger, who's pushing a sliver of lime into his Corona. 'Why are you single?' he asks. 'I mean, you seem normal and everything. Not nutty like some of these other girls.'

I laugh, but the anxiety-tide rises in my chest as I search for the right response. *Should I tell him about you, Steve?* Practice vulnerability, like Ruth suggested.

'To be honest, I haven't dated in a long time.' I lift my chin and look directly into his eyes. *I want him to see my heart. This is my opening, an area of life he could help me with.*

'I really loved my first boyfriend. And he . . .' I feel tears form in my eyes. 'He was killed in a car accident when I was twenty-four.'

Roger looks down and there's a long silence. I wait. *What's he thinking?*

'That's heavy.' He takes a swig from his Corona, almost finishing it. 'Do you think you're over it, then?'

I feel a surge of irritation, but in the moment I can't work out why.

'Well, it's been ten years. That's a really long time.' *I shouldn't have said anything. It's a second date.*

Roger tips his head sideways and I get the sense that he's

eyeing me like sack of damaged goods. There's more silence and I jump in to fill it. 'Tell me about your farm. You said you have cows?'

He pulls out his phone and shows me a photo of three cream-and-brown patched Jersey cows standing in bright green grass. 'This is Flopsy, Mopsy and Cottontail.' He flicks to the next picture, a bull. 'And this is Mr McGregor!' He laughs a deep cackle like he's thinking about the giant horned beast having his way with those lovely cows.

Roger describes how he bought the animals as calves. 'I'll probably sell Flopsy and Mopsy when they get bigger and just keep Cottontail, for breeding.'

'Sell?' After he named them, he couldn't.

'Yeah, for beef.' He sniffs. 'That's right, you're vegetarian. You probably don't like this stuff.'

'It's okay.' *It just seems so cold.*

'Cottontail is the best for breeding. She's got a small head and narrow shoulders, so her babies, you know, they come out easier.'

'Right.'

'And she's the last-born, like me.' He chuckles again and looks directly at my face like he's willing me gone. 'First-borns are usually the weakest. We don't keep them.'

David is a scientist working on a cure for cancer. He's thirty-one years old, at the younger end of my age range on eHarmony, and tonight is our second date.

I've established a rhythm to my weekly dating routine; I try to think of it as an extracurricular activity, like netball or art class. Throughout the week, I'll send and respond to messages on eHarmony, usually in batches. I'll schedule one or two calls with the most promising candidates for Sunday afternoons and then choose one to meet for a date, always 6 p.m. Thursday at The Victoria Room. I find comfort in the abundance of men in my pipeline. *Surely one of these guys is going to work out. 'Just around the corner,' like Dan said.*

My phone call with David had been exceptional. He's from London and speaks like he went to a fancy upper-class school. 'I'm over here doing my PhD,' he said, 'in molecular biology and cancer treatment.'

I saved 'David Scientist' into my phone along with Roger Farmer, Paul Accountant, Tony Finance, Henry Lawyer, Julian Games and Dan Sales. I scroll the list and it reminds me of collecting the toys that came with McDonald's Happy Meals when I was a kid. Each name and profession in my contacts represents a small achievement for the collection.

Our first date had been nice. David had short brown hair and wore a black collared shirt. 'I came out to Australia to surf, and the University of NSW is doing some awesome research in my space.' Our conversation flowed: he spoke, then asked questions; I spoke, then asked questions. He straightened his neatly gelled fringe with his hand.

Tonight, we've agreed to meet for a drink at Bondi Beach, where he lives. I've spent most of the day planning an outfit: laidback, beachy but still elegant. I found a long navy dress and a pair of brown leather sandals at a store in Paddington and had my toenails painted for the first time in months. I'm conscious that David is three years younger than me and earlier today I made the mistake of looking him up on Facebook. He stood at the beach in a huddle of mates and bikini-clad twenty-somethings with washboard stomachs. I'm thirty-four, wearing a push-up bra and Spanx under my dress.

I turn the corner up from the beach and there's music and a crowd outside the bar. Bondi Hardware is packed with young skin, tanned and glowing in tiny denim shorts and singlets. There are hanging plants, spanners and hammers fixed to a brick wall reading 'Tools Down'.

David greets me at the door in a polo shirt and shorts with their bottoms folded up in a carefully ironed line. He orders two Bloody Marys and we take seats across from each other at a high wooden bench. 'I had a late one last night,' he says, rubbing the side of his head. 'These are the best for hangovers.'

The bass pounds from two giant speakers. I lean forward and shout, 'What did you get up to last night?'

'What?' David cups his ear towards my mouth.

'I said—'

David waves me to stop. 'Let's go outside.' He gestures to the back door.

We exit to a garden courtyard with hanging lights, more leafy plants and steel tables. The seats are all taken but we find space on the concrete wall of a garden bed. *Think of something cool to say.* I sip my drink and bite the straw. 'You didn't tell me about your research the other night. What aspect of cancer are you looking at?' *That's not cool, Rebekah! That's what his mother's friend would ask.*

'Oh,' he says, like he wasn't expecting the question. 'I'm looking at sugar and the role it plays in cancer.' He holds up a fist. 'If this is a cancer cell, it needs glucose to grow. I'm working out what happens when it doesn't get any.'

'Wow,' I say. 'If I stop eating sugar will it stop me getting cancer?'

'I wish it were that easy. We can slow the growth sometimes, but not stop it. There's still a lot we don't know.'

We finish our drinks and David puts my glass on the table next to us. 'My flatmate comes back from London tonight, so I'd better get home.'

'Sure.'

I stroll down the beach promenade alone. I notice my sparkly toes through my new sandals and remember the effort I went to getting ready for this date. *I felt so out of place tonight. The bar, the noise, all those young bodies, David.* I run my hand across my waist and feel the bump of Spanx underneath. I imagine David discovering it in an act of passionate groping at his flat. Growing old just happened in an instant: one day I was young and the next I'm Bridget Jones.

I don't expect to hear from David again. *He's not ripe.* It's sad to admit that my banging Bondi club days are behind me. Kind of like when I realised that I'd never be an Olympic swimmer. Not that I was ever really into sport or nightclubs, but it's still disappointing to note that the window is closed.

At home, I log into eHarmony and go to 'Match Preferences'. I change my age range to '34–44' to increase the chance of finding a ripe one. On my phone I scroll to my last text from 'David Scientist'. Nothing since earlier today. I'm starting to feel more relaxed about not hearing back. The stab of each rejection seems to pierce my skin a little less.

Tom wears a purple cap with the badge for the Sydney Kings basketball team embroidered on the front. It's Friday night (Tom couldn't make it yesterday), and The Victoria Room is busier than usual. The bar stools that are often empty on a

Thursday are crowded with women in short skirts and men standing in circles. The mesh-shirt bartender is cheerily shaking up cocktails.

'Shall we go to the restaurant?' I suggest. 'It looks much quieter.'

Tom smiles and takes off his cap, revealing a shaved head and pink round cheeks. 'Sure, sounds good.'

Tom is probably around five-foot-ten, just a fraction taller than me in my heeled boots. He's not fat, but I expect he probably watches more sport than he plays. He lightly touches my shoulder as the waitress shows us to our table.

'Have you dined with us before?' she asks automatically. 'Wait —' her eyes shift from me to Tom then back to me '— I know you.'

I shake my head and scrunch my face as though trying to remember. 'Maybe a while ago?'

She raises one eyebrow. *Come on.*

'Could you please explain the menu?' I ask, holding one up.

'Oh.' She flashes a grin. 'It's a tapas-style menu. The dishes are designed to share.'

'Can we start with a bottle of sav blanc?' Tom asks.

Tom works at the Ministry of Education. 'I'm just a paper-pusher really, but it's okay.'

'What do you like about it?'

He stretches his shoulders back. 'The hours are great, nine till four. Everyone is out the door by ten past and the lights go off.'

We eat scallops, prawn tacos and gnocchi.

'Hey, do you watch *Q&A* on the ABC?' he asks.

'Yes! Every Monday night.' *Q&A* is a chat show where a studio audience ask questions to politicians and visiting scholars.

'Do you want to go on Monday?'

'Go, like be in the audience, on TV?' I've always wanted to get into the *Q&A* audience but never knew how.

'My friend is one of the producers. He can get us tickets.'

'Wow, okay. Let's do it.'

Tom pulls out his phone and his fingers pitter patter on the screen as he texts. Ten seconds later his phone dings. He looks up, beaming. 'Done.'

Impressive. This guy might be it.

Tom finishes the last of our wine and signals to the waitress that we'd like something else. He suggests I choose a dessert to share (crème brûlée) and he orders a beer, then another — two, three, four. I switched to lemon-lime-bitters an hour ago. We pull our chairs up right next to each other. His hand is on my knee now.

'Listen, do you want to get out of here? Go to another bar or something?' asks Tom.

'Sure,' I say, wrapping his hand around my back as we leave.

The Darlo Bar is only a hundred metres away, right opposite my apartment building. It's known for an eclectic mix of patrons — young hipsters, drunk scragglers and old men watching the horse races.

We step inside and I make a dash for the last available table. Tom goes to the bar. His cap is backwards now and slipped over to one side. He holds a tray with a lemonade for me and an empty glass and a giant jug of beer that looks like it's meant to be shared. He takes the seat opposite and pours himself a drink.

'So why are you doing the online dating thing, Rebekah? What are you looking for?'

'Um.' *How direct should I be?* 'I'm looking for a relationship.

A best friend, I guess. But something serious. Not just, you know . . .'

He chortles for a moment and then stops; eyes fixed with intensity. 'My parents divorced when I was ten. I thought I didn't ever want that, to get married or anything. But now —' he waggles his head both ways '— maybe.'

I lean forward. I can't quite make out the syllables in Tom's speech, except for the 'S's' and 'L's', which roll together with splutter from his mouth like a broken tap. 'My sister has three kids and all of my mates are having kids.' He's finished the first beer from his jug and pours another. 'I think I'd be a really great dad, you know.'

As Tom continues to speak and drink, his words become more and more difficult to decipher. I move my seat back to avoid the dribbly splutter. He pours another glass, then another.

'I eerie sslike slaalking slooo.'

'What?' I hold up my hand to shelter my face like an umbrella.

'I really like talking to you,' he shouts.

'Okay, I think we better call it a night.' I point to the door. 'Let's go'.

We cross the road outside the bar, and I flag a taxi. I open the passenger door. 'He's going to Randwick,' I say to the driver.

Behind me, Tom stands wide-legged to balance himself, with a blank expression like he's just lost everything. A part of me wants to take him in, give him milk and honey and lots of water, and nurse him back to health like a sick rabbit.

'Thaaanks Slebekah,' he says, reaching around to embrace me. Our heads are close now and I can smell the beer on his heavy breath. His lips are pink and wet and puckered. They lurch towards mine like a slow-motion zombie. I jolt sideways and feel dribble trickle down the side of my cheek. I squeeze the back of his shoulders in a hug.

'Good night, Tom.' I direct him into the back of the taxi, taking care to buffer the top of his head with my hand like the police do on television.

Two days later my phone buzzes:

> Tom: Hope you had a good weekend. I've got the tickets for tomorrow. Meet outside the ABC at 7? Dinner first?

Damn. I'd forgotten about *Q&A*. I'd love to go, but it seems wrong. Tom is sweet and I had felt attracted to him. But something happened when he got drunk, a switch was flicked that can't be set back.

> Me: Hi Tom, it was great to meet you on Friday. I had a really fun night, but I didn't feel there was enough of a connection for us to go out again. I don't want to give you the wrong idea by coming to Q&A. Sorry!

No reply for two, six, eight minutes.

> Tom: It's okay, I understand. We can still go to Q&A if you want, as friends.

I pace around my loungeroom for three, five, seven minutes.

> Me: I'm sorry Tom. You should go. Good luck in your search. You're a lovely guy and I'm sure you'll meet the right person soon.

Tom: No worries. Best of luck to you too.

I collapse onto the couch, holding my phone to my chest. I'm pleased with the interaction. I was honest, upfront and gentle. Back to eHarmony.

It's Thursday again at 5.30 p.m. I dart through the churchyard and around the corner to The Victoria Room. I scramble up the stairs in jeans and a T-shirt and spot the tattoo-sleeved waitress setting up tables. I wave to her and walk over. 'Hi.'

She stops setting knives and forks and looks up.

'You've probably seen me here a bit.'

She nods and puts her pile of menus down on the table. 'Yes, you've become quite the regular. With your —' she pauses and her eyes glimmer like a cat '— friends.'

I take a deep breath. 'Look, I wanted to let you know.' *How do I say this?* 'I'm doing this thing where I go on a date every week. And I really like this place. It's quiet enough, the lighting is good. So, I'm going to be here a lot.'

She lifts her eyebrows. 'Okay.'

'And I'd like you to try and act like you don't know me. Do the whole "Have you dined with us before?" script thing and explain the menu.'

She's giggling now. She holds out her hand and I shake it. 'I'm Gina.'

'Rebekah.'

She bites her bottom lip, smiling and nods like she understands. 'Sure. I can do that, of course.'

'Thank you.' I turn to the stairs and call over my shoulder, 'I'll see you in half an hour!'

Aaron is a personal trainer with a thick chest and thin waist. He jokes about his funny clients and tells me to eat green vegetables for breakfast. We decide to stay for dinner, but just after Gina places our tapas on the table there's a long silence. I've run out of questions.

Mal is in the Navy and his ship is docked at the port in Woolloomooloo. 'I'm actually a diver.'

'Is that dangerous?' I ask.

He puffs out a heavy breath and pushes himself backwards at the table like he's making way for the enormity of his importance. 'Well, I mean, I defuse bombs underwater. It's only dangerous if you don't know what you're doing.'

Martin arrives at our date with a face frozen in a permanent scowl. 'Are your family in Sydney?' I ask.

'I don't talk to any of them. Haven't seen them in years.'

'Oh.' Can I ask a follow-up question? Something really bad must have happened.

'We didn't have a fight or nothing. They just annoy me so I can't be bothered with it.'

'What about Christmas? Who do you spend Christmas with?'

He shrugs.

There's Ben who carries a motorcycle helmet to meet me at the bar, Nathan with impossibly small teeth, Ric the stand-up comedian whose jokes about his childhood are more disturbing than funny, Russel who tries to convince me that Scientology makes sense, Hamish who I could have predicted would be a wanker from the half-naked selfie on his dating profile, Kev the lift technician, Doron the bartender/actor, Ramses with dreadlocks, Gerard Landscaper, Garret Finance, Ken IT and Carl Engineer. *Phew!*

16. OUR BRILLIANT YOUNG LEADER

8 June 2012

I'm sitting at our boardroom table surrounded by glass walls, looking out over the office desks. Jen twirls her strawberry-blonde hair as she lines up her notebook and pen. Glen wears a black T-shirt with the Google logo upside down and the words 'Engineered in Australia' underneath.

I check my watch. 'We're just waiting on Don.'

Five minutes later, a thin bald man wearing a suit with brightly patterned socks strides in the front door. 'Don, we're getting ready to start,' I call.

He smiles and continues across the office to his computer.

'Don,' I repeat.

He stares at his laptop screen for five, ten, twenty seconds. 'Give me a minute. There's something I need to do.'

Josh steps in with takeaway coffees for Jen and Glen and green tea for me. 'Any plans for the weekend?' I ask, trying to fill in the time.

'We've got birthday drinks!' says Jen with her usual fervour. 'Is everyone coming?' She looks to Glen and Josh, who nod.

That's right, birthday drinks. I hunch my shoulders like a turtle retreating into its shell.

'Whose birthday?' Don enters, his laptop in one hand and iPhone in the other.

'Rebekah's,' says Jen. 'Well, it's tomorrow but we're celebrating tonight. At Sticky Bar after work. You coming?'

Don smiles with all his teeth. 'Gee, sorry, I have plans. But happy birthday for tomorrow.'

'Shall we start?' I say, switching on the TV to show our numbers for last week. 'We've signed up a hundred and seventy-eight new cafés and almost two thousand new users.' I sense an unspoken scepticism in the room. I muster every trace of enthusiasm I've got and project it outwards. 'We've now got three thousand, two hundred and eighty-eight shops and forty thousand, four hundred users on the app.' I scan the room for approval.

'Whoop whoop!' Jen claps her hands.

'That's awesome,' says Josh.

Glen says nothing and taps his foot under the table.

Don reads his mobile phone. *Should I say something?*

My whole body seizes with anger. I want to leap out of my seat and kick the bottom of his chair. *You arrogant twat, in your business suit and stupid socks.* I'm sure there is a *right* way to handle situations like this, but I'm lost. The board hired this guy.

I'm also sure that there is a *right* way to manage a team. A technique that inspires people to work hard, that gives them a sense of ownership in what they're doing. I've read the management books and consulted with Cameron, but I still don't get it. Maybe I'm missing the people-leadership gene.

I switch the display screen to a giant Google spreadsheet: a list of tasks around forty lines in total. 'Glen, when will your team finish the Facebook integration? Don, where are the new

HR policy handbooks? Jen, what's going on with the customer loyalty programme trial? Josh, why do we keep running out of toilet paper?'

The process takes an hour as they reply 'yes', 'no' or 'not yet' in subdued tones, heads down. The air in the room has cooled to a chill. By the end of the list even Jen and Josh, my bright sunflowers, look withered and weary.

I close my laptop and Don looks up. 'We're doing too many things. We don't need a loyalty programme.' He scans the group like he's the only grown-up in the room. 'I mean, I don't even get what this app is supposed to do.'

The anger pumps harder through my veins and I can't find a respectful reply. I sit back to take a few measured breaths and tilt my head in Don's direction. 'Okay. What's your idea? If you were in charge of the product roadmap. What would you prioritise?'

Glen chimes in from the sidelines. 'I'm think we're looking at the wrong numbers.' He pulls a book from his bag and slides it across the table. 'You need to read *The Lean Start-up*. What we talk about every week are "vanity metrics". They don't mean anything. It's irrelevant how many people sign up. It's about how often they come back. How much they actually use the app.'

'Okay.' I nod to Glen, who is staring down at the book.

Don tugs at his shirt collar and there's light sweat patches forming under his arms. 'Look, you're the CEO. It's not my job to tell you what to do.' He flares both nostrils and shakes his head. 'But this isn't what I would do. This isn't how you run a company.'

That evening, an awkward circle hovers around me at Sticky Bar. Jen valiantly works to fire up some birthday cheer.

'Here's to Rebekah, our brilliant young leader.' She holds up her lemonade shandy.

Oh Jen, please. I want to shrink into a crack in the couch. 'I'm not that young, and definitely not . . .'

Jen places her arm around my shoulders. 'What are you, thirty-four?'

I grit my teeth. *Should I say?* But last year we all celebrated thirty-three and technically my birthday's tomorrow.

Sticky Bar is a hidden room above a restaurant; you have to text the owner to let you up. Along the wall is a clutter of secondhand couches next to a tiny dancefloor and a tall steel bar stacked with coloured bottles of every shape and size.

'Happy birthday, babe.' Ainsley, my ex-flatmate and Saturday brunch partner, leans in to kiss my cheek.

I spot a grinning face at the top of the stairs. It's JD, my old friend from Wellington who lives in Melbourne now. 'Surprise!' He open his arms. 'I'm in town for work today. Jen invited me.'

There's a bunch of flowers in the middle of our table and a three-piece band setting up in the corner. As I scan the faces in our group chatting to each other, making an effort, I squirm at the sense that I've become a charity. No one *wants* to be here.

'I've got to get going,' says Josh.

'Me too,' says Glen, looking at his watch.

The drummer hits his snare and breaks into a beat. 'Let's dance,' says Jen, tugging at my hand.

Dance? There's no one else on the floor. 'In a minute. I just have to email something.'

'I'll dance with you,' says Ainsley. And she, JD and Jen start flaring their arms and legs and spinning about the empty room.

I push my back into the couch, refreshing my email over

and over and over and over and checking the news sites like I'm doing something important.

I wake early the next day. It's quiet. *Thirty-five years old. Halfway to seventy.* At least the faux birthday celebration is over. It's funny how at the time I just wanted to escape, but afterwards I felt happier. Even now, I feel good. As though the socialising altered the chemistry in my brain somehow.

I traipse through to the kitchen. *At least no one else knows.*

My phone buzzes. It's Facebook.

> Liz Johnson: Happy birthday!
>
> Kristy Erdelyi: Happy birthday Rebekah. Hope you have a great day!

And Katie, Danika, Graham, Cathy, Caro, Joanne, Freeda and 94 others. My insides twist with embarrassment. Thirty-five years old. *I should have done so much more by now.* I click into Facebook: Profile, Settings, Hide birthday.

17. THE MEN OF SYDNEY, PART 2

Nick is an investment banker (also wearing platform shoes) who's working his way up the ladder at Deutsche Bank. 'I'm on an emerging leaders track,' he grins with the eagerness of a school captain. 'One day I want to make CFO or even CEO.'

Nick is full of energy, management theory and quotes from businesspeople that I've never heard of. 'Have you taken the Myer Briggs test? We did it last week.'

'Yeah, my business coach made me do it a while ago.'

'What personality type are you? I'm an ESTP.'

'I think I'm an INFJ,' I say, 'but I can't remember what it means.'

He narrows his eyes disapprovingly. 'The rarest of the personality types. Let's see if we're compatible.'

He googles something on his phone. 'Here we go.' He clears his throat. 'INFJ is one of the worst matches for an ESTP. When paired with someone who operates primarily in these functions, it would bring out constant negative emotions and behaviours in the ESTP.' He looks up with four clear creases in his forehead.

Aiden is a graphic designer from Wollongong who I can't wait to meet. He's tall and works at an agency that builds phone apps. Our call had gone well: 'I can't believe you're the woman behind Posse. I love that app!'

We meet for a drink and, in minutes, my hope begins to fade as he talks around and around on a loop. 'I'm not really happy in my current job.' He sighs. 'My boss is optimistic about how much I can get done.'

At the end of our first drink I offer to buy another, but Aiden continues. 'I hate it. I just fucking hate it. He criticises everything I do. In front of everyone.' Aiden bangs his fist on the bar. I nod and wait for him slow down long enough to make an emergency exit.

Sanjay works as a surgeon at North Shore Hospital. He drives a red sports car and says he usually only dates women under thirty-five. 'But I'm thirty-five,' I say.

'And I usually go for blondes but — ' he flaps one hand ' — I make exceptions.'

I smile subconsciously as if I'm proud to qualify as worthy of an 'exception' and then mentally slap myself in the face. *What a jerk. Seriously. Who thinks like that?*

Then there's Scott, who works at the Fred Hollows Foundation, Oliver Consultant, Paul Marketing, Ali Physio, Bruce who goes to free-fighting, matches and Ivan the real-estate agent who only buttons up his shirt halfway.

On Sunday morning I take a walk to Rushcutters Bay Park and stroll beneath the tall old fig trees, with their thick branches and giant roots curling across the ground. Boats sparkle on the water and mums and dads with sweaters tied around their waists kick balls and throw frisbees to neatly dressed children. I sit for a while. The sunlight glistens through the leaves. The permanence, the magnificence of these trees, it makes me feel so small and temporary.

I pull out my notebook and flick to my goals. Posse is going okay: our growth is still strong, and we've started measuring how much people use the app. Don is a problem and I'm not good at leading a team. This I know as fact.

I smile as I re-read my personal goals. *One date every week for the entire year (52 total).* I scroll through my phone, remembering all the dates: Dan, Julian, Henry, Dean, Paul, Roger, Tom, Sanjay . . . Thirty-one so far! I imagine myself at age eighty looking back on this time. *At least I'll know that I gave it a good hot go.*

I recall the terror I felt writing these goals on that beach in Gili T. But so far, it hasn't been so bad. Although I haven't found 'the one' yet, and although I've run into some irritating characters, the men online are mostly normal people who genuinely want to find a relationship. I continue down the page.

My ideal partner

1. Smart: Be able to have good conversations, someone inspiring I can learn from.
2. Tall: At least as tall as me in heels.
3. Funny or fun: Makes me laugh, do fun things together.

Ruth said I'd change my list. I read through the phone contacts again. It's time for a retrospective, like we do at the end of each quarter at work. *What's working? What isn't? What do I like and not like in these men?* Not like is obvious: arrogance, insecurity and platform shoes. Still like: smart and funny.

The concept of *tall* sticks like a stone in my throat. I was so sure I wanted tall, but now it feels wrong. *Is a fragment of that Ken-doll vision still hovering in my subconscious?* I remember Sanjay, the doctor who 'usually goes for blondes', and how I'd felt judged and discarded. It strikes me that discriminating against men on the basis of height is no different. *I'm the same as Sanjay.* I'm sick with myself. I take a pen and draw a line through criteria number two. I'll adjust my eHarmony preferences at home.

I scribble another point in its place.

2. Sane and comfortable in his skin: Happy with himself and his life.

I think through my dating process. *How could I screen better for these qualities?* Smart is easy. I can tell by their profiles: do they read books? But sane and funny are better judged on a call. Yes, I need to be more methodical on my screening calls.

I make another list.

Guidelines for phone calls

1. Ask about his family and his work. A happy, sane person will talk fondly about both.
2. Ask what he did last weekend. Does he have friends, interests? Is he active?
3. Leave a pause in the conversation and see how he fills it. This will indicate how conversation will flow, or stall, on the date.

I imagine myself asking these questions of all the men I'd met so far. I could have saved so much time. I need to be hardheaded, like in business. Increase the quantity of leads, get better at filtering the candidates, and don't waste time on poor prospects.

At Posse, Jen and I developed a funnel to sign up new shops. I sketch something similar to help me think about my dating pipeline.

The dating sales funnel

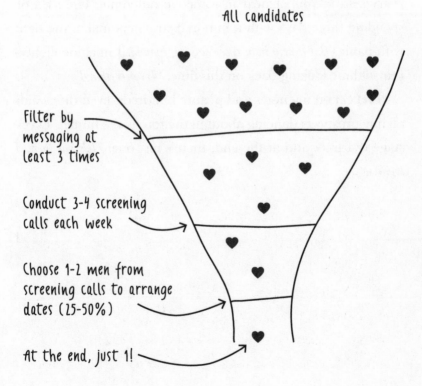

All candidates

Filter by messaging at least 3 times

Conduct 3-4 screening calls each week

Choose 1-2 men from screening calls to arrange dates (25-50%)

At the end, just 1!

To increase the quality of my leads, I need to increase the quantity of candidates at the top of my funnel *and* build better filters. If a business wanted to increase volume of its leads, it would look for new sales channels. And test to measure which channel delivered the best leads. eHarmony is just one channel. A different channel might find higher-quality men.

There's another dating site people use called RSVP. I make an asterisk on the page and a note to myself to join. And Jen keeps banging on about something called The Landmark Forum, a personal development course. 'It's the best place to meet guys,' she'd said. 'There's a hundred people in a room and every session you sit next to someone different.' The idea of spending three days with a hundred strangers makes me tight with panic. *But a new man every session, hmmm.* I imagine eighty-year-old me looking back on this time. *'Try everything!'*

I reflect on my notes and picture hundreds, even thousands of tiny prospects dancing about in the top of the funnel. Every stage is a filter and at the end, there's just one. *He's out there. I know it.*

18. SAND HILL ROAD, PALO ALTO

The Californian sun glares bright in my white hotel room. I'm staying at the Hotel Keen, a small hotel in the centre of Palo Alto. I turn on the television and an American voice makes jokes as he delivers the weather.

I pull on a T-shirt and head outside. Palo Alto is the capital of tech. Mark Zuckerberg lives here, Steve Jobs lived here. I'd expected it to bustle with lights and activity, but at 6 a.m. there's barely anyone about. The town is small, just a handful of streets on a perfectly straight grid. Hedges and flowerbeds are manicured and there isn't a spot of rubbish in sight. I jog from one end of University Avenue to the other in ten minutes and wonder if I've accidently slipped onto the set of *The Truman Show*.

I'm here to raise the next round of funding for Posse. Cameron has introduced me to a swag of venture capital firms, and I've spent the past week setting up meetings. Our team costs $75,000 per month (engineers are expensive). If I can't raise more funding, then we'll run out of money in December.

At 9 a.m. I start the car and key 2800 Sand Hill Road into Google Maps. I remember what Cameron told me about driving on the other side of the road: 'The passenger goes to the curb.' I steady my hands on the steering wheel driving past Stanford University and up onto a rolling highway with two lanes on each side. There are hills, green trees and farmland, but I don't see any buildings. *Is this the world-famous Silicon Valley?* On the right, an arrow that looks more like it leads to a winery than to an office reads: SEQUOIA. The building is made of panelled wood and set into the hill.

Sequoia is one of the world's most successful firms, best known as early investors in Apple, Google, LinkedIn, PayPal and more. I clutch my handbag. *Even if they don't invest, I have a meeting.* Just a few months ago, I was a sack of nerves at Launchpad Angels. *Now here I am.* I take a moment to let the sense of achievement root me to the ground and I pull open the heavy glass door.

An older woman wearing a cream silk scarf tied in a bow smiles as I approach the reception desk.

'Rebekah Campbell, here to see Bryan Schreier.'

She checks her computer and leads me down a corridor to a meeting room. 'Right this way.' The room is small, with a round grey table in the middle and a window to the carpark. 'Can I get you a water or a coffee?'

'Water would be great, thanks.'

Moments later she emerges with a bottle in hand. 'Bryan will be with you shortly.'

I let my eyes drift around the room. Bryan Schreier is the youngest partner at Sequoia. He just appeared on *Forbes* list of rising stars, thanks to his early investment in a new company called Dropbox. My heart jitters like I'm about to meet a movie star. Worse, *I'll* have to perform. I hunch forward in the seat and rub my arms.

I remember that TED Talk about body language again. The speaker described a study where a group were instructed to take 'high power' or 'low power' poses for two minutes before a job interview. Standing expanded, legs wide and with their hands above their heads like a victory 'V' increased testosterone, gave the participants a feeling of confidence and boosted their chance of getting hired.

I peer through the window to the carpark. *Can anyone see me?* I shift to the corner of the room behind the door and pump my fists in the air. 'Yeah, yeah!' I'm almost dancing now. *Come on testosterone.*

The door opens and I spin around. A tall man with refined stubble bounds towards me. 'Rebekah?'

'Hi.' I smooth my shirt to hide the air-punching crumples.

'I'm Bryan, great to meet you.' He takes a seat opposite and places a pen and notepad on the table. 'Cameron introduced us, right?'

'Yeah, he was my first investor,' I say with pride, feeling like a member of some elite club. *Cameron let me in.*

'We love Cameron. And you're from Australia too?' I nod. 'Great place, beautiful beaches. I've been looking for an Aussie company to back. Any excuse to get down there.' Bryan rubs his hands together. 'Let's hear about Posse.'

I reach into my handbag and pull out my laptop, ready to pitch. I flip open the screen and Bryan holds up his hand. 'Do you really need the PowerPoint?' His tone sounds disappointed. 'I'd like to hear the story. Why did you start this? What's your vision?'

My heart thumps. *But, but.* I've been planning the presentation for weeks. Every slide crafted with neat drawings and graphs to show our progress. Every sentence rehearsed, perfected and signed off by Cameron. I imagine his voice at my ear: *Stick to the script, Rebekah.* I wish I could magically transport him into the room. *I can't do this myself.*

Bryan leans forward to place his hand on my closed laptop. 'You know the YouTube guys sat there a few years ago, right where you are. They drew us a scrappy picture on that whiteboard and we got their vision straight away.'

My mind flutters, trying to remember how my PowerPoint started. I'm blank. I shuffle in my seat, then sit up straight to regain a power pose. 'I started in the music industry, I used to manage bands.' He nods. 'I learnt a lot about why people share music.' I pause. Ten, twenty, thirty seconds pass. There's a giant hole where my brain should be. 'I'm sorry, I can't do this without . . .'

'It's okay,' he says. 'Just do it however you want.'

I open my laptop, feeling like I've flopped at the first hurdle.

In the end we chat for around twenty minutes before he asks how much capital I'm looking for.

'1.5 million at a 4 million pre-money valuation.'

Bryan scribbles some notes on his pad.

'What's your process, from here?' I ask. 'How do you make a decision?'

'We have a partner's meeting on Monday. I'll take this to the group then and come back to you with an answer next week.'

My next meeting is at 11 a.m., at Kleiner Perkins. A receptionist offers me a bottle of water and leads me to another small room. I close the door and punch 'V' for 'victory' as I wait. At 1 there's Benchmark; 2.30, Andreesson Horowitz; 4, Accel Partners. Tuesday is another five meetings, and Wednesday another six. I pop about Sand Hill Road like a vacuum cleaner salesperson from the eighties. Almost every appointment is the same: a wooden building with glass doors, a receptionist who offers bottled water and directs me to a meeting room. The venture capitalist (VC) arrives: male, mid-thirties, Ivy League haircut, pastel shirt tucked in, cotton pants and boat shoes. We shake hands, I whip out my laptop and start the presentation. He smiles with white teeth, says how much he's always wanted to visit Australia, takes notes, makes positive noises and promises to be in touch.

On Wednesday, I arrive back at my hotel just after six and walk around the corner to Sprout Café for dinner. The salad bar is packed as a long line waits to order. I join the queue, eavesdropping on conversations around me. In front, a group of girls wear red shirts with 'Stanford' and big numbers printed on the front. They laugh loudly and lean in to one another. I order and take a solo spot in the middle of a row of tables. A couple next to me complain about an English assignment and a man wearing headphones waves to a young boy over Skype. I'm surrounded by the clatter of plates and chatter of voices. I sit eating salad from a box in the bright hub of big tech, feeling terribly alone.

I rack through my memory of the past three days. I've presented sixteen times, met sixteen different investors. I performed well each time and they all promised they'd come back to me. But I've developed a radar for men who say they'll follow up when they actually won't. I wish there was a woman in one of these meetings. I wonder what would be different?

It occurs to me that raising capital is very similar to dating. There's a face-to-face meeting, a game of question and answer, and then a request. Will you give me a million dollars? Will you go out with me again? This year I've met a lot of men, made a lot of first impressions, but something isn't working. None of the guys I've met in Silicon Valley are going to invest. And I'm still no closer to finding *the one*.

What am I doing wrong? I tip my head back against the seat. Is it me? Is it Posse? I throw my salad box in the rubbish and walk back outside into the warm Palo Alto evening air. The perfectly spaced trees on University Avenue are lit up like Christmas.

I don't know what's wrong. I kick a stone onto the road and imagine a *Truman Show* production assistant crouching in the background, ready to pounce and sweep it up as soon as I pass. *All I can do is keep trying.* Keep pitching to investors, keep lining up dates, keep looking for ways to improve.

My last meeting for the week is with a VC called Bill Tai at Charles River Ventures, who was introduced to me by my friend Lars Rasmussen.

I'd met Lars at a conference last year. Back then I was struggling to work with the website developers that I'd hired on Upwork. Someone pointed out Lars in a crowd. 'You need to meet that guy.' His thick blond hair and strong Scandinavian features put him a foot taller than anyone else in the room.

I bowled up and introduced myself, gave a thirty-second Posse pitch and asked for advice. We spoke for a while and agreed to meet for coffee. Lars had a broad smile and an inquisitive gaze. I immediately knew we'd become friends. 'Where do you work, anyway?' I asked.

'At Google,' he said. 'I invented Google Maps with my brother. We started it together.'

'Oh.'

When I mentioned I was travelling to San Francisco, he immediately said, 'You must meet my friend Bill.'

I pull open the glass door of the VC firm, and steady myself for another generic conversation. I step into the foyer and there's no one about. *Strange.* I poke my nose around the corridor. 'Hello,' I call. No answer.

Across the room a man in running shorts and a blue T-shirt bursts through the door. 'Rebekah?'

'Yes.'

'I'm Bill. Come through, I ordered lunch.'

Bill has bright brown eyes and the stature of someone who does a lot more push-ups than I do. We sit facing each other in a boardroom with two pizza boxes between us. Behind is a wall stacked with plaques celebrating the multimillion- and billion-dollar exits of the firm's portfolio companies.

'Do you kitesurf, Rebekah?'

'What?'

He pulls out his phone and files through photographs of himself flying high over blue water, attached to ropes and a board. I'm not sure where this conversation is going. I pull out my laptop. 'Shall I run through my deck?'

He opens a pizza box and signals for me to eat. 'We can talk about Posse later.'

I load a slice onto a plate and take a bite. 'I windsurfed, growing up in New Zealand. I wasn't that great or anything, but I loved it.'

Bill claps his hands together; his face is alight with glee. 'We must get you kitesurfing this weekend. I'll convert you.' He starts texting and looks back to me. 'Are you in town tomorrow?'

'Yes, but I've got to be at the airport by six.'

A few seconds later his phone vibrates. 'My friend will give you a lesson at 11. He'll lend you a wetsuit.' Bill turns to look for something and gets up. 'Hang on, I'll get a pen so I can draw you a map.'

Excuse me. I just sat down here to pitch my business. This whole scenario is bizarre. I don't want to try kitesurfing. I hadn't really liked windsurfing. All that sand, wind and seawater drying out my skin. I sit on my hands. *Just go with it.*

'I run a surf camp conference thing called MaiTai in Maui. It's for entrepreneurs and kitesurfers. There's some investors there too. You should come.'

'Okay,' I hear myself say, as if I hadn't deliberately formed the letters in my mouth.

'Mel and Cliff will be there. You must know them.'

I nod.

'Great!' He claps again. 'It starts on Monday, so you'll need to move your flight. See if you can stay with Mel and Cliff.'

Monday? Is he crazy? I can't get to Maui for Monday. I have investor presentations in Sydney and a board meeting.

'Okay,' I hear myself say again. I'm smiling too, and my chest is filling with nervous excitement. *Come on Rebekah, loosen up. Take a leap, a wild leap without a map.* 'I can't wait.'

We finish our pizza and talk about New Zealand and sport and the companies he's invested in. He flicks through gadgets on his phone like a master pianist, and my mind spins with all the tech I don't understand. 'I'll follow you on Twitter,' he says. *Note to self: Start Twitter account immediately.*

Bill looks at his watch. 'It's one o'clock, I have to run.'

'But I haven't even . . .' My laptop is still shut on the table.

'You can tell me about Posse later,' he says. 'On the beach.'

19. MAITAI

A crowd of fit twenty- and thirty-something bodies pile into a lecture theatre at the Maui campus of The University of Hawaii. The only flight I could get here was overnight, stopping in Honolulu. I landed at 6 a.m. and came straight from the airport. I close my eyes for a second and see tiny white dots floating like snow inside my head.

Bill Tai is standing at the front of the theatre, waving to every person like family as they step in the door. *What if he doesn't remember inviting me?* Bill jumps down from the stage and strides in my direction. *Someone important must be this way.* I check behind me. 'Rebekah. Wow, you made it!' He reaches out for a hug. 'Welcome.' My shoulders loosen. *Phew.* I continue down the aisle and spot Lars, Mel and Cliff in the second row from the front. I take a deep breath. *Thank you.*

Lars had introduced me to Mel last December after she'd pitched him her startup idea. 'I want you to meet this woman,' he'd said. 'She's from Perth but she'll be in Sydney next week. I thought you could give her some help with her presentation.'

We met at a bakery where we both ate pastries from cardboard boxes. My first impression of Mel was that she seemed very young, only twenty-five. She smiled a lot and asked questions. She was also beautiful, with clear skin and the kind of face you can't stop staring at. I searched for something wrong. *Her idea will be daft, I bet. No one is that perfect.*

Mel had perched her laptop on a steel table and told me about a business she'd started with her boyfriend to help schools design and print yearbooks. She clicked open her presentation. 'But this is what I want to build: a platform that lets anyone design anything.' She flipped through some mocked-up pages for how the website could look. And then finally, a strange leapfrog picture showing a chef's hat overtaking the Microsoft logo. 'We're going to be the future of publishing,' she said. 'We're going to beat Microsoft.' She pushed back her seat and waved her arms in wide ball shape like she was about to take on the world. I smiled and nodded encouragingly.

'What did you think?' Lars asked me later.

'Ah.' *How do I say this?* 'The plan didn't seem that clear to me, how they'd go from school yearbooks to beating Microsoft. I think a step-by-step timeline would help.'

'Right,' he said. 'I'll pass that on. But what about the vision? It's huge.' His eyes shone with excitement.

Mel and her boyfriend Cliff moved to Sydney a month later and we continued to catch up every couple of weeks. I expected they'd get a few knockbacks, give up and go back to yearbooks. I'd met with so many aspiring startup entrepreneurs for 'coffee and advice' and that's how it always went: a big crazy idea that would change the world, lots of enthusiasm and positive feedback from friends. Then some kicks from reality: can't raise money, can't get engineers to build the right product, can't get customers, run out of cash, run out of enthusiasm, disappear.

But Mel and Cliff kept charging forward with relentless determination. They registered the domain name canva.com and week after week they clocked up achievements: sign up a co-founder from Google, tick; hire engineers from Google, tick; raise seed capital, tick. They were a force that knew exactly where it was going and couldn't be stopped. Very early in our relationship, probably after three or so meetings, I felt the dynamic shift. *I* was learning more from watching *them* than the other way around.

Mel spins around in her seat and waves for me to join them. 'I've got a spot for you,' she calls, moving papers and a bag. I climb past Lars and Cliff and squeeze in next to Mel. I catch a whiff of my own musty skin smell, the kind you get after flying overnight, and spray perfume across my chest.

Bill signals for everyone to sit and takes the stage with a tanned blonde woman. 'Welcome everyone, welcome to MaiTai 2012.' The crowd whoops and whistles with anticipation for what's to come. 'I'm thrilled to introduce world-champion kitesurfer Susi Mai, the other half of this event.' Everyone claps again and a voice from the back shouts 'Go Susi!'

Bill and Susi introduce entrepreneurs and sportspeople to the stage. I recognise some of the company names: Twitter, Second Life, Tango. There's an ex-tennis star who's started an app for women to rate men after dates, a walkie-talkie app called Voxer, a cloud data storage company. They share their experiences in designing products, customer testing, team leadership and growth marketing. I frantically scribble notes in my Moleskine book. The talks are interspersed with interviews with kitesurfers. I suspect Bill wants the entrepreneurs to appreciate the parallels between elite sport and business. I wonder if it's a test. *If I learn to kitesurf — if I keep getting up when I crash — then he'll invest in my company.*

An hour later, the four of us make our way across the beach. A swell of tanned, toned bodies are lining up strings and boards and brightly coloured kites in the sand. I peer down at my pale skin and wrap a sarong around my waist. Mel points to a van loaded with boards. 'That'll be our lessons.'

As we walk past tech celebrities and glamourous sports stars I feel the onset of an illness: inadequacy. It started this morning as a queasy feeling in my stomach and it's getting worse. My head feels overloaded with inspiration and my brain has crashed into a flat dull tone. I imagine opening the top of my skull, reaching inside with my hand and squashing down my anxiety like a pile of rubbish.

That night, the bass thumps in the loungeroom of a Maui beachside mansion and I step out to the balcony for fresh air. My kitesurfing lesson earlier in the day hadn't gone well. I'd been dragged up and down the beach by an untameable kite, and swallowed so much water that a fish could be trapped inside me and I wouldn't even notice.

On the way here, I popped three St John's wort tablets when no one was watching. My anxiety won't flatten. It's a sharp knife jabbing up my spine, every muscle tightening in self-defence.

The bodies inside are dancing, there's strobe lights and a free-flowing bar of Mai Tai cocktails. I'm at the most elite tech party in the world. *How? Why?* I clutch the railing of the balcony to ground myself.

A man with a floppy haircut approaches me, his hand open. 'Hi, I'm Trent.'

Yes! Someone to talk to. 'Rebekah, hi.'

We clink our Mai Tais and begin to chat. Trent is an

entrepreneur who just sold his cloud services startup to Cisco. 'Bill was an investor in my company. He's backed me three times.' He shrugs as if building and selling companies is like flipping hamburgers. 'Now I'm just taking some time to think. Work out what's next.'

Trent seems different to the rest of the group. He's obviously here alone, a bit dorky and aloof like me. I check his left hand for a ring. *Of course, he's taken. The nice ones always are.*

'How are you finding MaiTai?' he asks.

I pause for a moment to design my response. It's amazing. It's inspiring. I love kitesurfing. I stop. *Be honest. See what happens. You'll break soon if you don't.*

'I'm finding it quite hard actually. Everyone here is so accomplished, they're young and their businesses are already so successful. And they're sporty and beautiful.' It's all pouring out.

'I know,' laughs Trent. 'I feel exactly the same. This is my fourth MaiTai and every year I swear I won't come back. All these amazing people.' He pats and grabs at his stomach. 'It affects me, physically you know. Right now, I honestly feel sick.'

I splutter my drink. 'What? You've sold three companies. That's crazy.'

'But I've never had a company list on the stock exchange.' He points inside to people scattered across the lounge. 'See that guy there, and there, and the woman by the kitchen?' I peer through the window. 'They've all listed companies. I'm almost forty, I should have done it by now.'

Is he serious? 'You really feel like that?'

'Yes,' he says. 'Absolutely. I think everyone here feels it to some extent.'

Is it true? Is everyone jealous of the person who's

accomplished just a bit more than them?

'I bet there's people who look at you and think "She's so amazing. I could never start a company." And go around feeling all bad about themselves.'

My head droops. *He doesn't know how useless I am. He thinks I'm successful because I'm here. But I'm not meant to be.*

I turn back to Trent. 'Do you think it ever stops? What about someone like Bill Gates? There's no one for him to feel jealous of.'

'Ha. What about Einstein or Tesla or Newton? I reckon Bill Gates goes to sleep thinking about them. Wondering how he measures up.'

I swig the remainder of my drink and feel a flood of relief. *Everyone is looking at everyone else. It's not just me.* Inside, I spot a pretty girl with a blonde ponytail in denim shorts. She's hovering awkwardly on the edge of the dancefloor like she doesn't want to look like she's standing alone. On the other side of the room, there's a guy with big muscles standing next to two men deep in conversation. I can feel his fear. He wants to join the group, but he isn't sure how to interrupt.

A warm breeze caresses my cheeks and ripples on the Pacific Ocean, glistening under the stars. *Maybe I can fit in here. Maybe I'm not so different.*

20. WHAT JUST HAPPENED?

My phone buzzes.

Cameron: Can you talk?

It's after midnight and I'm back at the rental house with Mel, Cliff and Lars. My bed is a thin mattress on the floor of a study. I sit up in my sleeping bag and dial Cameron's number.

'Hi,' I whisper. 'It's late here. I'm sharing a house so I need to be quiet. What's up?'

Cameron exhales through his front teeth. 'I tried calling yesterday.' He pauses. There's panic in his voice. 'It's Don. He's been in the ear of the board. He called a meeting today.'

The muscles in my chest clench together. 'What was it about? He hasn't said anything to me.'

'When you don't get invited to a meeting, then—'

'It was about me,' I interrupt. I pull myself out of my sleeping bag.

'He says you don't have clear direction. That the team's just flailing about, building random stuff.' Cameron shuffles about in the background. 'There isn't any easy way to say this. He wants the board to make him CEO.'

'*What?*' I want to spit. 'Don isn't a CEO. He's an operations guy.'

'I know, I know,' says Cameron. 'There was a vote. I voted for you, but the rest of the board are backing Don.'

Fuck.

'I've got to say, being in Maui isn't helping.'

'But I'm here raising money.'

'It's the optics. It isn't a good look right now. There's a perception that you're swanning around at the beach while the company is running out of cash. All those meetings we had set up for this week.'

'I've moved them,' I protest.

Cameron sighs and there's silence on the phone.

'What am I supposed to do now?' I ask. 'Am I out altogether?'

'Of course not,' he says. 'Everyone knows how important you are to this company. Look, we'll work it out when you get back to Sydney.'

'Cameron,' I plead. There's a scratch in my throat as I hold back tears. 'We've got to do something. Don's got no . . . He's just so bland. The team don't . . .'

'Trust me,' he says. 'I'll help you get through this.'

There's a long pause.

'Thank you,' I whisper. 'I don't know what I'd do without you.'

I set down my phone and slump my head onto the folded-up towels I'm using as a pillow. I feel paralysed, pinned to the floor. *Why didn't Don talk to me first?*

I close my eyes to sleep but every part of me pulsates. I picture Mel and Cliff upstairs sound asleep and smiling, tucked in with their perfect company. The corners of this tiny room seem like they're moving in on me. I want to vomit. *Hang on. I am* going to vomit. I clutch my stomach and stagger towards the bathroom. I flip up the toilet seat, hold my hair in one hand and wrap the other around the bowl.

'Morning.' Cliff grins in boardshorts and a T-shirt as he loads beans into the coffee grinder. 'We picked up some breakfast stuff yesterday, just grab whatever you want. Lars is out for a run.'

I drift into the room in my pyjamas, flop onto the leather couch and groan like a wounded animal.

'Rebekah, are you OK?' says Mel as she sips tea from across the lounge. I feel embarrassed. I don't want my friends to know what's going on. *They'll think it's my fault. They'll think I'm not cut out for this.* But I need help.

'I had a call with one of our investors last night.' I pause to sigh. 'The board want to replace me as CEO.'

'What?' Mel scrunches her face in disbelief.

'That's fucked,' says Cliff. 'You started the company. They can't do that.'

I haven't had much time getting to know Cliff but I always appreciate his directness. He's tall, solid and decisive, like his spine is made of iron. Nothing seems to shake him.

Mel sits next to me on the couch and our eyes meet for a second, then we look away as if we're unsure if we're close enough friends to hug. She smiles sympathetically and wraps her arms around my shoulders. Without a moment to spare, she positions herself ready to talk. 'Tell me what happened. And why.'

I fidget with the strap of my pyjama top. 'The board think I don't have direction. I keep chopping and changing. They brought in this guy Don to be COO.' I roll my eyes, picturing him in my head. 'He disagrees with me on pretty much everything.'

'Like what?' asks Mel, setting her empty mug on the coffee table.

'That's the thing. He doesn't have any solutions. He doesn't ever say what we should be doing. He just argues.'

Cliff steps through to the lounge and hands Mel and me big bowls of cereal and fruit. 'I did wonder,' he says. 'I mean, I think the app's really cool and that. But what's your plan for it? How are you going to make money?'

I put my cereal to one side and rest my forehead in one arm. 'We're just trying lots of things, I guess. Trying to work out what the cafés find useful.'

Cliff nods.

'People use Posse to find places near them. Recommendations from friends, you know. That part is going really well, but I don't think anyone's going to pay for it. I thought we could try adding vouchers, like Groupon, where we take a cut. But that model is kind of dying, so we're doing a loyalty thing instead.'

'What do you think?' I ask, turning to catch Mel's eye. 'I mean, you guys don't seem to make mistakes. Everyone just says yes.'

Mel splutters into her cereal like I just made a joke. 'That's not true at all. We've made loads of mistakes. It's taken more than a year to raise our funding and we still don't have enough. People knock us back every day.'

It's true. As much as I'd like to write off their success to a string of incredible luck, I know they struggle just like me.

'What am I doing wrong then? I mean, aren't startups supposed to pivot direction till they get to . . . What do you call it? Product market fit?'

Mel stretches her head back like she's serious. Her face is that of a radiant young woman but I can't help sense that behind those eyes is the mind of someone who's lived a thousand times before. 'I think it's okay to change how you do things, to pivot the business model perhaps. But the foundations of a company have to be solid.' Mel steps across the room, pulls open the curtain and sunlight blazes in. 'The problem you're solving and your vision for the future are the foundations.' She turns to look at me. 'What are your foundations for Posse? What problem are you trying to solve? What will the company look like in five or ten years?'

I cross my arms. *Think.* I read somewhere that speaking out loud uses a different part of the brain, that it helps to organise your thoughts more clearly. I relax my mind and eye the trees out the window, the golden sand and the lapping blue ocean.

'I know how hard it is to run a small business. I think technology can make it easier. I think we can help business owners be more successful, happier.' I feel determination rise inside me. 'In five years, I want Posse to support every aspect of a café's business. We'll help them get customers, take payments, run loyalty. We'll automate everything so the owners can focus on what they're good at.'

A smile sweeps across Mel's face and she holds up her hand for me to slap a high-five.

The Maui sun blazes down like a ball of fire in the sky. 'I'm going to give my lesson a miss,' I say to Mel. 'I'll stay here and try to meet some investors.' She lets out a disappointed growl and trudges off to the learner's area.

'Rebekah!' Bill Tai emerges from the water. He sets down his kite and strolls towards me. 'How are you doing? We haven't had a chance to chat yet, about Posse.'

'Of course. Do you want to sit down?'

'Great. Let me pull a few friends together,' he says. 'There's a bunch of people I think might be interested. You get set up and I'll round them up.'

Five minutes later an assembly starts to form around my picnic table under a tree. Bill flitters from group to group, pointing in my direction. There's an older man with grey hair, a couple with their arms around each other, two bare-chested guys still wet from the surf. More and more people cluster around. Bill returns in a wide-brimmed hat, holding two Coronas. His eyes shine with enthusiasm. 'This is for you,' he says, handing me a beer. 'Now let's hear about Posse.'

I must have stepped into an alternative universe. *This can't be real.* Just offshore, I spot Mel: she's standing on her board attached to a giant orange kite, scooting fast across the water and then *splat*, face-first. She surfaces, wiping wet hair from her eyes, and spins to her instructor with a beam of accomplishment. I perch as high as I can on the table so I can see the crowd. I flip open my computer and everyone squints as they try to read the screen. I use my hand to shelter the glare but it's no good. I close the lid and I look up at the circle of faces.

'My friend Matt opened a café last year, just around the corner from our office,' I start, working hard to project my voice. 'He had a dream to bring New York-style bagels to Sydney. But it's been really hard.' I start counting on my fingers: 'He doesn't know how to promote himself, there's no way for him build loyalty and stay connected with his customers, he loses business between seven and eight in the morning when there's a line outside his shop and he can't keep up. The rest of the day, it's quiet. Sixty per cent of cafés close down in their first year.'

I wave my phone to the crowd. 'I've invented a phone app called Posse. You can use it to find cafés that have been recommended by your friends. Cafés use us to run promotions and build loyal customers that they can contact again and again. Soon, we're going to add payments.' I spot Bill smiling from under his hat. 'We've already had more than a hundred and twenty thousand downloads and twenty-five thousand shop registrations from all over the world. My vision is to help café owners like my friend Matt use technology to run better businesses. We're going to revolutionise the industry, keep more people in business.'

I feel more alive than ever. My voice isn't coming from my head, it's coming from deep inside. I'm shaking but with excitement, not fear. The crowd leans in like they're waiting for what I'll say next. *I haven't even shared my step-by-step plan.*

I answer questions comfortably in between sips of Corona. Afterwards, Bill leads the group in applause. 'I'm in,' he shouts. 'Who else wants in?' A wave of hands go up and I feel confetti rain on me from above. *What just happened?*

21. READY TO MINGLE

The bass is thumping again and the dancefloor is packed. Lars waves to me as he twists his tall body in an awkward motion, grinning from ear to ear in a cluster of friends. Mel and Cliff are in the kitchen with Bill.

I exit onto a huge lawn lined with trees, bright flowers and palms. Fifty or so MaiTai guests chat in groups as waiters zip about with trays of hors d'oeuvres. I inhale the sweet Maui air and feel a soft blanket of confidence drape my shoulders as I saunter across the grass.

I spot a white plastic table staffed by a local lady in a pink patterned Hawaiian shirt. There are rows of stunning orange orchids and a charity donation box.

'Aloha.' She stands to greet me.

I remember the US currency in my wallet that I won't need back in Sydney tomorrow and tip a stream of coins into the bucket.

'What are these for?' I ask, touching an orchid. She hands me one.

'It's Hawaiian custom,' she says. 'You wear on the left side if you're married, like me.' She points to the bright flower above her left ear. 'And if you're not married, you wear behind your right ear.' She titters, jiggling her shoulders. 'That means you're single. Ready to mingle.'

The woman's eyes are warm and nurturing. *I can't date here. I haven't slept in days.*

'Are you single, dear?' The woman winks.

'Yes,' I say. *Deep breath.*

'A 'o ia!' She takes the flower and tucks behind my right ear. 'Now go. Mingle.'

The crowd continue to laugh and chatter. There are young men with slicked-back hair and women with glowing skin who glide effortlessly between conversations. I walk around the outside, looking back to spot my flower mother waving with encouragement.

I search for someone to talk to. *I hate doing this. Online dating is so much easier.* I hover on the outskirts of a group where a man is saying something about virtual currency and an online game called *Second Life* that he helped develop. 'I've heard of *Second Life*,' I say, proud to recognise words in a conversation. There's an odd silence. The man turns to me like I've interrupted with noise, then continues.

I step away. Next to the bar is a tall man with dark hair and thin glasses standing alone. He's quite handsome in an older professor kind of way. No flower, but no wedding ring either. The flower behind my ear feels like a 'For Sale' sign. *I wonder if he knows the custom.*

He steps towards me. 'Bonjour belle,' he begins in a smooth French accent. 'You are here alone?'

'Is that supposed to be a pick-up line?' I ask sceptically.

He tips his head back, laughing. 'I've got a joke. How do you tell the difference between an introvert engineer and an extrovert engineer?'

'How?'

'An introvert engineer looks at their shoes when they talk to you. The extrovert looks at your shoes.'

I laugh in a burst of breath and there's a tickle of interest that makes me step closer. 'Okay, that is pretty funny.' I reach out my hand. 'I'm Rebekah.'

'Pierre.'

'And what brings you to MaiTai?'

He takes a swig from his beer glass. 'I'm a bit odd here, you could say. I'm consult and I do some work at Stanford in robotics, algorithms. That kind of thing.'

'Stanford, the university?' I'm impressed.

'*Oui*, I'm a professor there. Or so they tell me.' He grins. 'What are you doing here? Have you got an app? Trying to meet some investors?'

I cringe at myself. 'Yes, I have an app. It's called Posse and it helps you to find cafés and restaurants.'

'A shopping app. Well that is a new idea.' He smirks and I feel about ten centimetres tall. 'So tell me, er, Rebekah. Why should I use your app instead of Yelp or TripAdvisor or one of the others?'

'It's social. It shows you places that your friends like.' I'm still shrivelled. Waiting for him to tell me why it won't work.

'Well best of luck with that, Rebekah. I'll look out for you on TechCrunch.'

Is he being rude? I fear he's making a joke. But there's something sexy about him.

'What do you think of the party, all these entrepreneurs?'

'I don't know,' I say. 'Everyone seems pretty nice so far.'

'Oh yes. Have you met the climbers?'

'The what?'

'You know. I'm only going to talk to you if I can get something from you. Everyone on a mission.'

'What about me?' I say. 'I don't want anything from you.'

Pierre pokes my stomach a little harder than I'm comfortable with. 'Ah, but you're only here because you didn't have anyone else. Standing over there on your lonesome. I saw you.'

I cast my gaze back to the lady with the flowers. She's giving me a thumbs-up. I smile back. Deep breath in, long breath out.

22. THE GOLDEN RULE

I arrive on the twenty-ninth floor of Cameron's building at Circular Quay. A man with a bowtie shows me to his office. I sit on the low leather seat, waiting.

A grey-haired mop pokes his head around the corner. 'Rebekah, good to see you,' says Gary. 'Cameron just ducked out for coffee. He'll be back in a minute.'

'Okay.' I reach forward to check my phone, and my black pants ride up to reveal the top of my socks and a patch of unshaven leg. I tug the material down.

'Look, I hope you're alright with the Don decision. I think you'll find it good. It'll free you up.'

I replay my phone call with Cameron. *The rest of the board are backing Don.* Hang on. Gary's on the board. That must mean—?

'Hey.' Cameron strides into the room and I stand. *Do I hold out my hand?* The etiquette is for men and women to kiss on the cheek once they know each other. *Have we reached that point in our relationship? Will he think —?*

He places an arm on my right shoulder, leans in then jolts awkwardly backwards like he's not sure. I feel myself blush and pat him twice on the elbow.

We sit and pour glasses of water in silence. He's waiting for me to speak first. 'I have good news,' I start, and place a stapled document face-down on the coffee table.

I'd arranged to speak with Bill Tai the Monday after I got back from Maui. 'I'll send you a link to sign up for Zoom,' he'd said. 'It's this new video-conferencing startup, way better than Skype. I'm their first investor.'

Bill appeared on screen with his trademark vivacity. 'Rebekah, so great to see you. Now tell me, how did you go with your lessons? Did you get up on the board? You have to stick with it. Persevere.'

Bill had spoken with his friends from MaiTai and together they'd agreed to invest $1.2 million. But I hadn't told him about Don or the board. Blades in my stomach churned as I imagined his response. I'm going to lose everything — Bill and the company.

'Bill,' I said, 'I have to tell you. I'm having some trouble with my board.'

He sat back and listened to each word, nodding. His response was calm, decisive and confident, just like how he surfs.

'Listen, who do you need on your board to make this company a hit?' He glared through the screen with intensity. 'You've got to structure this thing so that everyone has the best chance of success. You need the right people with the right skills.'

'Okay.'

'Talk to other founders in your network, get advice. Then send me in a term sheet. Let's talk tomorrow and get this done.'

I'd paced up and down Crown Street trying to imagine the challenges our business will face in the future. *Who are the ultimate advisors? Who will help me to grow the business?* Lars for technical decisions, Bill for a global perspective, Cameron to mentor me and help lead the team, an expert in finance and an expert in sales. I returned to my desk and drafted the investment agreement. I sent the document to Bill, who suggested some amendments. By Wednesday, we had a deal.

Cameron leans forward and turns over the document. I steady my composure. 'It's a signed term sheet for 1.2 million. From some of the best investors in the world.' My voice is slow with a pinch of smugness. 'There are conditions, of course. I'll stay on as CEO.' I watch his face stretch in disbelief. 'I did it in Maui,' I add. 'On the beach.'

Cameron blinks like he's making sure he's awake. 'Boom' he says. 'Well done. What a team, hey, you and me. You know, Rebekah, with this —' he gestures with the papers '—you've just enacted the golden rule.'

'The what?'

'The golden rule in business: the person with the gold makes the rules.'

Our eyes lock and for a moment I want to jump across the couch and hug him. He's my friend, my champion. I stop myself. *Be professional.* But the emotion is overwhelming.

'Thank you so much,' I say. 'I couldn't have done any of this without you. You're just . . .' I shake my head, thinking how lost I'd be if we hadn't met. 'Just incredible.'

We stand and he pats me on the back. 'Like I said, we're a team. I'm always here. We'll do this together.'

I exit the lift and step outside into the towering buildings and trucks and people at every intersection. I feel buoyed by my conversation with Cameron. *We did it!* Or, did *I* do it? I skip two steps. Maybe I'm more capable than I thought.

I decide to walk back to Surry Hills instead of getting a taxi. I'll use the time to think. *What have I learnt from this experience?* All those meetings on Sand Hill Road seem like a waste of time now, like first dates without any spark. But if I hadn't been there, I wouldn't have found Bill. My meeting with Bill went off-script; he just wanted to talk about sport. Normally, I would have forced the agenda back to my pitch. But I went with it, I didn't try with Bill. I assumed he wasn't interested, so I relaxed. When he suggested I come to Maui, even though I had other plans I went with it. Then there was Mel and her advice.

I picture myself again at that picnic table by the beach. When I spoke, it felt almost like I wasn't there. I wasn't trying to remember a script. I was a channel for a vision much bigger than me, and words flowed from my heart to the crowd. They wanted to be involved; I didn't need power poses or testosterone. I was high on inspiration.

I continue all the way up Macquarie Street, past Parliament and into Hyde Park. I need to define what happened in Maui. Get it down on paper.

I sit on a park bench in the middle of a grand tree-lined avenue leading to the war memorial. Families dawdle like tourists in both directions. I pull my Moleskine book from my handbag and make a new heading:

Who to be

1. Every success is underpinned by a lot of effort. Be someone who works hard and doesn't give up on pursuing what's important. Even when it feels like you're not making progress, have faith!

2. Don't try so hard. Relax and be yourself.
3. Be confident in your vision. Speak from your heart, not your head.
4. Be open to serendipity. Luck is created by effort, and you have to be open to it. Be prepared to go off-script, take chances and say yes to crazy adventures.

It strikes me that points one and two contradict each other. You should make a huge effort but then not try? No, they're separate points. The secret to finding the right investor was taking all those meetings, putting in the effort, being resilient. The secret to inspiring the right investor was being relaxed, confident in myself and speaking from my heart. Yes, have a plan and go for it with ruthless determination. And be open to serendipity, be willing to go off-script when you need to. That's when the magic happens.

When I think back through all those generic investor meetings — shake hands and say hello, then pitch from the PowerPoint, then ask for money — it's the last part that's off. An entrepreneur–investor relationship is so close; this is someone who will be by my side, helping to build the company for the next five to ten years. Kind of like a marriage. I'd been asking to get married on the first date. *No wonder they all said no.*

What worked was building a friendship with Bill. We spent time getting to know each other without the pressure of me asking for anything. When I finally pitched him Posse, it seemed natural. *Have I been too desperate on all these dates? Too focused on the outcome?*

23. SCREENING CALLS

I unzip my white puffer jacket and head briskly up the hill towards Darlinghurst Road after my regular Sunday walk in the park. I'm coming to the end of another jam-packed weekend of nothingness. Every hour, a scheduled activity: go for a jog, shower, dress, get nails done, pick up dry cleaning, buy birthday present for Mum, watch *The West Wing*, yoga class, speak on phone to Mum, do supermarket shopping. This is how I fend off the dark cloud of loneliness that catches up to me every time I stop.

Saturday nights are the worst, late when the world goes quiet. The cloud always catches me then. Last night at around 11.30, I lay in bed listening to possums scuttling across the roof. *Or were they possums?* I pictured a man wearing a balaclava scratching at the lock, climbing up the drainpipe to the kitchen window. I darted out of bed to check the door, the window, the door, the window: nothing. I was too tired to sleep, too scared to switch out the light. I clung to my pillow like a liferaft. 'Steve,' I whispered. *Please God, let me dream about him tonight. Bring him back, just for a moment.*

Steve had appeared in my dream last night, although I can't remember the details. I woke with my heart in a bath of light and peace, like someone had opened up a plug and let out a decade of stress all at once. Seconds later, reality squashed me with a ton of regret.

This afternoon, I've set up my first screening calls in a month. I haven't been out on a date since I arrived home but I have set up an RSVP account and registered for the Landmark Forum, which is next month. Unlike eHarmony, RSVP is free. The morning after I set up my profile I found 114 messages in my inbox, mainly from guys with photos that reminded me of the 'Wanted' segment on that *Crimewatch* show I used to watch. I found an option to 'Hide my profile' — for $45 per month I could browse the men's profiles, and they couldn't see mine unless I contacted them first.

Today I'm doing four screening calls: Creed at 4, Sean at 4.30, Jacob at 5.30 and Eddie at 6. I fix myself a cup of tea and sit at the dining table. Creed and Jacob are from RSVP, Sean and Eddie are from eHarmony. *Four lottery tickets.*

I dial my first call. A deep voice answers. 'Hello'.

'Hi, is that Creed?'

'Hey. Rebekah.' He stretches out the words like he's just waking up. 'How's it going?'

'Yeah, good. I've just come back from the park. What have you been up to this weekend?'

'Oh Rebekah, Rebekah.' His voice is almost a whisper, inflecting upwards like he's smiling. 'I've just been, you know, hanging with the boys.'

'Oh.' There's a pause and his breath muffles against the phone.

'Rebekah,' he says. Hearing my name like that is making me shiver.

'Why are we talking on the phone? We could just meet up?'

I roll my eyes. 'I wanted to speak first, to learn more about you. See if we have a connection.'

'A connection, hey.' He whispers. 'Why don't I just come over and we can find out? I'm free now. I can be there in twenty.'

I take a sip of tea and press the red button on my phone. Screening calls are a *great* idea.

'Hi, Sean speaking.'

'Hi Sean, it's Rebekah. From, you know, eHarmony.'

'Hi, I was expecting you to call. How's your weekend been so far?'

Sean and I chat for twenty minutes. Sean is an investment banker who recently left a highflying job at Macquarie Bank to start a company. He's spent the weekend camping down the coast with a group of friends. He grew up in Melbourne and is close to both his parents. 'Dad is my best mate. We're really similar.'

'Look, I need to be straight with you,' he says out of nowhere. *Here comes the catch.* I brace myself.

'I've got a son. His name is Sam, he's ten years old. I'm not with his mother — actually, I've never been with his mother.'

'Okay,' I say. I stand and pace the room.

'It was a one-night stand. She worked for the same bank but at the Sydney office and we'd just finished putting a deal together. I was up from Melbourne and we went out to celebrate. We had too many drinks, and . . . you know.'

'Wow.' I'm curious but I don't know how much to ask. *He put it out there.* 'You didn't use protection?'

Sean laughs regretfully. 'I went to get a condom and she said she was on the pill. I didn't see her again but a few months later I heard she was pregnant. She said it wasn't mine. But I knew people who knew her, and when the baby was born, I did the maths.'

'What did you do?'

He exhales loudly. 'I had to get a court-ordered paternity test. He's mine. I've been fighting to be a part of his life ever since.'

'What's the deal now? Do you still see him?'

'Yeah, I get him every second weekend from Thursday to Monday. I moved to Sydney to be close to him. When his mum got a job in New York, I moved to New York. We've been back three years now. It's hard, and the mother hasn't stopped fighting. She doesn't want me involved.'

'I'm really sorry, Sean. I can't even imagine.'

'Yeah. Look, I wanted to tell you because it's a big part of my life. Some women don't want to date guys with kids.'

I haven't considered this before. I want my own children, of course. I try to imagine a blended family with older half-siblings for my little ones.

'I don't mind at all,' I say instinctively. 'It's a bonus.'

'It's shattered me, this whole experience — emotionally, financially. But I wouldn't change it for a second. Becoming a father is the best thing that's happened to me. It's completely changed me.'

I sit back on the couch. I hadn't expected this conversation on a Sunday afternoon screening call. They're usually so superficial. Sean is open, vulnerable, and he's taking our date seriously.

'How has it changed you?' I ask.

He lets out an *Ahhhh* like a rush of love. 'I used to be so selfish. Life was all about me. I work in finance,' he laughs. 'Now it's about him. His voice cracks with emotion. 'I love taking care of him. I'm a lot softer now, you can probably tell.'

I feel my heart wriggle in my chest. *I can't wait to meet this guy.*

Jacob and Eddie are quick calls. Jacob is an officer in the Australian Army and lives in army accommodation in Paddington. Eddie is a film student completing his second Master's degree. They both sound nice enough, like unread books with semi-interesting cover blurbs. I arrange dates for Thursday and Friday evening to make up for the weeks that I travelled and didn't date. I set up Sean for Wednesday. *Three nights in a row, a new record.*

24. MONEY IS A RELATIONSHIP

My car glides along the highway between Canberra and Sydney. Outside, the sun is peeping above the vast brown flat of Lake George. 'I'd love to run out there,' says Sarah, rolling down the window and twirling her arm in the cool morning air.

We left at 5 a.m. after two intense days in the Australian Future Leaders Dialogue, a programme designed to encourage collaboration between emerging leaders in business, politics and not-for-profits. My head is still spinning with all the conversations I've just had — meeting CEOs, journalists, the prime minister.

To me, the most interesting person there was Sarah. A thirty-something blonde who owns a multimillion-dollar business and lives half the year in Bali and the rest in Beaver Creek, Colorado, skiing. 'How do you run your team?' I ask her, turning the car radio down.

'Everyone's remote. We all work from home.'

I imagine Sarah drinking coffee at her laptop, with couple of part-time mums doing admin support from their kitchen tables. 'But you guys are huge.' Sarah's business Wealth Enhancers is one of the best-known financial advisory brands in Australia. Something doesn't fit.

She turns to face me, long hair blowing in the wind like some free-living hippy. 'We *are* huge. And we're good at planning.'

Planning. Financial planning. That's what Sarah does. I reflect on the hire-purchase BMW I'm sitting in, my expensive rented apartment, the tax bill that I'm dreading. I flinch whenever the ATM asks if I want a receipt and select no. I'm scared to see the balance. Money, I recognise, is another area of life where I procrastinate.

'Maybe I should come and see you,' I say tentatively. 'Get some financial advice.'

Sarah flashes a smile. 'We've got three hours. What do you want to know?'

'What do you see? With people like me. What are the big mistakes they make with money?'

Sarah rolls up the window and crosses her arms. 'Entrepreneurs like you are usually terrible with money because you're optimistic, right?' She cocks her head to catch my eye. 'And it's not just entrepreneurs. It's most people our age.'

'Most people our age what?'

'Well.' She pauses. 'People wait. They put their head in the sand, thinking that someday something magic will happen. They'll wait till they find a partner or get a promotion. Maybe they think they're going to sell a business and just become wealthy. Then they'll get financial advice.'

I shuffle in my seat. But one day I *will* sell the business. I *will* become rich.

'Wealth doesn't work like that,' she continues. 'Wealth is about habits. Because even if something does happen — even if you do make money — it won't stay around unless you have good habits.'

'Okay.' I grip the steering wheel tighter, staring forwards.

'Just imagine that I don't have good habits. I made some money in my last business, but I spent a lot of it.'

The highway narrows to a single lane as we wind over green fields with spotted cows.

'Money is a relationship. Everyone has deeply held beliefs, usually going back to childhood. Ideas like "you have to work hard to get money" or "money's hard to hold onto". Think about what you believe and then question it.'

I believe that money will come. Posse will grow huge and one day sell for a billion dollars. But there's a bubble of sick in my stomach. *What if something magic doesn't happen?* 'What else?' I ask. 'What practical things can I do?'

Sarah tucks long strands of hair behind her ears. 'The most important thing is to start now. Think about the lifestyle you want to create for yourself, and your family too if you want kids. It's not about saving for a rainy day; that's boring. It's planning for your best days, then working towards it. Put some good habits in place.'

'Habits like?' I feel like a bear rolling over to expose its soft belly. 'I'm really bad at this. I hate to admit it.'

'Do you have any shares?'

'No.'

'Property?'

'No. I've got a savings account,' I say in a hopeful tone.

'Term deposit?'

'No.'

She scratches the side of her nose. 'Save a little every week in cash and the same in shares.'

'In shares?' I shake my head. 'I don't know anything about the stock market. I wouldn't know where to start.'

Sarah puts her arms behind her head. 'It's really easy. There are apps that'll invest twenty dollars a week for you. Start with a hundred dollars, get comfortable with it dropping to $98 and rising to $105. Learn as you go. People who just save cash don't want to risk losing it, so it'll be a very linear journey for them.'

'What about property? Mum wants me to buy an apartment.'

Sarah nods. 'Do it. But don't use all your money. Keep some for shares and some for cash saving.'

'Okay, but Sydney apartments are expensive.'

'Buy a cheaper one.' Sarah open her hands. 'The best advice I can give you is not to put all your eggs in one basket. Most people will clean themselves out of cash for one property that they'll pay off for the rest of their lives. And that's okay if it all goes to plan, but what happens if there's something unexpected?'

I notice that I'm instinctively massaging the crown of my head with one finger. *I must get onto this.*

'You don't want to end up living paycheque to paycheque,' she continues. 'It's stressful.' She's leaning forward now, checking my eyes to make sure I'm listening. 'Your relationship with money will flow on to your business, your personal relationships too. And the longer you leave it, the harder it is to catch up.'

25. SEAN

The Winery beer garden is alive this evening. Men in tight T-shirts rest their bottles on rustic wine barrels. I take a seat on a corner bench next to an open gas heater and bury my head into my woollen scarf as I wait for Sean.

I want to make a good impression tonight. I feel a trickle of anxiety. *Come on, don't be nervous. This time two weeks ago you were on the beach on Maui.* I picture myself there, confident and full of vision.

'Rebekah?' A man wearing a plaid shirt waves as he walks towards me. He leans in to kiss my cheek. 'Before I sit, I'll go to the bar. What are you drinking?'

'Vodka lemonade please,' I reply.

I settle back into my scarf and grip my hands together. This could be it. Remember your notes: take your focus off the outcome, start with friendship, relax.

Sean returns with two drinks. He's not tall, not short, probably the same height as me. I check his feet: ordinary flat leather shoes. He squeezes next to me on the bench.

'Tell me about your company,' I ask. 'The technology you're building, is it an app?'

'It's a bond trading company, an exchange like a market for short-term bank borrowing.'

I know so little about finance. *Think of an intelligent question.*

'That sounds big, launching a new stock market.'

His eyes fizz with enthusiasm. 'It's a really big problem. Banks trade bonds over the phone. There's no transparency, no liquidity in the market. We're going to change that.' He pauses, raising his eyebrows. 'Or at least we're going to try.'

Our conversation flows naturally. We share stories and laugh. It's almost as if we've forgotten we're on a date. At eight o'clock Sean hugs me goodbye and asks if I'm free next Tuesday night.

'I've got Sam this weekend.'

Six days later we're at The Victoria Room, sitting across from each other on maroon velvet seats at the back. 'How was your week?' Sean asks, spooning creamed potatoes onto my plate.

I think back over the week. On Thursday I met Jacob Army, and Friday Eddie Film. Jacob had been sweet but very nervous. His wide jaw and number-one shaved head reminded me of the serious young man in the army recruitment commercial. He kept catching my eye then giggling nervously like he hadn't sat so close to a woman in years.

For five minutes Eddie had seemed interesting and confident. His profile said that he loved to tell stories, and he did. Longwinded stories about missing a flight to Thailand, about temporarily losing a neighbour's dog. The stories went on and on and on. I probably said two or three sentences all night. We had one drink; I didn't offer to buy a second. And at the end of the date: 'It was very nice to meet you, Rebekah. I think it's important to be honest and upfront. Integrity is everything, you know.' I twisted my brow, confused. 'I just,' he continued, 'I just don't feel like there's chemistry with us.'

But I won't share these stories with Sean. 'It's been a quiet week. Lots of yoga, work. You know, regular stuff.'

I remember. 'Actually, something did happen this week. I started a blog.'

He smiles and gestures for me to continue. 'And you write about . . . ?'

'What it's like being an entrepreneur. It's really hard. I feel like I learn something important every week.'

'I know exactly what you mean.' He nods. 'Starting a company is the most intense education. It's like a bootcamp and the stakes are so high.'

'Exactly. I've been trying to capture it in a notebook. But I figured, why not make it public.'

I pull up rebekahcampbell.com on my phone. 'I made it myself on WordPress. Look, nine people shared my first post.' I beam with pride.

Gina appears with dessert menus. 'Yes please,' says Sean, taking the leather folders. Gina slips behind his back and gives me a thumbs-up. I smile impishly and lean in to listen.

'I write too,' he says. 'I've just finished a book actually. Well, the first draft. It's a novel.'

Now I'm impressed. 'Wow, I've always wanted to write a novel. What's it about?'

Sean scratches the side of his face. 'It's a passion project, okay, so don't laugh.'

I shake my head and hold up my hands.

'It's about Mr Big. You know, from *Sex and the City*. He's such a well-known character and I feel like we never learned much about him. What's his background, what makes him tick? I wanted to tell his side of the story and give women an insight into how men think.'

I stop for a second. I've always been a huge *SATC* fan. I must have seen every episode. 'You know, that is a really clever idea.'

'If you want to read it, I can email it to you. I'd love some feedback. Like I said, it's just a draft.'

As we step down the stairs, I feel relaxed. *He is going to kiss you. Prepare yourself.* We face each other on the street, his breath steaming in the cool midnight air. *I'm waiting.*

Sean lunges awkwardly and kisses my right cheek. It's like a badly coordinated dance where we step on each other's shoes. There's no pash. I frown on the inside.

'Thanks Rebekah, for a lovely night. Let's catch up again soon okay?'

On Saturday morning, my phone rings. It's Sean.

'Hi Rebekah. How's your Saturday morning?'

'Yeah, good thanks. I've just been out for a run. Stunning day.'

'I wanted to see what you're up to. If you want to get coffee or something?'

Today? I've got plans for today. There's yoga at 11, then the shops to buy makeup, then a date at 5 with Lakshan Management Consultant. The day is laid out like dominoes in my head. *I can't just shuffle them last minute.*

'Sorry. I'd love to but I've got a bunch of things on. How about later in the week, or next weekend?' The words tumble from my mouth and I want to smack myself. *Remember spontaneity!*

'I've got Sam next weekend, but we can do the week after.' I hear Sean flick through pages in a book like he's checking a diary. 'How about Wednesday, 5 September. Drink at The Winery?'

September? That's years away. I want to retract what I said. I *can* do coffee this morning. But that would sound flighty. 'Well, um, sure. Let's do that. And do you want to send me your book? I'd love to read it.'

I stroll down Campbell Parade, and across the road Bondi Beach sparkles like a giant gold treasure chest. I step into Trio Café and scan the rows of white tablecloths for Sean.

We'd met on Wednesday at The Winery, like we planned. He was out in the beer garden when I arrived, chatting to someone.

'This is Aram,' said Sean. 'We worked together at Macquarie. He's been stood up.' A plump man with thick eyebrows smiled timidly.

'RSVP,' said Aram.

'Do you mind if he joins us?' Sean asked.

It is kind of weird, inviting someone else to our date. 'Sure.'

'Hey Aram, you've got to check out Rebekah's app.' Sean pulled his phone from his pocket, throwing me a wink. We sat as a threesome and chatted about new tech, new companies and new ideas. 'Have you guys seen Canva? They just launched.'

Sean and I were a team, like boyfriend and girlfriend or an old married couple. Or maybe just really good friends. My shoulders tightened. *Is that what this is? A friendship?*

At the end of the night I looked to Sean. *A kiss tonight, maybe?* 'Hey, you wanna come to the beach on Saturday?' he said. 'It's the first day of spring. You gotta get in the water.'

'Sure, sounds fun.' *Still waiting, Sean.*

He patted me twice on the arm and spun to leave. 'Great, we'll get coffee first.'

Trio Café clatters with plates and lively Bondi locals, chairs scrape on the ground as they're pulled in and out. I spot Sean in the back corner on his laptop. He spots me and smiles. 'Rebekah, hi.' He stands to hug. 'I'm just reading your feedback of *Big Time*. It's great. You've done a lot of work.'

I'd read Sean's book earlier in the week. I wasn't sure what he wanted, so I tried to be as useful as I could. I'm a stickler for grammar so I copyedited the whole thing, making plot suggestions in the margin. As I filed through the pages, the two sides of my brain debated.

Right: *Just tell him you love it.*

Left: *But my changes make it so much better.*

Right: *You wanted to find a writer, remember, just like . . .*

Left: *Steve would not have written this book.*

Right: *Remember Ruth's advice. Stop looking for what's missing.*

Left: *Hmmph.*

I pull up a wooden chair. 'What have you been up to since, when was it, Wednesday?'

Sean narrows his eyes pensively like he's about to test the cold, early-spring ocean with his foot. 'Actually.' He pauses. 'Last night I went on a date.'

I sit back. *Okay.* I swallow and process the information. His head is still, like he's waiting for my reaction. *Am I hurt?* I sense a bruise, but what is it? I know that I like this man — he is fun, smart, confident, everything I'm looking for. Except he's calling it: we're friends, that's all.

I scan my body for the bruise. My heart. Is it sad and broken? *No.* My skin, dormant, still waiting to be touched? I look at Sean's pink hands and imagine them sliding across my hips. *No.* Then why do I hurt? I scan some more. My shoulders, my neck, my head. *Ah, there it is.* My ego. That's what's been struck.

Even if I don't want him, I still want him to want me.

I know it's wrong and nasty, but I can't help it. I'm pissed off that he said it first. *Who does he think he is?* And I'm disappointed with myself for feeling angry. *Don't be a bitch!*

I place my hands square on the table. I'm lucky to have found a nice new friend. 'Tell me about your date,' I say. Our eyes meet and it's as if a whole conversation just passed between us in an instant. 'Who is she? Any funny stories?'

26. MADELEINE

I shuffle in a plastic seat, trying to get comfortable. The room is a beige rectangle with the windows half-covered by blinds. Two women stand at the front. One has dark hair and black-rimmed glasses; she introduces herself as the Landmark Forum leader. The other woman is large, with long blonde hair. Around me, about a hundred people sit in perfectly straight rows. There are kids who can't be much older than twenty, an old couple holding hands who must be close to ninety. There are suits and tracksuits, turbans and burkas.

The dark-haired woman starts by asking if anyone in the room thinks this is a cult. 'If you don't want to be here then it's fine to leave now. Madeleine will give your money back,' she says. I don't know much about this thing. Jen described it as a self-development course with lots of available men, so I signed up. *A cult?* I'm intrigued.

We make our way through the day, sitting for two- to three-hour sessions. The forum leader does most of the talking and other people from the group get up to share their insights. I position myself next to a different man each time; within seconds I'll scan their left hand for a ring. So far I've met Ian, Dee and Sunil — all married.

The blonde woman, Madeleine, plays a support role. She marshals the group back from breaks and hands around a microphone when people stand to speak. We've made eye contact a couple of times. *Why does she keep looking at me? Has she noticed that I'm only sitting next to men? She must hate me because I'm thinner than her.* I scold myself for being judgemental. I imagine her turning up to an online date. *She must be so insecure, so lonely.*

By the time we re-enter the room for the fourth session I'm feeling more comfortable. I notice two men in the front row chatting with each other. The first is young, probably around twenty-one, with sun-bleached hair swept to the side. The other might be early thirties: he's tall with flawless skin and dark shoulder-length hair. There's an empty seat next to him. *Should I take it?* I feel a rush of terror. *He's way out of my league.* I hold my breath and sit.

'Hi, I'm Rebekah.' I reach out my hand.

'Hi.' He smiles and light beams from his sparkling brown eyes. 'I'm Joe.'

There's no ring! My heart skips like a nine-year-old girl doing jump-rope as we turn and wait for the session to start.

'How are you finding the course so far?' asks Joe.

'It's okay. I mean I'm sure it's good for some people.'

'What did you get out of the last session? I got some great stuff about my relationship with my dad.'

The content so far today has been interesting but hasn't applied to me. In the last session the forum leader described a principle called 'already always listening'. She said that how we listen and interpret others is filtered by our own experiences and ideas. I don't get it. *I'm objective and open-minded.* She said that these filters are 'always on' and will 'impact how you're listening to me right now'.

'Oh.' I love it that everyone here is so open. 'Tell me?'

'I guess I always thought Dad didn't listen to me. I speak to him like I expect he's not listening, never really say anything meaningful. But it's a filter.' He shrugs. 'Maybe he would listen if I spoke to him properly.'

I nod to show I'm understanding. 'My mum doesn't listen to me either.'

Madeleine toddles down the aisle to the front of the room. She flicks her hair purposefully as she catches me chatting to Joe, and she waves. He raises his eyebrows in acknowledgement.

'Do you know her?' I ask.

'Yeah, why?'

'I just don't think she likes me. She keeps looking at me, kind of like she doesn't want me here.'

Joe tosses his head back and snickers. 'Three words: already, always, listening.'

The muscles under my ribs clench together. *He's right.* I'm filtering Madeleine, I'm presuming that she's insecure and spiteful. I cross my arms and hunch back in my seat.

The forum leader writes the word 'stories' on a whiteboard at the front. 'Humans are meaning-making machines,' she says. 'Something happened — ' she draws a circle '— and you made up a story about what it means.' She draws a second, overlapping circle. She draws a big loop around both and runs over it again and again and again.

She instructs us to think back to a time when we were very young, when we felt like something wasn't right. 'What did you make it mean about you?' We take a couple of minutes to think.

My mind drifts back to Year 2 in primary school. A popular girl called Rachel was having a birthday party; there'd be canoes and a giant bouncy castle. Everyone was excited. One morning

I'd arrived at class to find little envelopes on every desk except mine. I sat on a cold concrete step outside with my head in my hands. *Why didn't I get invited? What does it mean?*

Girls with pigtails swung on the monkey bars. They were so pretty, so natural, so *likable*. I began to rationalise. Likeability must be a gene. One that God forgot to install when I was being put together. *In order to be liked, I will need something else.* I'll need to have something or achieve something that other people want to be around. I will need to be impressive. *Being me will never be enough.*

It's midnight when the last session ends. As the group files out through a beige hall, I notice Madeleine standing in the doorway.

She steps towards me, hand outstretched. 'Hi. Joe said we should meet. You sat next to each other.'

'Oh, Joe.' *How could I forget.* 'The—'

'The one who looks like Orlando Bloom.' She winks. 'He's my fiancé.'

I picture God pointing at me and laughing from above. 'Your *fiancé*?'

'I thought we could get lunch tomorrow in the break. Joe thinks we'll get along.'

I close my eyes for a second and open them again, consciously working to remove my filters. The person before me has a presence like I've never seen before. She glows with charisma. *I need to know this woman.* 'Of course, I'd love to.'

The next day at 1 p.m., I meander towards the corridor feeling more nervous than I would on a date. I haven't stopped thinking about Madeleine since we met. *What's her secret?* I need to know how she and Joe met, how they fell in love. Whatever she's got, I need it.

'Hi!' Madeleine is wearing a navy blue fitted dress with long sleeves and a necklace made of thick gold rings. Her hair is out today, and her eyes sparkle like she knows we're about to become lifelong friends. We walk to the food court and order Thai noodles.

Madeleine doesn't seem interested in bland conversation. She hasn't asked me about work or where I live or where I grew up. 'So why are you here,' she asks, 'at Landmark?'

'Honestly, I didn't know much about it before I came. One of the girls in my office said it's a good way to meet men.'

She chuckles. 'Tell me more about that. Why do you want to meet men? What are you looking for?'

I take a deep breath in. 'Where do I start?'

I ramble though the synopsis of my love life: Steve, my hopes for a family, recent attempts to date. She nods and squints, kind of like Ruth does when she's listening intently. 'I have to ask,' I say, 'about you and Joe. He seems like an amazing guy.'

She smiles like her whole self has just filled with sunlight. 'You want the story?'

'Please, I want to know everything.'

'Well I'll start by telling you that I didn't have a boyfriend until I was thirty-two. Joe is my first and only.' A sense of togetherness passes between us. *I know what it feels like to be single for a decade: the longing, the loneliness, the fear that no one is going to want you.* Madeleine forks in a mouthful of pad see ew and bobs her head as she talks. 'I always knew I wanted a family. I did a bit of RSVP and hated it. I think I went on three dates and they were awful.' She stretches her face like she just swallowed a frog.

'So, is that it? Three RSVP dates then Joe?'

'No, no, no.' She wags her finger. 'That was five years ago. Then I was in a theatre production and one of the stagehands asked me out. I was *so* flattered. I couldn't believe anyone would want to go out with me. I mean, I didn't like myself very much.' She closes her Thai food box and sets it aside. 'I changed myself. I acted all giggly and pathetic. I wore shoes and clothes that weren't comfortable. We went out two or three times and he stopped calling. He flat-out ignored me.' She shakes her head. 'I was shattered, absolutely heartbroken. I thought this was it. I'd imagined a whole future. I'd named the babies. It seems crazy now.'

'And . . . ?' I lean in.

'After a while, the pain started to fade. I decided never to put myself in that position again. I'd focus on my career. I was certain I'd be single for life. And I was okay with it.' She shrugs. 'There was a point where I decided that my happiness wouldn't be determined by whether I had a relationship or not. I focused on what I could give to the world, where could I make a difference. I started working with a cause I was passionate about. To be honest, I felt quite at peace with myself, and then . . .' Her face breaks into that light again. 'And then I met Joe.'

'Okay.' I sit back, thinking how to phrase my question without being offensive. 'Can you tell me how it happened? What was it about you that he fell in love with?'

Madeleine raises her eyebrows. *She knows what I'm suggesting.* 'I'm sorry.' I bite my lip; I don't want to blow this friendship. 'I just want to understand.'

'We met at work,' she starts. 'We became friends. All the women in the office called him 'Hot Joe'. I didn't ever think of him romantically. I mean, he was *Hot Joe* and five years younger than me. One night he dropped me home after work and we got talking about movies. We ended up sitting in his truck for hours. The next day he asked me out for dinner.'

Madeleine rests her head on her hands. 'We met at an Indian restaurant up on Harris Street. I didn't really take it seriously. I thought: "Is he deluded?"' She laughs. 'He said: "I've got two questions for you: Do you want to get married — not necessarily to me, but in general — and do you want to have children?"'

'What?' My head springs back in disbelief. 'He actually said that, on a first date?'

Madeleine nods. 'I remember sounding like a thirteen-year-old, I was like "*Yeeees!*" And he said: "Good, if you'd said no to either of those questions I would stop right here." The whole date was so effortless. We knew we wanted to be together.' She pauses, rubbing her chin. 'And then I asked him the one thing that I couldn't stop thinking about. We were being honest, so I had to put it out there. I said: "Do you have an issue with my weight?"' Her eyes glass over. I hold my breath.

'He took a few moments, wiped his mouth with his napkin or something. And he said: "I don't have a problem with it, but I'm worried about what my friends will think."'

I scrunch my nose.

'It felt like a stab in the heart. My first thought was: "Right, I have to change myself."' Madeleine sits back and taps her fingers on the table. 'He said he'd think about it. I sat at home that night feeling like the biggest idiot. I'd ruined my one chance to be happy. And then I remembered my strength. My life is full, with or without a relationship. I'm perfect.' She points to her phone on the table. 'I sent him a text. I said: "I've thought about our conversation and I'm unwilling to be with someone who doesn't think I'm the sexiest woman on the planet. You've got twenty-four hours to decide if that's me."'

She smiles. 'I kept waking up to check my messages. Probably around 2 a.m. he replied: "That's the hottest thing anyone's ever said to me. I'm in."'

Our eyes meet and there's tears flowing down both of our cheeks. 'We arranged to go away to the beach the next weekend. I was so terrified. I remember asking my friend to explain blowjobs to me. I said, "We have to talk about this once and then we'll never bring it up again."'

I tilt my head sympathetically.

'When we got to the cabin, he cooked dinner,' she says. 'We sat on the balcony, looking out to the ocean, and it felt like a dream.' Madeleine gives me a look like there's one more secret. 'He brushed his hand on my chin and said: "What's that?" And I was like: "What?" He said: "There's something on your chin." I went inside and checked the mirror. "It's a chin hair, Joe. Usually I pluck them, but I must have missed this one."'

We laugh and the joy in her heart is obvious. 'The rest of the weekend was amazing. We could have got married right then. We just decided to wait a year so everyone else wouldn't freak out. But we were clear it was forever.'

For a second I remember the internal dialogue I'd had about Madeleine when I'd seen her onstage yesterday. *Why did I think that? Am I a bad person? Who is that little voice in my head? Is it me?* I don't like the person behind that voice.

I reach across the table to squeeze Madeleine's hands. She is striking: the most authentic, strong, beautiful woman I've ever encountered. 'Can we be friends?' I ask. 'I'd love your advice, as I go through this dating thing.'

She smiles with the certainty of someone who knows I'll be okay. No matter what happens. 'Of course.'

27. THE SENATOR

It's been a long day at the office. I flop onto my soft corduroy couch at home, phone in hand, laptop to one side, ready for work. My dating sales funnel is flowing well and the past few weeks have yielded promising candidates (Murray Construction, Donnie Engineer and Mick Electrician) but no second dates.

I start by checking eHarmony. I do this on my laptop because men on eHarmony like sending long-winded messages and seem to expect similarly thoughtful replies. I've created a folder in Google Drive for 'Dating prospects' and a working document with template eHarmony messages that I cut and paste into conversations. There's a message for 'first contact' with gaps for me to personalise.

> Hi ___,
>
> Great to connect! I noticed your profile, especially that you like _____. I'm also a fan of___. [Insert comment about my relationship to the sport/movie/band/holiday destination.]
>
> I grew up in New Zealand (yeees, still have the accent) and I moved to Sydney in 2000 (not an Olympian, just coincidence). I'm currently obsessed with The West Wing, as you can probably tell from my profile. I enjoy politics and current affairs. I like to read and get outside as much as possible.

Anyway, as I said, your profile intrigued me and would love to hear more about you.

Rebekah

I've tested numerous 'first contact' approaches and this one gets the most replies. It's a good length — not too long, which looks desperate. It shows genuine interest in the man and his profile, not just a cut and paste job. There's a touch of humour and a statement about what's important to me.

Each time I respond to a message, I copy what I write into the Google Doc so I can reuse paragraphs when someone else asks the same thing. Tonight, I have messages from Lance, Toushar, Trent, Grant and Alfin.

I start by replying to the messages; this is the most time-consuming part of my night. I've worked out that three back-and-forth exchanges is the optimal amount of contact before suggesting a phone call. Any longer and there's a risk I'll waste time on poor prospects, and I've noticed guys often go silent if I ask for a call too early. My aim is for a healthy funnel with just the right number of chats going at once: not so many that I can't keep up, but enough so I hardly notice if someone disappears.

The other document in my Google Drive folder is a spreadsheet. This is for me to take notes on the screening calls so I can remind myself of their stories before our date. I started the spreadsheet after my date with Donnie Engineer when I asked him about his sister, the teacher in Adelaide. He looked confused. 'I'm an only child,' he said. 'My parents separated before I was born.' I'd racked my brain. He continued, 'Remember we talked about . . .' *Whoops! That was Murray Construction with the sister in Adelaide.*

Next, it's time for what I've come to think of as 'fishing'. This is when I scan through men on both eHarmony and RSVP and fire out as many first contacts as possible. This will fill my funnel with a week of new prospects. Today I scan through the sixteen new 'Matches' on eHarmony and send five messages using my template email. RSVP is more of an open market, so I search using filters just like when I searched for my apartment on realestate.com. Instead of 'location', 'price' and 'number of bedrooms', it's 'location' (within twenty kilometres of Darlinghurst), 'education' (Bachelor's level or above) and that he's checked either 'Wants' or 'Possibly wants' children.

Now with forty-two dates behind me, I've learnt what to look for in online profiles. A chiselled jaw in a photograph has zero correlation with physical attraction in person. Instead, I scan what they've written for two important signs:

- Indication of depth: Do they reference books, music, travel, people who inspire them?
- Are they genuine about their search for a partner? Have they taken time to fill in their profile thoughtfully or have they just slapped something up for fun?

And I've developed a radar to filter out men. I check the age range they've specified as their 'ideal partner': I'm looking for maybe five to seven years younger than them, up to their age or older. If their age range dips to include eighteen-year-olds then we won't be a match. And there are stop signs. Tonight, I've sifted through profiles that say:

Please only apply if . . .

- Looking for light hand luggage, no heavy divorces or kids.
- A curvy woman who is a good cooker and socialiser benefits in attracting me.

Yuck, yuck, yuck, scroll.

A few months ago, there were hundreds of men to choose from, but now my feed is littered with faces I recognise: dated, called, filtered. Tonight, there's only a handful I haven't seen before. One profile stands out because there's no photograph. I usually discount these, but tonight I need prospects. I click in and begin reading.

Mozart70, 42, from Double Bay

I'm an easy-going, genuine and caring person who would like to find a partner to share adventures with. I am a loyal person. I value family and long-term friendships. I am in awe of my parents, who have just celebrated 50 years together.

I have a big job which requires me to travel and work long hours, but I'm incredibly passionate about what I do. I'm a patriot. I love Australia and am committed to making a difference.

I enjoy good food, the arts and classical music. I often attend social events for my work.

I'm looking for a partner who is caring, honest, loving and has a bright outlook on life.

I look forward to meeting you for a coffee, a nice dinner or a play.

Genuine and thoughtful: tick, tick. He sounds serious but why hasn't he included a photo? I fire off an invitation for him to view my profile and keep scrolling.

Five minutes later my phone pings with a notification from RSVP: 'Mozart70 has sent you a message'.

> Hi Rebekah,
> Thanks for contacting me. What have you been up to this evening? I've just come home from a function with Tony Tan which was fascinating.
> There isn't a photo on my profile so here are two attached.
> Hope to hear from you soon,
> Matthew

I open the photographs. There's a slightly podgy but friendly face with short dark brown hair, and a second picture of him standing tall at a kids' soccer game. He looks nice. *Why didn't he want these photos made public?*

I type 'Tony Tan' into Google and learn that he is the recently elected President of Singapore. I search again, this time adding 'Sydney' and today's date. There's nothing. This guy is either important enough to get invited to a private event with the President of Singapore, or he's a fake. Either way, I'm intrigued.

We message back and forth a few times and I try to sound intelligent about politics and art. Matthew says that he's a member of the Sydney Theatre Company. We arrange to chat.

That Sunday, I key Matthew's number into my phone. He answers with a boisterous 'Hello!' and tells me he's just been out helping his sister shop for a wedding dress. He speaks quickly and sounds eager to please.

'I have to ask,' I say tentatively, 'what is it that you do for work?'

There's a long pause on the phone. 'Look, I uh . . . ' He switches from hesitation to candor. 'I'm a senator in the New South Wales parliament.'

'Right.' There's a hint of scepticism in my voice. *Why would a senator be on RSVP?*

'My name is Matthew Marino. Look me up if you want. I'm on Wikipedia.'

I quietly key his name into Google. 'Which party?' I ask, trying to sound casual. Trying to sound like I'm not about to leap out of my seat.

'The Liberal Party.' He takes a breath. 'Oh god, you're not a Greenie are you?'

A small flurry of disappointment stirs my stomach. I do quite like the Greens. 'To be honest, I used to be a member of the Labor Party. But I haven't been in ages.'

He sniffs. 'That's alright. I don't mind Labor, there's some sensible people in Labor.'

The flurry settles. I can live with Liberal. He sounds nice and he's a senator!

I step from my lounge to the bathroom, to the full-length mirror in my bedroom and back to the lounge. I picture Matthew arriving at The Victoria Room right now. Gina will show him to the table I've booked. If I leave now, I'll make it by 7.05. *I don't want to keep the senator waiting.*

I feel my legs tremble in my patent heels as I step across the road towards the restaurant. I've been preparing for this moment all week: I've bought a new outfit (fitted leather skirt and a blue silk singlet), had a spray tan, my nails painted, eyebrows waxed and tinted. I've read up on every production at the Sydney Theatre Company this year. I listened to classical music playlists on Spotify and strained my brain trying to remember the names: Bach, Beethoven, Schubert, Chopin.

In between preparation there was dreaming. I imagined walking arm in arm with Senator Marino to public events. He'd get invited to the Mayor's New Year's Eve Party at the Opera House. *'Welcome, Senator.'* The Mayor would shake his hand and Matthew would turn. *'Let me introduce my wife, Rebekah.'* I stand tall, refined, important.

I step into The Victoria Room, shoulders back, head straight. I can do this. This is it.

Matthew sits at a table reading his phone. He looks up and his eyes smile like they're pleased with my appearance. He gets up to kiss my cheek and my whole body wants to melt — he's so tall and distinguished. He wears a white collared shirt and a navy tie, like he missed the casual Friday memo at the restaurant. I want to jump up on chair and announce to everyone in the place, *'Do you recognise this man? He's a senator. I'm dating a senator!'*

Matthew pulls back my chair for me to sit.

'Here's the menu.' He hands me the leather folder. 'Before you look, I want to be clear that this evening's dinner is on me. No arguments.'

A cascade of thoughts flash across my mind at the same time:

- He's a gentleman. He's trying to be chivalrous.
- He hasn't been on many dates before. He doesn't know that's an odd thing to say.
- I feel like a small child. 'Kid, I'm paying. Pick whatever you want from the menu.'

We make small talk about art and theatre. 'Did you get to the Archibald this year?' he asks.

'Ah.' I'd seen something on TV about the winner. 'I followed it but . . .'

'Tim Storrier won,' Matthew prompts. 'Fabulous painting. The traveller choosing good or evil. It was quite an abstract one for them.'

I nod like I knew that already. Gina appears to take our orders. 'Have you dined with us before?' she asks, flashing me a wink.

I wish she'd stop doing that.

'I haven't,' says Matthew. 'First time.'

Gina looks to me and I squeeze my eyes sarcastically.

'It's a tapas-style menu, designed to share.'

Matthew turns to me. 'Is there anything in particular that you'd like, or shall I order for both of us?'

I feel a surge of panic. *Do I tell him that I'm vegetarian?* I want to be easy-going.

'You go ahead,' I say. 'I'll eat anything.' *Gulp.*

'Wonderful.' He opens the folder. 'We'll have the chicken liver and dried fruit to start. And for mains, the lamb albondigas, roasted chorizo and beans, the crispy potatoes and almond broccolini.'

The panic has reached my mouth now; salty sick swirls around my tongue.

Our food arrives and Matthew heaps it onto two plates. 'Just a small amount for me, of the lamb and chorizo.' My plate is round, piled high and staring at me like an enemy. When I was ten years old, I rescued a starving orphan lamb from my friend's farm. I named her Charlotte and bottle-fed her three times a day until she was strong enough to go home. Now, I dig around the flesh and mush for something safe and spoon potatoes and beans into my mouth. I swallow the chorizo without chewing and try not to picture the squealing pig. Matthew excuses himself for the bathroom. I scoop the lamb into a napkin and stuff it into my handbag.

He returns, striding across the restaurant with the air of a suave Alec Baldwin. 'Right, where were we?' Our eyes meet across the table. He is confident and charming and handsome, but I also sense fragility, like he's trying really hard to be perfect. I wonder if I've discovered a rare gem; a sweet, gentle senator who's been afraid to date.

We continue to chat about his life and his work. He rattles off his background like it's a stump speech he's given a thousand times. 'Dad immigrated from Italy. Came here with nothing and started an import business.' I'm careful not to ask anything that could make him uncomfortable. There's no discussion of politics, past relationships, RSVP dates or dreams for the future. I assume he wants kids. *Every politician needs a cute family for the campaign posters.*

Just after ten Matthew checks his watch. 'It's getting late.'

He folds his napkin and places it on the table. 'I'd really love to see you again.'

'I'd like that.' I hold my mouth closed so he won't see my grin.

Outside, Matthew offers to walk me home. 'It's cool tonight, take my jacket.' He places his broad-shouldered suit jacket over my shoulders. It's warm and heavy and smells of aftershave. We step through the churchyard to my apartment door.

'This is where I live,' I say, stopping outside the stone art-deco block. I scan his face and neck and chest, working hard to absorb every feature so I can bring him to life in my imagination later. I can tell he likes me but he's much too nervous to try and kiss or even hug. *He doesn't want to come on too strong. Afraid of the risk.* He takes hold of my right hand and kisses the top of it, eyes fixed like a prince.

In my mind our tongues are entangling, I'm tugging at his blue tie and unbuttoning his shirt, sliding my fingers across his chest.

An hour later I lie in bed and my phone buzzes.

Matthew: Great to meet you! Let's catch up again next week.

I rest my arms across my stomach and my gaze on nothing in particular. My heart is peaceful and confident. *This guy really likes me.*

What will we do at Christmas? *Will our relationship have developed enough by December for us to spend the holiday together?* I calculate the number of likely dates between now and then and resolve that, yes, Christmas together is a very likely scenario.

Where will we go? I skim through options in my head. We should rent a house somewhere close to Sydney so his family can visit, and he can make daytrips if he needs to get back to parliament. I open Airbnb and search through the listings. We'll invite my parents for a few days too. They'll insist. I squirm, picturing him in conversation with Mum and her breasts and Dad with his honorary lifetime membership to the Greens.

I spend the next hour investigating rental options and settle on a white wooden cottage next to the beach. I picture myself snuggling into Matthew after a day in the surf.

I message the owner:

> We are a professional couple interested in renting your cottage between Dec 23 and Jan 6. Would you be willing to reduce the price if we take the full two weeks?

I turn and close my eyes with my phone on the pillow next to me. You've done it, Rebekah. You are the girlfriend — soon to be wife — of a New South Wales senator.

28. THE LARGE COST
OF SMALL LIES

Matthew and I spoke on Sunday afternoon and Tuesday after work. I studied the news each day and made notes on topics I could introduce in conversation. I stayed clear of international politics, climate change, social welfare — every issue where we might not agree. I looked for inane stories about art, entertainment and food, where I could demonstrate thoughtfulness and not be controversial.

I cancelled the screening calls I'd set up for Sunday. There'll be no more dates. The pipeline is closed. I have found my man!

Tonight we're meeting at the Almond Bar, a cute corner restaurant in Darlinghurst. I'm wearing fitted black jeans, a cream silk top and a beige patterned scarf. I bought the scarf a year ago after noticing other women in the city looking dignified with scarfs draped across their shoulders. I'd study the women on the train. *How do they tie the scarves so neat?* Every attempt I made seemed to flop into a flat scruffy pile down my front. This afternoon I googled 'How to tie a dress scarf' and watched a video by Nordstrom. Time to try again.

I arrive at the restaurant first and there's only a few people here, all couples sitting face-to-face at intimate two-person tables. It's a tiny place, almost like an underground corridor, with cream-painted brick on one wall and Syrian wood carvings on the other. I use my reflection in the window to fluff up my scarf, and pull out my phone to look busy.

Matthew has to stoop through the low door. He beams as our eyes meet. *God he's handsome.* Tonight he's wearing a maroon tie with a navy suit jacket slung over his shoulder. He looks like he's just come from a meeting where big decisions were made.

I stand for a kiss on the cheek. 'Rebekah.' He places his hands on my shoulders and scans me up and down, as if something's surprised him.

'What?' I ask. 'Is something wrong?'

He shakes his head, smiling. 'You look good. You look really good.'

I wonder if he's assessing my appearance for social events. *He's imagining me on his arm.* I feel like I've just sneaked into a private club. *I am a dignified scarf-wearing woman!*

We sit, and a waitress brings an assortment of coated almonds to our table. Matthew checks his surroundings. 'What is this place? Syrian?'

'Yeah, the food is amazing.'

'Gosh.' He makes a face. 'They've had a rough time lately.' He pauses a moment like he's expecting me to make a leftie comment about refugees.

I catch the words in my mouth.

We chat back and forth with measured ease. Matthew describes his younger sister: 'We're really close. Too close, probably. I mean, we were never apart growing up.'

I ask about her wedding. 'Do you like the guy she's marrying?'

'Look.' He inhales slowly. 'No one is ever going to be good enough for my sister. The guy is decent, he treats her well. But he's a bit —' Matthew tumbles his hands like he's struggling to articulate what's wrong — 'well, he doesn't read books, let me just say that. Not full-length books anyway. He didn't go to uni. He works as a tradie. But she's thirty-nine, she wants kids. I just hope she's not, you know, settling.'

I feel like someone just poked me with a hot stick. *I'm thirty-five. I want kids.*

And for a moment I reflect on the disparity of men and women in this stage of life. *You're forty-two! You probably want kids but here you are breezily dating in Darlinghurst.* I imagine his younger sister trawling through RSVP, piling on lipstick for every date, her panic deepening with every birthday. She'll have seen the same news headlines I have: 'How long can you wait to have a baby?' The graphs with fertility dropping off a cliff after thirty-five. So now, at thirty-nine, she's found someone nice who treats her well. Matthew sits safe and smug, sipping lemonade through a straw. He doesn't have to worry.

I take charge of ordering tonight. We eat pumpkin balls, haloumi, calamari and toasted fattoush. I try to loosen my shoulders without letting them slump. *Relax, smile.* I feel like I'm in a job interview. My mind is a whirr as I try to focus on what he's saying, design intelligent follow-up questions and store ideas for new things to talk about in case there's a pause.

The waitress brings coconut ice cream which we've agreed to share. We look at each other like we're unsure if we should split it into two or if we're okay to dig in and exchange spit. I break the moment by scooping the first piece. *Best to show that I'm not grossed out by his fluids.*

As I plan the next segment of conversation, it occurs to me that we've spent the entire night, and the previous date, talking about him. I'm sure this is because he's nervous and hasn't dated much. I decide to throw out a piece of information and see if he takes the bait.

'I've been writing a blog,' I announce. It's clunky to start a conversation about myself. 'It's about starting the business and everything I learn each week.'

'Really?' He raises his eyebrows. 'Can I read it? I'd love to read it.'

'Sure.' I pass him my mobile phone. 'I've only been doing it for a couple of months, but look, more than fifty people shared this last post. It's getting a bit of a following.'

'"The Large Cost of Small Lies."' Matthew reads the headline. 'Can you email me the link?'

'Of course. I'd love to hear what you think.'

Matthew pulls out his mobile and passes it to me. 'Did you see my new website? I just upgraded it.' A huge photo flashes up on the screen. Matthew's speaking at a podium, surrounded by media microphones and solemn grey-haired men. The picture is taken from below, looking up at Matthew as a giant important figure. He scrolls across the navigation options. 'There's videos of all my speeches here.'

An hour later I'm back in my apartment. Matthew had given me a warm hug at the end of our date. *We're working up to the kiss.* He'd invited me to his house next Friday for dinner. 'I want you to see where I live. Come over and we'll get a movie.' My whole body tingles with excitement.

I snuggle back into the couch and pull my laptop onto my knee. I write Matthew a note with a link to my blog. And I key 'wedding inspiration' into my browser. *Indoor or outdoor wedding?* I've always wanted to get married outside amongst rolling green hills. *New Zealand?* No, his family and friends are all here.

He'll want to invite his colleagues. *Maybe the Premier will come?* I imagine the looks on the faces of my parents' friends. *Rebekah has done well.*

I decide on an indoor Sydney wedding because my skin looks best in soft lighting. The sun is much too harsh. I scroll through venues and click on an image of an auditorium filled with candles and ice sculpture: 'Sydney Convention Centre Weddings'. *Too much?*

Matthew and I have had several charming calls this week. I notice that we both switch into a higher pitch whenever we speak. I googled to see if this is a *thing* and read articles on 'Phonetic Convergence: The Similarity Attraction Hypothesis'. Researchers say that people who are attracted to each other will unconsciously modify their voices to sound similar. *More evidence he likes me!*

Tonight feels like a milestone: dinner at his apartment. Tonight, we will definitely kiss. We *have* to kiss. Tomorrow, I fly to New York to do media interviews for Posse and we won't see each other for two weeks.

My phone buzzes.

> Matthew: I'm outside.
> Me: I'll be right down.

I pull on my brown leather jacket, check my lipstick and dart out my apartment door. Matthew is in a shiny blue convertible with his sunglasses on. He waves.

'Nice car!'

'It's a Spider,' he says, revving the engine. The wind smacks my hair to my face as we turn the corner to William Street. 'Sorry, do you want me to put the roof up?'

'It's okay,' I lie. 'It's nice actually.' I feel fragments of foundation slide into my wrinkles. Mascara mixes with water from my eyes and dry crusts form at the edge of my lipstick. *Just try to enjoy it.*

We pull up to a strip of shops in Double Bay. 'I can't remember if I told you, but I used to be the mayor here, before I went into parliament.'

'You didn't say, but I read it on your Wikipedia.' I want to nudge him in the side like I'm poking fun, but I hold back. I'm not sure he'd find it funny.

'Let's order pizza,' he suggests. 'There's a great Italian place on the corner.'

Matthew ducks inside and I wait on the street. I glance around. Shiny shopfronts with pastel dresses in the windows, manicured gardens, neatly parked four-wheel-drive Porsches in every lot. I cross my arms and slouch against the wall.

I pull myself up just as Matthew emerges with two boxes of pizza and a garlic bread.

'I've got to warn you,' he says, 'people recognise me around here, because I used to be the mayor. They stop to chat. It's *very* annoying, but —' he holds his hands up '— it comes with the job.'

'Okay. Shall we head back to your place then?'

Matthew looks down the busy shopping strip. 'Hang on, I need to get a magazine. The newsagent is just over there.' He links my arm into his. 'Shall we walk?'

Matthew strides tall as we make our way down the path. In my mind I see paparazzi jumping from the bushes and the headlines to follow. Page one of the *Wentworth Courier*: 'Matthew Marino has a new girl! Matthew Marino engaged!' He nods to passersby, who look back at him blankly. After a minute or so he frowns. 'This is really strange. Usually I get accosted.'

I want to make a joke, but Matthew seems annoyed; his image is important. This realisation both draws me in and concerns me. I can see he's vulnerable, a little boy handicapped by an overgrown ego. *I could protect him.* But I'm fearful of what happens when his ego takes a hit. Will he cry, explode, disappear? I tell myself to be careful. *Watch what you say, watch what you do. Don't ever offend him.*

We step back into the car and drive slowly around the block. 'See that kids' playground?' He points. 'I did that, when I was mayor. And that garden over there. And the new parking stations.'

'Wow, really?' I emphasise my awe.

He pushes out his chin. 'Let's take a detour home. I'll show you a few things.'

After a twenty-minute tour and commentary of Matthew's involvement in every Woollahra landmark, park, bus shelter, library and community hall, we arrive at his apartment with cold pizza. *This is it. We're a couple. I'm at his apartment and tonight, we're going to kiss.*

We climb up the steps to the second floor and Matthew holds open the door. He looks nervous, like his place might not live up to my expectations.

'Here it is,' he says.

I step inside. The lounge is large with light grey carpet. There are brown leather couches, a glass coffee table and a big-screen TV in the corner. The walls are bare except for a framed poster in Liberal Party blue: 'Matthew Marino for Woollahra Council'. There's a bookcase lined with family photos and pictures of him with politicians (Tony Abbott, John Howard).

'Is this your sister?' I pick up one of the frames.

'Yeah.' He smiles. 'That's Gabriella.'

The apartment strikes me as plain and functional. There aren't any special touches like coloured cushions or a rug on the floor. *This place needs a woman. I could make it so much nicer.*

'I got a DVD that I thought we could watch. It's the latest James Bond. I've been meaning to watch it for ages.'

A tiny red flag peeps up in the back of my mind, almost so far off that I can't see it. *It would have been nice if he'd chosen a movie that I'd have liked.* I silence the voice. *I'm at the senator's house.* Matthew crouches by the television. He presses play and steps back to sit next to me on the couch, our legs almost but not quite touching.

Fifteen minutes into the movie and I wonder if I'm going to have to sit through the whole thing. I feel like a teenager sitting close to a boy I like, too nervous to know what to do next. *What's he thinking? Should I make the first move?* I slide slightly closer so our legs connect, and it feels like electric currents colliding. *Did he feel that?* I hear him breathe in nervously, but his gaze is fixed forward. *Are we silently having a conversation about making out?* The television plays on in the background: another ten minutes of fighting, computer hacking, men leaping from skyscrapers, and I'm ready to try again.

I wonder if the whole dilemma only exists in my head. *Maybe he's just watching the movie.* I decide to shuffle closer still, just by an inch. I nudge him again from the side. *Was that obvious enough?*

'Are you alright there?' He turns. 'Do you want a cushion or something?'

Okay, enough. I decide to risk rejection and make a bold daring gesture. I lean over his knee and rest my hand his thigh. His looks down at it. It's as if I can hear his heart thump in his chest. This big, important man who runs Australia is scared of little unimportant me.

He looks up to meet my eyes. I lean in a few inches and a magnetic force draws our lips together. I take his hand and place it on my waist. The kiss is tender and sweet. His lips are soft and his breath smells of Listerine.

'Thank you,' he says awkwardly, as he turns back to the television. 'That was lovely.'

An hour later, Matthew is driving me home. 'Hey, did you check out my blog?' I ask.

'Yes, I did.' He pauses. 'It's good.'

Why didn't he mention it earlier? Did he actually read it?

'Is there anything in particular that you liked? A favourite article?'

He pulls up his car next to my apartment building and turns to me. 'I liked all of it.' He brushes the side of my chin with his hand. 'You are a very impressive woman, Rebekah.'

The little red flag at the back of my head is sticking all the way up now and there's another behind it. Both are bright red. I blink hard and they're gone. All I can see is Matthew, his charming eyes leaning towards me as we kiss.

I'm floating across the sky in so many ways as I recline my aircraft seat on route to John F Kennedy airport. I've had two glasses of champagne and watched a silly Jennifer Aniston comedy that made me laugh and cry. I usually feel a jolt of disappointment when a movie ends: back to my loveless reality. Today, I feel bubbles of happiness as I remember where I am and how wonderful life is with my new senator boyfriend.

I take a deep breath in like I've just completed the biggest challenge on earth. I close my eyes and let my dreams wander. I'm way past the Christmas holidays and the wedding. Matthew and I are in the backyard of our big Sydney house. I'm standing on lush green grass with my hands on my hips while Matthew tends to flowers in the garden. Two young children and a golden retriever play in a sprinkler. Droplets of water fall like glitter in the sunlight.

I would only have been eleven or twelve when I picked the names for my children: Finn for a boy and Iona for a girl. 'Finn Marino. Iona Marino,' I whisper over and over. Should I register the domains when I land? *It'll be good for the children to own their dotcom addresses.*

29. ELECTION DAY
IN NEW YORK

6 November 2012

8.15 a.m.

I draw my coat tight around my waist as I step out from my Airbnb apartment onto East 8th Street at St Marks Place. The icy morning air swirls with the smell of hot coffee and toasting pretzels. People flow in both directions like they've all got somewhere to go. A man shouts 'Come on' to a taxi that doesn't stop, a siren blares, car horns beep and the New York City traffic drones on and on and on. I stop for a second to take it all in. The city opens its arms and welcomes me back like an old friend.

Every day in New York is a thrill, and today the excitement in the air is so thick I could reach out and touch it. Today is the 57th presidential election. Tonight, either Barack Obama or Mitt Romney will claim victory. Of course, I want Obama to win and I'm feeling optimistic. I notice a skip in my step as I pace up 3rd Avenue and across to Union Square. There are campaign posters everywhere, Obama stickers plastered across garbage bins and street signs.

This morning I'm meeting Posse's publicist, Andy Morris, for breakfast in midtown. I've got an interview with online magazine *Refinery29* at 10, Bloomberg News at 10.45 and a meeting at *The*

New York Times at 12. Cameron and Gary arrive in town later this afternoon and have organised a dinner for Aussie entrepreneurs in New York. Then I'll find somewhere fun to watch the election results. I smile to myself as I swipe my MetroCard through the barrier at Union Square station. *This is going to be a great day.*

10 a.m.

Andy Morris wipes yoghurt from the corner of his mouth with a napkin. We're in the NoMad Hotel restaurant at Broadway and 28th Street. Our table sits to one side of a long dining hall under a high glass ceiling.

Andy wears stylish glasses and a trimmed beard. He'd been introduced to me as 'the best tech publicist in New York'. He glances at his phone. 'Lisa will be here any second,' he says. 'I asked her to write this piece because she's the food and drink editor. She won't be so interested in the startup business story, so try to focus the interview on how Posse helps people to find cafés and restaurants. A lot of influencers read *Refinery29*. It's a great audience for you.'

A slight woman with dark, sharply cut hair and a red backpack steps through the glass door and waves to Andy. 'Here she is,' he says, pulling his chair to stand.

I spend the next hour chatting and drinking tea with Lisa and Andy. I show her the app and she discovers that lots of her favourite cafés have already signed up. She records our interview on her phone, and I smile for a photo. At 10.45, a short cheery guy called Doug arrives and I spend another thirty minutes answering questions for Bloomberg News.

'How did you get Bill Tai to invest? And Lars Rasmussen? Wow.'

12 p.m.

I step through swinging glass doors below giant silver letters: The New York Times. I run my fingers across the cool marble pillars in the foyer to make sure they're real. *I'm here. Square in the heart of our modern universe.*

Andy saunters through like it's just another office building. 'Remember, Loren won't write an article. This is just a meeting for you to get to know each other.' We hand our drivers licences to a security guard and I snatch mine back quickly so Andy won't spot my birth year. 'Once Posse becomes a big company — once you're raising twenty or a hundred million dollars at a time — then he might write about you. And it'll be good you made the connection now.'

I feel like a kid at Disneyland. As a teenager, I'd dreamed of becoming a journalist. I'd even started a communications degree before getting side-tracked into business. *The New York Times* is the ultimate. *I know they'll never write about me.* The glass lift scoots up through the centre of the building, revealing floors of bustling reporters carrying bags, microphones and piles of paper. A man in a leather cap whispers to a young woman sitting at her desk. The whole place pulses. It's election day and I can smell the hustle. *Just to be here, it's incredible.*

Andy leads me to another reception and flashes a smirk as he notices me taking everything in. I sense that he just brought me up here for fun. I'm all the way from Australia and it'll be a treat for me to see inside one of the world's most iconic newspapers. *He knows they'll never cover Posse.* For the first time today, I feel relaxed. This isn't an interview, it's just a tourist stop and chat with Andy's friend.

A tall man with slate-grey hair appears from behind a door

and grips Andy in a tight hug. 'Great to see you,' he says.

'This is Rebekah from Posse,' says Andy.

'Loren Feldman. I'm the business editor here.' Loren reaches out a long thin arm to shake my hand.

He isn't at all what I expected. I'd pictured someone with a sharp nose and a tailored suit. Loren wears a long-sleeved polo shirt tucked into the kind of jeans my dad would wear. His face is friendly and open.

'Come into my office.' He beckons. 'I've got twenty minutes.'

Loren's 'office' is a wooden desk with papers piled to the roof and no windows. He leans in. 'Now, I hope Andy's told you we don't cover startups. But I like meeting new people and who knows what might happen. Maybe you're the next Steve Jobs. I'll be able to say I met her when . . .' His eyes sparkle. 'You're from Australia, right?'

'Actually New Zealand, originally.'

Loren jokes and asks questions, and I've forgotten that we're sitting in the offices of *The New York Times*. It's as we've known each other forever.

'What's been the hardest thing?' he asks. 'Was there a time where you wanted to give up?'

I roll my eyes. 'My God,' I say. 'I want to give up every day. I mean, it's impossible.' I pause to pinpoint a moment. 'A few months ago, the board tried to fire me.'

Andy and Loren exchange a glance like they're shocked at my candor. I feel like I'm chatting to old friends; it's safe to say anything. *This must be why Loren is such a successful journalist.* His demeanour is so warm and unassuming.

He motions for me to continue.

'I was changing direction too much. "Pivoting" is what we

call it in the startup world. I kept pivoting the plan and the investors got nervous.'

'And what happened? How did you get out of it?'

'Well, I clarified the business vision, what problem we're solving and where I want the company to be in five years' time. And I focused. I raised money from some people in Silicon Valley who supported the vision and supported me.' I shrug. 'That was just one obstacle. Every week there's something else: the website crashes, a customer complains on social media, I struggle to get my team motivated, I stuff up a media interview. You know how it is. I'm learning so much though. I mean, you can't buy an education like this.'

Loren folds his hands together. 'Have you thought about writing all this down? What you've been learning?'

I laugh. 'Ha, yes. Actually, I've started a blog. I'll send it to you if you like. It's pretty out there — no sugar-coating, lots of blood and bone and pain.'

Loren knocks his wooden desk twice with his knuckles and scrunches his eyes together like he just had a thought, then checks his watch. 'It's 12.30, I've got to run.'

9 p.m.

Cameron holds up a bottle of red wine to offer me another glass.

'Sure,' I say, leaning across the table. I'm seated near the end of a long bench at ABC Kitchen in the Flatiron District. Stylishly mismatched ivory chandeliers hang from rustic beams overhead.

I've decided to break my two-drink rule tonight. It's not a date after all, and I have a loose plan to get a bit tipsy. It's been a good day and I hope that a few glasses of alcohol will both soften the nerves I feel dining with a group of strangers and enhance the thrill of New York City on election night. Kind of like a chemistry experiment.

Three large television screens have been wheeled in to blare out percentage counts from the first polling booths. I glance along the table at the bright, youthful faces Cameron and Gary invited along. There's a woman who runs programming at YouTube, the founders of a mobile advertising startup, an online photography marketplace, some investors. Australian and American accents overlap in boisterous conversation, laughing and making new connections.

I watch Cameron introduce himself to a woman with square glasses who's sitting next to him. Gary is deep in discussion with a guy at the other end of the table. Everyone else yaps away in clusters of two or three and I sit alone, an empty seat to my left and the back of the YouTube woman to my right. I reach for the wine. *It'll help my confidence.* I take big sips — one, two, three, the glass is empty. I reach for the bottle.

'So Rebekah, how's life?' Gary appears at my shoulder, standing with the swagger of a few beers. I'm still wary of Gary after that incident with the board. He's like a dog whose jaw I can't quite trust.

'Life?' I don't know what he's asking. The wine is warming the inside of my brain and the left and right sides are arguing again.

Left: *You've known these guys for a year, been through so much. It's time to lower that personal/professional wall.*

Right: *Gary is an investor, he's on your board.*

Left: *Being CEO is so lonely. Gary and Cameron are fun. You can forgive what happened with Don.*

Right: *Gary is not your friend! To him, you are a machine. You exist to make money, that's it.*

'Posse is going well. The team's on fire, we've got a clear roadmap, we're growing fast.' Be steady, be professional, project confidence. 'You've seen the numbers.'

Gary smirks like I've missed the point of his question. 'I didn't ask about the business. I know Posse is doing well.' He pauses. 'How's the rest of your life? What do you get up to when you're not working?'

The wine versus sense balance in my head is starting to slip.

'Oh.' I casually throw open my hand. 'Yoga, exercise. I read. And, um.' I know what he's asking. *Do I have a boyfriend?* 'And I hang out with my boyfriend.'

There it is, that word. *Does four weeks qualify as boyfriend?*

Gary raises his eyebrows. I can tell what he's thinking: *The ice-queen has a boyfriend. I've cracked her.*

'A boyfriend, hey?' He smiles, rolling his hands like he wants more details.

'He's a senator actually, in the New South Wales parliament.' My face burns hot.

'A senator. Wow. Which party?'

'Liberal,' I reply before adding quickly, 'One of the good ones.'

Thirty minutes later and the wine has settled like a blanket of mist around my head. In my hand is a pile of business cards I've collected along with promises of further introductions and coffee catch-ups next time I'm in town. I check the nearest television. Talking heads flash maps with red and blue patches, but still there's no winner.

I flop back into my seat near the end of the table and

Cameron pulls up next to me. He cocks his head to one side and runs his tongue back and forth across the inside of his cheek. There's a moment, a sharp precise moment where I feel our relationship change. He's looking at me differently. His eyes burn holes in my head, down through my heart and deeper still.

'A senator, eh? A Liberal guy,' he says, coy.

Cameron and I have never discussed our personal lives. I know he's divorced with two teenage kids. I've heard him describe himself as a chardonnay socialist, which I find endearing. I guess he's mid-fifties, not an appropriate age for me to date. Besides, we work together. The fact that we could technically have sex is not something that has ever crossed my mind.

I try to work out what's changed. Him knowing I have a boyfriend, knowing that area of my life is not completely shut, has given him an opening. I notice the shape of his chin and shoulders. And there it is: the opening is there for me too.

I run my eyes across his chest and see myself sliding his navy V-neck over his head. In my mind, we're back at my Airbnb. I'm a seductress, unbuttoning my shirt, placing his hands on my body in case he doesn't think he's allowed. '*Do you want to walk me home?*' I test out the question inside my head.

Right: *Shut this down right now! This is your most critical relationship.*

Left: *But it would be hot. Those fifty-five-year-old hands on your thirty-five-year-old skin.*

Right: *Hot? You're no seductress. You're way too scared.*

Cameron smiles like he's reading every thought that charges through my head. I catch his green eyes, wrinkled in the corners. A flood of unspoken feelings hovers between us. There's a closeness. Maybe in another world, something different.

11 p.m.

Back at my apartment, I'm alone watching CNN. No one's called a result yet but the number of blue patches on the map is creeping up. Outside I hear horns blaring and people whooping with excitement. *I want to be a part of this.*

I pull on my puffer jacket and step out into the icy night. It snowed earlier today and there's still slushes of white banked up against the edges of the sidewalks. CNN is broadcasting from Times Square, so I walk two blocks to Broadway and follow the road uptown. My feet break into a trot as I cut through the still air.

The street is oddly quiet. The occasional car hoons past waving an American flag with someone shouting 'O-ba-ma!' from the window. Bars are packed and hushed as hordes of people squish in to watch the screens. *They'll call it soon.* I jog past 34th Street and stop for a second to take in the Empire State Building lit up in blue and red stripes.

I reach Times Square at 11.16 p.m., and two minutes later it happens. A short man with a beard clutches papers as he breaks the news. 'CNN projects that Barack Obama has been re-elected president. He will remain in the White House for another four years.'

The crowd explodes like someone just took the lid off. A girl grabs me in a giant hug. There are screams and howls and I'm hugging and kissing a pile of American faces. I take a selfie with a group of kids in front of the giant flashing billboards and text it to Matthew.

Me: Party in Times Square!

Ten minutes later, I trot across two blocks and hail a cab. From the warmth of the backseat, halfway down 3rd Avenue my phone buzzes.

Matthew: Looks like you're having fun. Shame about the result.

The message hits me like a shower of faeces. I breathe in, then exhale. *We can have different opinions. It doesn't mean anything.*

30. SIX WEEKS

I arrived back in Sydney yesterday morning and slept most of the afternoon. It's 4 a.m. and I'm wide awake, eyes pinned open with jetlag. My mind buzzes with everything that's happening. Posse is on the way up. *Refinery29* put us on their homepage and two thousand people downloaded the app. 'You should think about moving to New York,' said Andy. 'This could really hit.'

Matthew and I have Skyped most days and I can feel the warm flutter of love in my chest. Tomorrow night is our debut as a couple at the Future Leaders programme Christmas party in Kings Cross. We'll be together, in public.

I roll and spot three email notifications on my phone. *Don't check it. You won't get back to sleep.* I turn the phone face-down and snuggle into my pillow. *Hang on, what was the name on that message?* I can't help myself.

'Loren Feldman.' I whisper aloud. *Where's that name from?* In a fog of confusion and half-darkness, I read.

Hi Rebekah!
Great to meet you last week and thanks for sending over the link to your blog. The post you wrote about lying is very, very good. I'd like to publish it and see what kind of reaction we get.

You'll be paid $400 which is our standard rate. Let me know if this is OK and I'll have our admin center send you a contract.

Thanks,

Loren

I sit in bed and read the email over and over, tapping the side of my cheek to make sure I'm not dreaming. *The New York Times is going to publish one of my blog posts.* I pull myself out of bed and to the kitchen to fill the kettle. It's still dark outside and completely quiet. I flick on the television to distract myself. There's something on about wrinkle cream.

Two hours later I've agreed to make three easy payments of $29.99. I pull on a T-shirt and step outside to greet the early morning street-sweeper on Darlinghurst Road. The air is already balmy and bursts of anticipation power my feet in the direction of Rushcutters Bay Park.

I stroll next to the sparkling harbour and the tall fig trees rustle in the breeze. My mind jumps from *The New York Times* to Matthew and tomorrow night. I'll introduce him to my friends. 'This is my partner, Matthew. Do you recognise him?'

Tomorrow night will mark six weeks since our first date. What are the averages? I sit on the grass and open Google on my phone: 'How long to wait before saying I love you?' and 'How long before having sex?' I browse a list of links and a men's forum on Reddit. The consensus is three months for 'I love you' and four to six weeks for sex.

On our phone call minutes earlier, my old flatmate Ainsley said to 'rip off the Band-Aid'. I called JD, my friend from Melbourne, to check how long he dated his wife before they did it. 'It was six weeks,' he said. 'Of course, I was ready earlier. I tried but she made me wait.' My mind is all shaken up with advice. I don't want to but I *do* want to. So far as I can tell, either way I'm stuffed. I text Ruth.

Me: Can you talk?

My phone rings almost immediately.

'Look, I know this is going to sound like a strange question.'

'Yes,' she replies, stretching her voice.

'I've been seeing this guy for six weeks. I really like him. And, you know I'm a bit shy in the —' I pause, noticing the quiver in my voice '— you know, with sex.' I hear Ruth chuckle. 'I wanted to ask you, how long is normal to wait? Do you think he's expecting it?'

Ruth sighs a long breath. 'Look,' she says firmly. 'The most important thing is for you to be ready, for your relationship to be ready. Talk about it with him. If you don't feel like you can talk about it, then you're not ready.'

'Okay,' I say. 'But what's normal, in your experience? Everything online says six weeks.'

Another sigh from Ruth. 'I guess so. Six weeks is probably average, but like I said . . .'

Ruth's words splutter, swirl and suck down a giant plughole till they're gone. Only one sentence remains fixed in my head: '*Six weeks is probably average*'. I stamp one foot on the ground and begin to pace back up the hill.

Late in the afternoon I cross Oxford Street on my way home from the office. The concrete footpath is meltingly hot as I pass trendy bars, falafel counters and dark staircases up to shops and nightclubs whose clientele must slink in and out in the shadows.

Throughout the day I'd run a leadership team meeting, approved the design for a new feature in the app and debated sales strategy with Jen, but my mind remained captive to one event: tomorrow night. Excitement and terror pulsed through my body in equal measure.

Excitement: *I'll wear a short dress, get my makeup done. I'll look hot.*

Terror: *He's expecting to have sex. Six weeks is the average. Everyone says so, even Ruth.*

Excitement: *We'll walk into the party together, heads will turn. 'Rebekah's got a boyfriend, and so handsome.'*

Terror: *You've started a lie. You kissed him, remember. You pretended to be confident.*

Excitement: *Word will spread that he's a senator. 'How impressive. Haven't you done well.'*

Terror: *I can't remember what to do. He's going to think I'm a freak. Or worse, a virgin.*

I recall Madeleine asking her friend about blowjobs. *Could I call her? No, she thinks I'm a success.* I've worked hard to cultivate my glossy professional exterior. I've learnt, yes, to expose vulnerabilities like business mistakes. But this? No way.

I look to the hot dusty sky, my stomach churning. It's time to get proactive. Where could I do some discreet research?

My eyes catch on a fluorescent yellow bar overhanging the footpath: 'Adult XXXX City: Adult Supermarket'. I check the street both ways to make sure there's no one I know, and I sneak three quick steps into the pink-lit staircase.

At the top, the staircase opens to a wide room that might

be an alien planet. The ceiling is high like a warehouse, and in the middle like a monument stands a giant round pink creature with a contraption on its back. On inspection, I conclude it's meant to be a bum with flaps for the cheeks. Signs for cock rings, bondage toys, anal toys, dongs (?), machines (?), swings (?), pumps (?) and lingerie blast me in the face and I cringe with embarrassment.

There are two other customers in the shop: an older man with grey hair, and a muscular guy carrying a motorcycle helmet. From behind the counter, a pale skinny man in a black beanie eyes me. *You're not doing anything illegal. Just relax.*

Rows of porn DVDs line the wall: colour photographs of huge boobs that look like balloons about to burst. Names like *Tit Woman, Bang Bro* and *Girls Getting Wild* leap out and choke my breath. I flinch, I can't look. I feel dirty, like I'm complicit in the exploitation of these women just by looking at the covers. A bitter taste shoots into my mouth. Do I run?

'Can I help you with something?' The beanie man is leering at me. His two front teeth are missing.

Shit! I scramble for something to say. What *am* I doing here? I shake my head. *You're an idiot, Rebekah.*

'Hellooooo?' The man pipes up again. 'Are you looking for anything in particular?'

I glance at the videos and back to the man. 'Do you have something more . . . instructional?'

The man stares and then lets out two giggles which descend into a smoker's cough. 'Like a "how to", you mean?'

I nod.

He shakes his head. 'I'm sorry, we don't have anything like that. But it is a good idea.' The pitch in his voice is high, part polite, part horror-film predator. 'We do have this.' He holds up a DVD of a woman bending over a stool while a man wearing leather straps holds up something tall and pointed. 'It's one of our more basic . . .'

'It's okay.' I wince. 'That's not really what I'm after. Thanks.'

I grit my teeth as I dart down the stairs and back out onto the street. My heart pounds. Quick check both ways again. Nobody saw me. Phew. Walk like nothing happened.

At home, I sit alone on my couch. My chest is tight. *You'll be fine. It'll come back to you.* For a moment I remember Ruth. *Should I just be honest? Tell Matthew I'm nervous?* But that's far too embarrassing to admit. He'll think there's something wrong with me. There must be a reason no one's wanted me for so long. And I don't want to burden him with the heavy truth of Steve. *My ex-boyfriend died, I'm still not over it.*

Out the kitchen window, buildings start to light up in the distance as sunlight drains slowly from the sky. I wonder if there are other women out there just like me. Maybe they're still sitting at office desks, working late to fill up time before catching a bus home to their one-bedroom apartments. They'll cook something healthy, pour a glass of wine and settle in to watch TV. *Under their Carla Zampatti suits, are they afraid too?*

31. JUST LET ME PASS

According to the ABC, today is the hottest November day in thirty years. I worked from home so I could get down to MAC for makeup at eleven. The theme for tonight's party is the eighties. I'm wearing a short blue sparkly dress, red fishnet stockings, a big pink bracelet with matching hoop earrings, and platform heels that I spray-painted silver.

I've just ducked out to buy condoms from the pharmacy and a glass vase from the two-dollar shop in the mall. I am ninety per cent certain that Matthew will bring flowers tonight, because:

- We haven't seen each other for two weeks.
- Tonight is a big date.
- He's the kind of man who wouldn't show up without a gift.

I imagine opening the door. *'Wow, you look amazing,'* he'll say, handing me a sweet-smelling bouquet. I'll smile, thank him, and plop the flowers into the vase like I get them all the time.

My makeup melted a little in the heat so I have to touch it up in the mirror at home. My eyes are circled by thick, 1980s blue to match my dress. I look into my pupils. *Are you ready for this?*

There's a knock at the door. I open it to Matthew, tall and handsome in his navy suit. 'I had to come straight from work. I haven't had time to dress up, sorry.' He kisses my cheek and steps inside. I check his hands: no flowers, no gift. *Oh well. At least he's here.*

Thirty minutes later we're in an underground nightclub on the edge of Kings Cross. On stage, a band bashes out a cover of Tears for Fears. Tony and Sharon, my friends from the Future Leaders programme, are at the other end of the bar doing shots. Matthew orders a lemonade. 'You want a drink?' he asks.

'Just lemonade,' I say. 'I don't need to drink tonight.' I'm lying, of course, and when Matthew excuses himself for the bathroom I knock down two shots of tequila with Tony and Sharon. I wipe my mouth with the back of my hand and scutter back to where Matthew left me. *I should wait.*

The room is packed with faces I recognise. I wave to Sarah the financial planner and her friend, who flail about on the dancefloor like they're having the best night ever. I stand in my spot, fidgeting with my lemonade and waiting to parade Matthew about like a prize pony. I check my watch. He's been gone fifteen minutes, then thirty. My glass is empty. Sarah waves for me to join them. 'Dance with us,' she shouts. 'It's Christmas!'

'I'm waiting for my boyfriend,' I yell back.

'What?' She can't hear me. 'Come on!'

I shrug. *Where is he?* It must be forty-five minutes now, and I decide to dance. I don't want him to think I've been waiting.

My body twists to the music but my head is a pool of anger. *This is so rude. I brought him here.* I had plans, a vision in my head for exactly how this night would go and he's ruined it. I want to crumple him into a paper ball, toss him to the ground and stomp him down with my platform shoes.

'Hey, there you are.' A warm voice in my ear. A hand on my shoulder.

I spin. Matthew grins. 'Sorry, I had to take a call.' He holds up his phone.

'It's okay.' I smile back, and my anger evaporates. My friends stop dancing and huddle towards me. 'This is Sarah. We did the leadership programme together.'

She reaches over to shake his hand enthusiastically. Matthew looks calm and poised, ever the politician.

He presses his mouth to my ear. 'Do you want to get out of here?' he says.

We only just arrived. I want to dance and drink and catch up with old friends. 'Sure.' Suck it up. Keep him happy.

We link arms and walk back through Kings Cross and up to my apartment. Hot, dry dust rises from the footpath and sticks to the sides of my legs. I feel a blister forming at the heel of my shoes. We grumble about the heat but otherwise don't talk much. It's obvious that the plan from here is to have sex. That's why he wanted to leave early. I just want to get it over with. I'm not going to get an A, but if I can scrape a Pass then we can move to the next phase of our relationship.

We hover outside my door. 'Shall I leave you here?' he says. I know what he's doing — he's being a gentleman. He doesn't want to assume.

'No way.' I open the door and pull him inside by the hand.

My lounge is a sauna, and droplets of sweat trickle down my chest. I switch on a portable fan but it's no match for the engulfing heat.

I reach for Matthew's other hand and wrap it behind my back, embracing him close. I lean in, kissing him on the lips. 'Do you want to come through?' *Just fake confidence. It's sexy.*

I feel myself trembling as I push open my bedroom door.

'Okay,' he says with an expression I can't read. 'Sure.' His words are short whispers like they're not coming from anywhere solid.

I perch on the edge of the bed and point to the zip on my dress. 'Do you want to take this off?'

His big fingers fumble and catch in the top of my pantyhose. 'Got it.' He breathes out tenseley.

I pull the dress over my head and reveal red pantyhose, black lace undies, a black bra and platform shoes. He stands back, his brow crooked. *What's that look? Is it desire?* I'm not sure.

It's so hot in my bedroom. 'We're going to need the fan,' I say.

'I'll get it.' He's out the door in a flash and I hear him scrambling about with the wires in the lounge.

I kneel on the bed and look down at my pale skin. I don't look like the women on the DVD covers yesterday. If my breasts are balloons then someone let the air out. There's a fold of flab over the top of my pantyhose, a mole under my left breast. *God, just let me get a Pass. All I need is to pass.*

Matthew plugs in the fan next to the door, blowing dry air onto the bed. He takes off his shoes and crawls awkwardly across the bed towards me. He moves my hair to one side and kisses the top of my neck: passionate, sloppy. His tongue stretches deep into my mouth and twiddles, reminding me of a boy who kissed me once on the side of a skating rink in Year 8.

I clasp his face between the palms of my hands. I wish I could read what's going on inside his head. *Do you want this? Are you going along with it because you think it's what I want?* He's a man. Of course he wants it.

His mode has shifted, and mine has too. Everything is getting faster. His shirt is off, his pants, he tugs at the legs of my pantyhose till my feet pop out, my bra, my undies. Suddenly we're both naked. Our pink bodies slap together, groping, kissing, tumbling.

I catch his eyes again and I'm quite sure that his look is terror. For a moment, it's clear we're both thinking the same thing: *'We should stop, we should talk about this. I don't know what to do, you don't know what to do either. We're not ready.'*

But there's an unspoken conversation as well.

Him: *I can't look scared, I'm a senator. I don't want to offend her by pulling back.*

Me: *Remember: fake-sexy and confident. It's been six weeks, he's expecting it. If you stop then you'll embarrass him, you'll lose him.*

'Ah, I —' he stutters, breaking the silence. 'I don't have a condom or anything.'

I'm in my animal brain now, focussing only on surviving the fall. 'I've got one.' I reach for the box I'd put in my bedside table. What happens next is a blur of legs, fear, pain, penis and regret.

We lie next to each other on the bed, dripping with sweat, ice-cold in disappointment. *Oh well, it's done. Now we can cuddle.* I tell myself it'll be better in the morning. He'll want to stay with me and make sure I'm okay. We'll wake together, make breakfast and talk. *This experience will bring us closer.*

'I should get going,' he says. 'I've got a breakfast thing tomorrow.'

A rock drops from my throat to my stomach. 'Right.'

I walk him to the door wearing a towel. He kisses my cheek and looks at me for a second. Another unspoken acknowledgement flashes between us: our relationship is over.

'I'll call you in the morning,' he says, flipping his suit jacket over his shoulder.

I return to bed and collapse there in a pile of panic and loneliness. *That flash that I saw about us breaking up, that was just my imagination. He'll call. He always calls.*

The next morning, I'm on the couch watching *The Bachelorette* and eating a cinnamon scroll for comfort. My phone rings, it's Matthew. My chest relaxes. *He wants to talk.*

'Good morning!' I sing like a bright bird.

The phone is quiet. Matthew's voice is in the background calling out instructions. 'Look I've said it a thousand times, that centre has to move.'

There's rustling of papers.

Matthew has bum-dialled me. I chuckle to myself.

'Hello!' I shout down the phone. There's no answer, just more rustling.

I listen for ten minutes as Matthew paces about, ordering instructions down another phone. He sounds manly and important.

I shout again. 'Hello! Toodeloo! I'm here, can you hear me?'

There's nothing. Just more talk in the background and then a click. I'm gone.

I picture him in his apartment, standing over his desk. Didn't he say he had an event this morning? It seems odd that he called me by accident. Was it an accident? I text.

> Me: Haha, you just bum-dialled me. Hope you're having a good morning.

There's no reply.

Twelve hours later, it's 8.30 p.m., I decide to call. The phone rings, four times. 'Hi, this is Senator Matthew Marino. I can't get to the phone right now. If your matter is urgent, then please try Susan from my office on . . .' I hang up. I text.

> Me: Did you still want to chat today? I'll be up for another hour then gotta sleep.

There's no reply. The next morning I text again.

> Me: Hi Matthew, did you want to catch up today? I'm planning a walk to the park later.

There's no reply.

By Sunday night my panic has turned to despair. There's a whole world at threat: our summer holiday at the beach, wedding with the Premier present, house with a garden, a sprinkler, two children. The two children! Iona and Finn Marino, what will become of them? The loss is too big to think about all at once. I text again.

> Me: Hey, it would be good to talk sometime. Can we chat tomorrow?

There's no reply.

As I walk to work on Monday, I'm still holding a thread of hope.

'How was the party?' asks Jen.

I smile and show photos of me and Matthew with our arms around each other.

'Rebekah,' she says, jaw dropped. 'He's so distinguished.'

I want so much to fold into the joy of the moment, but I restrain from feeling anything. 'Yes, he is.'

All day my stomach is wringing out my organs like wet clothes. I don't eat a thing. That evening I stare at my silent phone on the coffee table, remembering Ruth's advice. 'As soon as you start chasing someone, they'll run.'

But Matthew owes me an explanation. He can't just disappear. We can fix this. I wonder if the rejection is all in my head. *It's only been three days. He's just been busy. He'll call later.* I text again.

> Me: Hi. I'm sure you're busy but would be good to chat.

By Wednesday I can't stop shaking. I sit at my desk but my brain is fog and I can't concentrate. My stomach is still squeezed so tight that there's no room for food. I've barely slept.

By Friday I'm so exhausted that I can't make it to the office. I crouch in the corner of my apartment and cry. I cry and cry, feeling relief that there's any emotion left in me at all. I text again.

> Me: I'm feeling really quite hurt. Please call me so we can talk.

By Sunday my pain turns to anger. *What an arsehole. What a scared little creep.* I pound my fist against the wall until my hand is agony. I stamp the ground so hard I almost crack a floorboard. I dial his number and it cuts to voicemail after only one ring. 'Hi, this is Senator Matthew Marino. I can't get to the phone right now—' I hang up and try again.

'Hi, this is Senator—' Click.

I'm numb now. I imagine him on his couch watching my calls come in. I'm the scary woman chasing him down the street but I don't care anymore. *Does he care how I'm feeling?*

The weeks that follow are like waking up from surgery. At work, voices I recognise ask questions and hand me pieces of paper to sign. 'What? Sure, okay,' I reply. Outside, outlines of people blur on the street.

An email arrives from Loren Feldman in New York.

> Hi Rebekah!
> Your post is up and it's getting a terrific response! You made the top ten most shared articles in NYT Business today (see list below).
> Yahoo Finance has published it too so expect some syndication royalties. Here's the link.
> I'd like to speak with you about writing a fortnightly column. When suits to chat?
> Thanks,
> Loren

My phone flashes with notifications. More than a thousand new people are following me on Twitter. Someone from CNBC has sent a message on LinkedIn asking for an interview. Life is a surreal blend of emotion: pain, elation, fear. Days and nights are a jumble of team meetings, graphs showing the growing number of people using Posse, board reports, *The New York Times*. It can't be real.

32. THREE MISTAKES

I hand Madeleine a bottle of pinot noir and slump onto the charcoal leather couch at her and Joe's apartment. Madeleine, stunning as always in a light blue dress that ties in the middle, heads to the kitchen to fetch two glasses. Joe darts around in the background, holding a tea towel and preparing dinner.

Madeleine doesn't have to ask. She raises a sharp brow, pours the wine, and everything inside me gushes out: Matthew, his politics, stuffing lamb into my purse, his disinterest in me and my opinions, the disastrous sex, the humiliation, his disappearance.

'When I say it all out loud it sounds pathetic. I sound pathetic.' I let out a deep sigh. 'I don't know what's wrong with me.'

Madeleine sits still like a statue. I comb the edges of my fringe as I squirm about uncomfortably. 'Let's start at the beginning,' she says. 'You want a relationship, yes?' I nod. 'How do you imagine it looks? Who *are* you?'

'Um. I want to have kids. I'd like to be a mum, a wife.'

She shakes her head. 'But who are *you*?'

'What do you mean?'

'Look.' Madeleine gently touches my arm. 'Can I give you some honest feedback?'

'Yes.' I motion eagerly. 'Please, go ahead.'

'When we met for lunch that day, you . . .' She stops as if she's working out how much to say. 'You weren't what I expected.' There's a nervousness in her breath. 'Joe told me you were a successful businesswoman. Someone I could learn from. But the way you walked, carried yourself. I remember you being stooped over, hair in front of your face, self-conscious, weird in the way you used your hands. And something about your voice. It was so quiet, with no power behind it. Zero conviction.' She tilts her chin down, waiting for me to respond.

'Okay,' I say, as a hundred bricks crash down on my skull.

'I'm sorry. I just couldn't work you out. I kept thinking: this woman is successful, attractive. What's wrong with her?'

I wriggle further into the corner of the couch, taking a healthy sip of the pinot noir. *Is that really how I come across?*

'Can you give me a hand?' Joe appears in the doorway wearing red oven gloves.

Madeleine stands. 'Back in a minute.'

Alone in the lounge, my brain feels like a mess of lost puzzle pieces as I try to process everything I've just heard. *Who am I?* Pictures emerge in my mind, the faces of three different women. All me, but different.

Woman 1: The Rebekah I think I am

Outwardly confident with an air of untouchability. Her tech startup and *New York Times* column are perfect props to ensure the viability of a successful outward persona. But inside, there's a little voice in her head that judges others. She doesn't like the voice, and she can't work out how to switch it off. She's fears being exposed as a fraud. She's terrified of someone discovering that underneath the tough exterior is a scared, lonely, not very nice person.

Woman 2: The Rebekah that Madeleine sees

Outwardly successful, yes. Impressive in a way that frightens people. Comes across as aloof, a bit cold, maybe confused. Others wonder if she doesn't like them or if she doesn't like herself.

Woman 3: The Rebekah I want to become

A strong woman who loves with her whole heart. She's someone who contributes too. She gives herself when she thinks she can help others.

I try to zoom out and look down on myself from above. *Who is this woman with red hair and pale skin sitting cross-legged on the couch?* I wonder if the woman Madeleine sees is actually what everyone sees. *People are nice to me out of pity.* Woman 1 is just in my head. So is Woman 3. *Could I become her? Is it possible?*

Madeleine returns, licking her finger like she just tasted something delicious. 'You figured it out yet?'

Is she kidding? I can't construct myself in two minutes.

'Come on,' she says, signalling to the kitchen. 'Joe's got dinner ready.'

I pick up our glasses and set them next to plates on the high kitchen table. Joe beams from beneath dark locks of hair. He sets down a steaming casserole dish that smells like baked cheese. Madeleine drapes her arm over his shoulder affectionately. *Is there anything he can't do?*

'Madeleine tells me you've been seeing some guy. Sounds like a bit of an idiot,' says Joe.

'Ha. Maybe I'm the idiot. I don't know.'

He spoons slops of potato and vegetable casserole onto my plate.

I turn to Madeleine. 'You've heard the story. What do you think I'm doing wrong?'

She smiles and sips her wine. 'It's simple but it's not easy. You need to get out of your head. Stop trying to fix yourself.'

'Fix myself?'

'What is it that you think isn't enough? It'll be impacting your choices in relationships, I mean.' She looks at me, quizzical. 'Didn't you figure this stuff out at the Landmark Forum?'

'Well, yeah. I know that I have this belief that I'm not likeable, not naturally anyway. It goes back to not getting invited to a birthday party when I was seven. I thought that in order to be liked, I'd need something else to impress people. Like managing bands, starting a tech company . . .'

'Dating a senator,' adds Madeleine.

The room falls quiet and I feel my cheeks flush.

'Shit.' I reach for my wine glass. 'You're right.' *He wasn't even nice to me.*

Madeleine smiles. 'There are three big mistakes I see women make in romantic relationships. You just made the first. You looked for a man to fill something you think is missing in yourself. For you, it's status. You don't think you're likeable so you chase men, jobs, clothes, whatever, to prop up your status. Yes?'

I nod, feeling tears swell in my eyes.

'Women do this all the time,' she continues. 'Most people

have something they think is missing. It's usually looks. They're not confident in their appearance so they'll only go for good-looking men. They tell themselves it's about physical attraction but it's not. They *need* looks. If they're with some handsome guy, then they must look okay too.'

She closes her hands into fists and softly bangs them on the table. 'Imagine what kind of guy you'd find if you stopped looking for someone to plug your insecurities? Just go out and find a nice, decent man who likes you, who you can have good conversations with.' She motions to the street outside. 'There's loads of them out there.'

I take a deep breath and smile, remembering all those faces on the dating sites that I'd quickly disregarded. 'What are the other mistakes?'

'Well.' She cocks her head to the side with a playful confidence. 'The second is trying to change yourself for a man, especially early in a relationship. Think about my story, what I told you last time we met. If I hadn't been upfront with Joe about my weight, if I'd tried to change myself, then I'd be totally screwed now.'

'How do you mean?'

'We've been living together for a year. We're going to be living together for the next fifty years. Do I want to count calories the whole time? Worry about what he's thinking when I eat a chocolate bar? Imagine what he's thinking when we're having sex?' She bangs the table again. 'Fuck, no! I like chocolate! I need a man who thinks I'm a goddess exactly the way I am. That's it.'

I laugh out loud remembering the awful assumptions I'd made about her when we first met. *I love this woman. She's hypnotising.* Joe pulls a tray of sweet-smelling dessert from the oven and slices it into bowls.

'Work out who you are and live your life without excuses. Because whoever you are when you date is who you'll get a match for.'

'What do you mean, get a match for?'

'I mean, if you're a confident person and you pretend to be shy and demure, then you'll end up matched with someone who's overbearing. If you have strong opinions but you pretend that you don't, then you'll get someone who isn't interested in what you have to say.'

This one is like a cold fish. 'Matthew wasn't interested in my opinions. He never read my blog. I pretended not to care that he spent so much time on his phone. If we'd ended up together . . . ' My mind drifts.

'You would have spent your whole life pretending. You would have been miserable, you probably would have ended up divorced.'

'Right, yes.'

'There are risks, of course, in this approach,' she says. 'Joe could have said that he did have a problem with my weight, and I would have lost him. I might have ended up alone.' She shrugs. 'But I still think that's better than being in a bad relationship — hating him, hating myself.'

I look up. 'I still haven't figured out the first bit. What you asked before, about who *I* am in a relationship.'

She frowns. 'People waste so much time trying to *find themselves.* You already know who you are, who you want to be.'

'Okay.' I feel like a dumb student who isn't getting it. 'What if it isn't obvious? When I picture myself, that woman you described before with no confidence. I'm not sure that's me.'

'But that *wasn't* you. The way you were when we met, your attention was on yourself. I bet there was a voice in your head. *How am I coming across? What does she think of me? What can I get from this conversation?*'

I lean back in my chair, folding my arms. 'Yeah,' I say. 'There's always a voice in my head asking those things. I hate that voice.'

'And who is that voice?'

I shrug. 'Me, I guess.'

Madeleine stops eating and places her knife and fork on the plate. 'It's not you. It's just your judgements and evaluations. They're automatic, from somewhere in your unconscious.'

I notice I've been holding Madeleine's gaze for an unnaturally long time and I look away.

'You did it again,' she says.

'What?'

'What did that voice in your head say?'

Stuff it. Be honest. 'The voice said that I'd been looking at you too long. That you'd think I'm weird.'

'See, you weren't being yourself. Because your attention was on you. Worrying what I'd think of you. Can you think of a moment, one time in your life when you weren't thinking about yourself? When you were just going for it?'

A scene flashes into my head: pitching Posse on the beach in Maui. I uncross my arms and nod.

'Who were you in that moment?' Who are you now?'

I remember what Mel said about the importance of vision for a business. *I need one too. What are my 'foundations'?*

'Inspiration. Someone who makes things happen. Someone

who cares about people. I'm a leader.'

Her mouth turns up into a smile. She points her finger at my chest. 'Be that person, when you're on the dates. See what happens.'

We chat and laugh and eat the delicious pudding. I turn to Joe. 'I have to ask, what was it about Madeleine that got you interested? I want to hear your side.'

He smiles lovingly at his fiancée. 'We were friends first, at work. He taps his finger over his mouth like he's thinking. 'I guess I really liked the way I felt when I was around her. I'd just come out of a relationship where the woman kept trying to fix and change me. Madeleine seemed to think I was great just how I was. Isn't that right, honey?'

She puts her arm around him for a squeeze.

'I looked at her and I thought: If I end up with this woman then my life will turn out awesome.' He laughs. 'I did. I thought I'd be mad to miss this one.'

At the end of the night I gather my things. 'I almost forgot,' I say. 'You said there were three mistakes women make. What's the third?'

'Ah,' says Madeleine. 'The third is how women sabotage their relationship once they've found the guy. Come back and see me when you think you've met someone. We'll talk about it then.'

33. CHRISTMAS DAY

The whitecapped waves crash onto smooth golden sand at Noosa National Park.

'So Rebekah,' says Mum, 'what are you plans for the year? Any resolutions this time?'

The three of us have walked five kilometres through the bush to work off our Christmas morning pancakes. The beach is hemmed by green — no roads, no people. Grey heron birds scatter about with their heads held high.

Mum is wearing a ridiculously large sunhat and a red shawl. Dad's in a floppy hat tied under his chin and sunglass lenses sticky-taped over top of his regular glasses. Here we are again, an oddball collection of three.

'What plans do you have?' Mum asks more sternly this time, like she's annoyed I haven't answered.

I drag my toe along the sand, carving out a wobbly line. I'm not where I'd hoped to be at the end of 2012, but I am pleased with how far I've come. The lonely woman of last Christmas, out walking the streets of Whangarei at 6 a.m., peering in other people's windows, filled with longing but completely stuck. She knows so much more now than she did a year ago.

What about this next year? What will I keep? What will I throw? I haven't dated since Matthew. Last night I logged into my dating profiles for the first time in months. They reminded me of untended gardens, overgrown with new faces and unanswered messages. I noticed Matthew's profile back up and I imagined him dining with other women. *'I want to make it clear that dinner tonight is on me.'* The thought makes me laugh.

My plan for 2013 is fifty-two more dates, but this time I'll succeed in my mission. This time I know what to do: be compassionate, don't judge, ask questions, especially about his mum, don't ask if he wants kids until the third or fourth date. Be confident but also vulnerable. Look for friendship (but not for whatever happened with Sean), have a plan, be spontaneous. Don't change yourself to please anyone, don't look for someone to fill your insecurities. 'Just go out and find a nice, decent man who likes you, who you can have good conversations with.' And most importantly be yourself, but don't focus on yourself. My brain whizzes like an overheating computer.

I've decided to shift location. I'm done with the men of Sydney with their dyed hair and platform shoes. *Me and Sydney men just don't click.* I need a new pool of talent in my dating funnel. Somewhere with endless options, where the men are ambitious, creative, smart, energetic, cultured and fun.

'I'd like to move to New York,' I say.

Mum turns to me, her shawl flapping in the wind. 'Do you think that's a good idea? For your dating, if you want to settle down.'

'Yeah,' I say, squinting into the sun. 'You've seen *Sex and the City.* There's heaps of single men in New York.'

We're halfway down the beach and a sole pink figure appears in the distance. New York *is* a good idea. I'd felt excited just then, when I said it out loud. I've signed up to start my *New York Times* column in February. I'll have to raise more money for Posse by

December. We've got customers there. Yes, New York is it.

The pink figure is closer now. It's a man with fluffy hair and . . . I search the pink for another colour. Something to indicate cloth down there.

'Mum, I think he's—' I'm not close enough to tell.

'It's a nudist beach, Rebekah, didn't you know?'

'*Muuuuuum*, gross! Why didn't you say?'

Dad chuckles. 'What's the problem? What's so embarrassing?'

I bury my face in my hands. 'Arrrrrgh. I'm going back.' I spin and run in the opposite direction.

34. A WHITE ROOM IN THE EASTERN SUBURBS

'm on the eighth floor of an office tower in Bondi Junction. The woman opposite me is named Priya. She has long dark hair and I imagine she's wearing a designer blouse and a thin necklace under her doctor's coat.

'How old are you?' she asks.

'Thirty-five. I'll be thirty-six in June.'

She makes an expression like I'm pushing my luck. 'This is the time to do it then.'

There's an enormous frame on the wall, packed with photos of newborn babies: pink, brown, fat, scrawny, naked and dressed in cute bowties. All, I imagine, products of Priya's work.

'What's the process?' I ask.

She places my GP referral letter to one side and passes me a glossy folder titled 'Fertility Preservation, IVF Australia'. *Is this how I have children? This white room, this smiling specialist. All by myself.* It's not how I'd dreamed it would happen.

Priya opens the folder. 'First we do a couple of tests. A scan of your ovaries and your uterus, and a blood test. We want to know how many eggs you have left.'

How many eggs I have left? My brain starts to calculate. *I've had my period since I was thirteen. That's twelve years. Hang on, no. That's twenty-two years. Shit!*

'On the first day of your next period, you come in and we give you some hormones to take.' She holds up a box of syringes. 'It's to stimulate egg production, so we get as many as possible.'

I grimace.

'It isn't painful,' she says. 'They're very small needles.'

I picture myself on the couch at home, hunched over, a handful of tummy flesh in one hand, an egg-stimulating needle in the other. *This isn't how I dreamed it would happen.*

Priya turns a page in the folder and uses her pen to point to a picture on the page: a clear sack filled with little round balls. 'After about ten days we collect the eggs.' She turns the page again and a sharp instrument is piercing the sack.

'Do I get put to sleep?' I ask.

She shakes her head. 'We give you a bit of gas. It's uncomfortable. But honestly, it looks worse than it is.'

I cross my legs. 'What's the success rate? Of babies, born like this?'

She throws her hands gently. 'It's still fairly new, but look: for someone of your age, I'd expect we'd get between ten to twelve eggs. Seven to nine of them will be suitable for storing. Most will fertilise when —' she looks up tentatively '— when you're ready to do that.'

When I'm ready. I feel a shower of judgement fly across the desk. She thinks I'm prioritising my career. I'm being selfish. I'm angry now, but I need numbers so I storm forward. 'How many of those become babies, on average?'

She shrugs. 'Look, there's no guarantee. But in my experience, it's about twenty to thirty per cent that'll develop into a pregnancy.'

I do the maths in my head: one baby per batch. 'And what's the cost?'

Priya turns to the back page in the folder. 'The initial tests are three-hundred and fifty dollars. A cycle is eleven thousand, including collection, then there's a small monthly fee for storage.'

$11K. I compose myself, holding my face motionless to mask my shock.

'Unfortunately, Medicare doesn't cover egg freezing. Unless it's for medical reasons.' She stresses the word *medical*.

What about my reasons? I look at the babies on the wall again and feel my heart sting. I don't want to miss having a child. Life only happens once. But I'm torn and I start to question. Is she right? Is my career the reason why I'm so late to start looking for love? I've only been dating for a year.

I imagine my little eggs frozen in a test tube, waiting. Another image emerges in my mind. I'm at a dining table sitting across from my twenty-year-old daughter. *'You were born from a frozen egg. I was busy working for most of my thirties. I didn't have time for relationships, so I just popped you on ice until I was ready.'* I sink in shame.

Priya closes the folder and leans across the table, smiling as if she senses my unease. 'Have you thought about just having a baby now? I mean, it's much easier. You might not need any of this.'

Is she kidding? She thinks I'm here for fun. 'It's not because of work, you know, or anything like that. I just haven't —'

'You're not in a relationship,' she interjects.

'Yeah.' Now she's going to think I'm a loser who can't find a man. 'I was seeing someone. I thought he was it.' I shrug. Why do I have to justify myself? I have a right to do this.

'Egg freezing is a good option then,' she says. I can't decide how I feel about this woman. Is she here to help me or is she here to make money? I imagine her beyond these sterile walls. I wonder if she has children herself. If they holiday at fancy resorts with giant swimming pools.

As much as I'd like to know I tried everything I could to have a family, this whole thing seems like a massive gamble. I take the folder and Priya hands me a stack of medical forms. 'Joan at the front desk can schedule the tests for you.'

'Thanks,' I say, stepping towards the door. 'I'll think about it.'

35. THE MEN OF NEW YORK

'You look amazing,' gushes Jen. She's sitting on the couch of our midtown Manhattan apartment. I'm wearing a blue Lycra top that rides off one shoulder, tight black jeans and high leather boots. Ready for my first date in New York City, my first date in months.

'Would you mind taking my photo? I need a new profile pic.'

Jen and I have been in New York for a week, bunkered down in a tiny eighteenth-floor, one-bedroom unit, each of us taking turns on the couch. We're here to market Posse, learn what American customers want and build relationships with prospective investors.

I've decided to hold off on freezing my eggs for now, but I've made a mental note to keep aside $11,000 in my bank account. I'll give dating one more year. If I haven't met my man by my thirty-seventh birthday, I'll definitely go back to the clinic.

A few days ago, I started a Match.com profile because it's the site I'd seen advertised here on television. On Match, you have to give yourself a tagline. I'm capitalising on my foreign appeal: 'Aussie gal looking for new adventures in the Big City'. I'm already in contact with eight candidates.

So far, I've discovered some differences in dating etiquette. On Match, guys will message only once or twice before suggesting a date. I've asked for phone calls twice now, and both times the 'matches' have disappeared. I'm trying a new strategy: meet as many men as possible, always in public places that are easy to escape from.

Tonight I'm meeting Gabby from Brooklyn, who's invited me to the NYC Whiskey and Spirits Festival on 11th Avenue. The evening spring air is cool as I walk briskly along 34th Street. I dart past the foot of the Empire State Building, holding my arm out to hail a cab. Horns blast and lights flash like they always do. I pause for a second to take in the magnificence.

As my cab approaches a brick building with a glass arched entranceway, I spot Gabby waiting by the door. He has long black hair and his hands in the pockets of his hooded sweatshirt. 'Hey, Rebekah.' He waves, smiling, and I get out to greet him. 'I've got the tickets. Come this way.'

The next hour is a whirlwind of sample cups and tastings: whiskey, vodka and tequila. Hundreds of brands I've never heard of, each company with a small white stand. Gabby asks questions and charms the proprietors with his interest. I follow behind eagerly, my mouth awash with sweet malt.

'Now there's an actual way to smell a whiskey,' he says, holding a plastic cup to his nose. 'You bring the cup up till it's too sharp, then back away a little, then away altogether to think about what happened.'

I lift the cup to my nose.

'Hang on, hang on. You've got to open your mouth.'

At the end of the night, Gabby walks me to a cab. 'Thanks for coming. That was fun,' he says.

'Yeah.' I wait. I have no idea what this date is. Does he want to see me again? Or am I just a prop to enhance his evening?

I imagine his calendar on the wall at home: Wednesday night Whiskey Festival: ticket, tick; date, tick.

'I love your accent by the way,' he says as he closes the door of the cab. 'Super sexy.' He blows me a kiss.

On Friday afternoon I meet Brett at Aldo Sohm Wine Bar on West 51st Street, a few blocks from where he works as a private wealth advisor. He wears a maroon tie matched to a perfectly folded pocket handkerchief.

'How do you like New York?' he asks.

'I love it! Of course.'

He orders fancy cocktails and lists New York attractions he thinks I should visit. 'Get to the Hamptons in summer,' he insists. 'Get an invite to one of the parties.'

On Sunday I meet Jim, an NYU professor, at an organic vegan restaurant called Caravan of Dreams on East 6th Street. I order the huitlacoche quesadilla and Jim gets the macrobiotic platter. We cosy up under the low ceiling of hanging plants and talk about his research into gender and sexuality in medieval Islamic societies. The conversation is fascinating, if not a little one-sided.

On Tuesday, I meet Howard, a product manager who was an early employee of DoubleClick and made a fortune cashing in his stock options when the company sold to Google. On Thursday is Teo, an aspiring actor who wears a backpack and carries a bottle of water when he meets me outside Union Square station. There's George, who takes me to the Soho House in Tribeca on Friday night. We sip cocktails on the sixth floor while New York's elite strut like they're straight from a film set.

Then there's Clint Chef, Gerrit Banker, Tyler Insurance,

Kyle Banker, Dylan Advertising, Mitch Consultant, Chris Architect, Derek Art Gallery and Brian Banker. We've strolled through Central Park, visited the Museum of Modern Art, sipped iced tea at the famous Coffee Shop in Union Square, eaten burgers outside at Shake Shack in Madison Square, discovered hidden wine bars, laughed, danced, kissed. Not one of them has asked me out on a second date.

A man in a top hat is playing piano as I stroll through Washington Square Park to meet Jarrod, my latest match. The ground is in full bloom with bright red and yellow tulips, and pink cherry blossom trees border the path. I feel a rush of joy in my chest, like New York City just kissed me on the cheek. It's hot today and I'm wearing the navy summer dress and sandals I bought for the date with Bondi James last year.

Afternoon light shimmers against the sandstone buildings and a woman tugs on the leashes of five dogs as she crosses the lights at 7th Avenue.

Jarrod is a bartender at a place called Due West. 'There's usually no one around on Tuesday afternoons,' he'd said on his message. 'We can hang out till I knock off.' I arrive at 189 West 10th Street, put Google Maps back into my handbag and cup my hands against the window to peep inside. The place is empty except for a sole bartender wiping glasses and adjusting his thick dark fringe like Luke Perry on *90210*. I feel a small insect flutter its wings in my tummy. I know I'm trying not to be superficial but *he is delicious!*

'Hey,' he says, looking up as I push open the door. 'Rebekah, right?'

I smile, my tongue twisted.

'What can I get you to drink?' he asks.

I don't think I've ever encountered such an exquisite face. His cheek bones are high, his skin soft-looking, his eyes brown and clear and he has perfect straight white teeth. 'Um, a vodka lemonade,' I say, reaching for my purse.

'Pft.' He waves away my money. 'I work here.'

The place is boutique, with white brick walls and a mirror behind the bar. I pull up a black leather stool and search for a suave first question to ask. I need to break the silence. 'Did you grow up around here?'

He lifts one eyebrow as if my dart has totally missed the board. 'Yeah. Well, New Jersey.'

We chat for a while about Australia, Posse and his work in New York. He's a writer who wants to get into film and television. 'I just work here to pay the bills.'

A group of four guys burst through the door and form a circle at the other end of the bar. Jarrod winks at me while he pours them jugs of beer.

I'm confused. *This guy is way out of my league.*

He returns with the vodka bottle and I hold my hand over my glass.

'I can't,' I say. 'I've got a really big day tomorrow. I'm presenting at New York Tech Meetup. It's a huge thing.'

'Okay,' Jarrod says. His face settles into a confused, disappointed expression.

The group convene on a blue velvet couch at the back of the bar and Jarrod pulls up a stool next to mine.

'Hey, can I ask you a question?' he asks.

'Of course.' I sit back.

'How have you found New York so far? The dating, I mean.

Or am I the first?'

'Ha. No. I've done, I dunno, maybe twenty.'

'And?'

'They've been fun. Everyone's been really nice, interesting. But . . .'

'But what?'

I pout. 'No relationship.'

'Is that why you're dating? For a relationship?'

I nod firmly. 'Isn't that why everyone . . .'

Jarrod returns to the other side of the bar and pours himself a gin and tonic. He's moving more purposefully now, not the slow flirtatious waltz of before. 'Show me your phone. Bring up your Match profile.' I reach for my phone and hand it to him. '"Aussie Gal looking for new adventures,"' he reads, eyes gleaming. 'That doesn't say "relationship". That says "This girl wants to have fun". Or in guy talk, "This girl is up for it".'

'What?' My face contorts.

He points to my phone. 'Look at that girl in the tight blue top. She's Aussie, sexy as hell, looking for adventure. Oh yeah.' He laughs.

'You think that's what these guys expected?'

'Maybe not on a first date. But I mean, they'd expect some chemistry, some fun. They're not there for marriage.'

I lean in towards Jarrod. I must make the most of this opportunity, learn whatever I can. 'Okay then. What advice can you give me? I want a relationship. I want my, you know, my forever person.'

'And you want to find him on Match?' He raises his eyebrows. 'Two things. First, change what you say on your profile. Say you're there for love, a relationship, whatever. You won't get as many dates.' He smirks for a second. 'You'll get a lot less dates, okay. But they'll be higher value.'

'That makes sense. God, I feel like an idiot.' There's a pause and I wonder if he wants me to go. But I want more intel. 'And what else?'

'Look, this is what you need to understand about men.' This is it. I lean in. 'Men think about sex all the time.'

'I know that.'

'No,' he says. 'Women think they know, but they don't understand the scale of it. Sex is about more than getting off. It's validation.' He takes a gulp of his drink. 'If I went on a date with you and we had a nice conversation, but I didn't get any signals, tension, flirtation — whatever you want to call it — then I'd think you didn't like me. I'd go home feeling shit, like I'd been rejected. That's why they're not calling you.'

I take a moment. 'And if we're both clear that we're there for a relationship?'

'You still need chemistry. It can't just be a nice chat.'

I rummage through my brain. 'How do you go from nice chat to chemistry? Isn't it just there?'

He tenses his face. 'No, it's not *just there*. You have to flirt.'

'Okay. I just want you to pretend, for a second, that I'm really hopeless at this. That I have no clue what to do. Give me some tips.'

His voice cracks into chortles of laughter. 'You're really something.' He shakes his head. 'Touch is the best signal. If you're a guy, you're always looking for signals. The moment a woman touches you, brushes your arm or your back or whatever, it tells you something. You know she's interested . . .'

36. THE NEW YORK
TECH MEETUP

'Posse.com helps people find the best cafés and restaurants wherever they go.' Over a thousand faces watch me from row on row of red seats in the NYU Skirball Center for Performing Arts. Andy Morris is in the front next to Cameron, who's holding his head with both hands and looking even more nervous than me. Two robotic cameras stream to thousands of viewing parties and homes all over America. At 8.30 a.m. back in Sydney, our team is huddled around a laptop watching.

New York Tech Meetup is one of the highest-profile pitch events in the world. Held twice a month, it's watched by the media, other founders, influencers and investors as a showcase of the world's hottest emerging apps and products. We're only here for two reasons. First, Andy Morris is a great publicist. Second, my *New York Times* column has become something of a viral hit.

So far, I've written articles about my social panic at networking events, jealousy almost crippling me at MaiTai, how I stuffed up a sales meeting at Clear Channel, learning to manage engineers who think I'm stupid, and the unique challenges of being a woman in the crazy male-dominated world of tech. The more pain in the story, the more people seem to share it. Kind of like the transfixing appeal of watching a natural disaster unfold, or maybe just a realistic portrayal of starting a business other entrepreneurs can relate to. Last week Sheryl Sandberg wrote me an email via Lars (who now works at Facebook). 'Tell Rebekah I loved her piece on gender. I'm so glad she shared her story.' *Sheryl Sandberg read my article? Sheryl Sandberg even knows that I exist?* The world seems upside down.

I hold up my phone to the Skirball Center crowd and my screen broadcasts on a giant display behind the stage. 'Imagine I'm new to town and I'm looking for somewhere to get good coffee.' I scroll through the cutely designed recommendations from my friends. Jen steps on stage to play-the role of a shop owner and I cringe at our school nativity play-like performance.

People are shuffling in their seats. I finish with a strong statement about my vision for the company. 'Retailers do it really tough. People put their lives, their dreams into launching a café, and three out of four will fail in the first five years. Our mission is to give café and restaurant owners access to a platform that lets them find new customers, take payments and build loyalty, all in the one place.'

Rows of faces stand in applause. I look to Jen, sweat streaming down my chest. My phone flashes with Twitter notifications.

Just seen the next Four Square @rebekahposse #NYTM
Great presentation @rebekahposse. Downloading @posse app now #NYTM

Andy Morris claps and whistles from the front row. He's lined up interviews with more media who I'll meet in the green room afterwards (Mashable, TechCrunch, Buzzfeed). Two girls who look like university students step towards me nervously. One is tall with plaited brown hair and the other shorter with red-rimmed glasses. The girl with the glasses nudges the other like she wants her to talk. 'Can we take a selfie with you?' asks the girl with plaits. 'We love your column.'

I smile for the photo, feeling certain that someone I know will see it online and laugh at me for pretending to be famous. As I turn around, I almost walk into a navy shirt and brown leather jacket. 'Cameron.'

'Boom!' He steps backwards, smiling and raises his arm to pat my shoulder.

'Thanks, there's definitely things I'd change. Next time.'

He shakes my shoulder playfully. 'It was perfect. You nailed it.'

'I can't believe you came all this way.'

He lifts his other arm. One hand on each shoulder 'Are you kidding? This is huge, I wouldn't miss it.' He winks as if to say something neither of us knows how to interpret. A bubble of fizz swells inside.

Back at the apartment, I feel like a junkie coming down from a massive hit. There's only me and Jen, our couch (which this week doubles as my bed), the TV and our laptops. The highs and lows of startup life have put me off-balance: I'm in a tiny apartment, we're running low on cash, our user numbers are high but we still don't make revenue, the NY Tech Meetup crowd loved us, my column is a hit, the team back at home need me to raise capital, and without revenue I'm not sure I'll pull it off. I look at Jen and her optimistic face. She relies on me to pay rent, buy food, travel, do everything. I can't let her down. I think of Cameron: how much faith he has in me, the other investors who've trusted me with their money, and I feel a tight squeeze in my chest.

37. BILLY MANN

The train glides over murky water, grey highways and brown housing projects on the way from Manhattan to Connecticut. Today, I'll celebrate my birthday by exiting the city and visiting my friend Billy Mann and his gorgeous family of five.

Jen flew back to Sydney last week, so I woke this morning to an empty room. I made myself a cup of tea and turned on the TV to fill in the quiet. Outside on the street an old man with a pipe and a grey hooded coat walked straight into me, not looking up. 'Watch it,' I said as he scurried past. Thirty-six years old. There aren't any messages on Facebook this time. No one *really* remembers.

I met with a dozen different investors after NY Tech Meetup. A Russian billionaire committed to $300K after a single Skype call, a friend of Cameron's is tipping in another hundred, and a New York group that backs female founders seems likely to invest two hundred more. The minimum I need to close the round is $500,000. My aim is to raise $1.5 million, but in five months I won't be able to make payroll so right now I just need the minimum.

I've started to hear the voice again. The one in my head that Madeleine told me to ignore. It seems to get louder when I feel stressed. *You won't make it. This is all going to collapse.*

I rest my head back against the seat of the train, feeling the track clunking as we pass. I met Billy Mann at a hotel in 2008. He'd been introduced to me by the head of EMI Australia as a renowned songwriter, famous for hits with Pink and Kelly Rowland. He'd just been appointed as EMI's global head of creative and would help guide one of the bands that I'd signed to my management company. I distinctly remember the first time I saw him in the lobby. He was huge, more than six foot with shoulder-length black hair, a long stride and an aura so bright I couldn't stop looking at him. We drank tea and talked music, politics, life goals. He gushed about his wife Gena and their young children back in Connecticut.

The next evening, we met for dinner at a place called Est near his hotel on George Street. 'I know this sounds strange,' I said, 'but when we met yesterday, I felt like I knew you or something, like we're—'

'Family?' He grinned. 'Yeah. Sometimes that happens, in life. There's soulmates out there, people we're meant to meet.'

The restaurant felt magical: high ceilings decorated with carved wood, the crisp white tablecloths, the silver candle sticks and twinkling lights. Billy's eyes were so sharp, I felt them pierce my deepest thoughts.

'Have you got a boyfriend?' he asked.

'Ah, there was someone once. A long time ago.'

'And?'

My heart squirmed in my chest, trying to dodge the question.

'And we broke up, then he died in a car accident. I was twenty-four.'

Billy leaned back in a kind of stretch, with his arms folded above his head. 'I lost my first wife when I was twenty-five.

Stomach cancer.' He paused, rolling his tongue under his bottom lip. 'I bet they got together, I bet they're right here at the next table.'

I glanced to the table. Tingles spread across my back.

'What was his name?'

'Steve.'

'You still love him?'

I nodded.

Billy placed his phone face-up in front of me. On the screen was a photo of a woman with long golden hair. 'This is Gena,' he said. 'We've been married seven years.' More pictures: two young boys and a toddler girl snuggled in bed, heads touching. 'I'll tell you why they wanted us to meet. What Steve wants me to tell you.' He thumbed through photos on his phone again: Billy and Gena hugging on a red carpet, the children in a swimming pool, on a slide.

'This is the beginning and the end,' he said. 'It's everything. Don't miss it.'

I wiped under my eyes, smudging my makeup, but I didn't care. I reached my hand across the table, needing to be grounded. 'So life goes on.'

Billy gripped my whole arm in his hand and widened his eyes. 'Yes. Life can still be incredible, but you've got to go after it.'

The train pulls to a stop at Wallingford station. There's a concrete platform and no one else getting off. It's been five years since my conversation with Billy at the restaurant. We'd only met in person a handful of times since, but we speak often on the phone. He'd squealed with glee when I told him about my plan to date fifty-two men. 'You're going to do it,' he'd said. 'This is your year.' That was 2012, when I was thirty-four. I step onto the platform and my hair flaps in the hot summer wind.

'Happy birthday!' Billy jogs down the steps towards me, his whole face shining. He draws my head into his chest like a brother. 'I'm parked over here. Gena and the kids can't wait to meet you.'

I climb into his silver Tesla and half an hour later we pull up to a huge rambling New England house. Gena waves from the porch and three children tumble out the front door, laughing and screaming. Billy turns to me smiling as if to say *Here it is. Everything.*

Inside, Gena has put out lunch on a big wooden table. There's breads, jams, cheeses, salad and space for everyone to sit.

'So,' starts Billy.

'So?' I know exactly what he wants me to tell him.

'So what's happening? With the dating, the men?'

I look to Gena, hoping she'll change the subject, but she smiles like she's adding a second question mark.

'Where to start, honestly. I've done, what, seventy-eight dates now. I'm starting to think, well . . . I'm starting to wonder if there's something wrong with me.'

'Seventy-eight, wow. I'm impressed you kept count.' Billy's voice is low. He's taking in the magnitude of the number.

'You know me, what do you think? What's my problem?'

Billy opens both hands. 'I think you're great. You're a superstar. Honestly.' He shakes his head. 'I don't think you've found the guy yet. You've got to keep looking.'

Around the table the two boys clamber for bread rolls, and

across the room the little girl pounds notes on a piano. Billy and Gena sit so close they move like a single unit.

'And how do you know if you find the right person? How did you guys know?'

The two heads of the unit smile at each other. 'We were friends first,' he says. 'I wasn't ready. But whenever we were together it just felt like I was home.'

'I knew before he did,' Gena says squeezing in closer. 'Everyone in his life could see it. I thought he'd be on my side no matter what. That's really important.'

Yes, life is beautiful for them, but I'm not sure it's coming for me. 'I'm thirty-six years old, I've done seventy-eight dates.' I wait for a reaction and the boys scuttle off to play. 'I'm really starting to wonder.'

Billy brushes aside the plates and jams, and reaches across the table to grasp both my elbows. 'Listen, there's seven billion people out there. The universe is conspiring with you. You have to trust it.'

38. THE STOCKTAKE

I'm finding it difficult to get to sleep at night. I stay up watching *House of Cards* on Netflix and the True Crime Network on cable. I toss into different positions in bed, but I'm never comfortable. The Russian billionaire and Cameron's friend have signed their paperwork, but the women's investment group keeps asking more questions. Every day they insist I meet someone new: an accountant to drill me on the numbers, a café owner to drill me on the product plan. All time that I should be spending with my team, growing the business. Back home, two of our engineers have taken new jobs.

I took Jarrod's advice and changed my profile on Match. My tagline now reads: 'Looking for something serious?' Jarrod was right — my profile is getting a lot less action. I'm now only messaging two or three guys at once and they're all happy to speak on the phone before we meet.

So far I've met: Caleb, a researcher in Governor Andrew Cuomo's office; Sumit, a mathematician doing a PhD at Columbia University; Tim, a primary school teacher from Queens; and Muhammad, a lawyer from the Dominican Republic. We went through the motions, had drinks, smiled, asked each other questions. But inside I felt flat. There was no excitement, no instant fantasies of children, weddings and holiday destinations. Caleb and Sumit both asked me out again, but the second dates weren't any different.

I open up Match and there's two new messages. *Here we go.* I let out a long sigh, feeling queasy like I'm about to bite into a tuna sandwich that I know is off. *Please don't make me do it.* I feel paralysed, but there's a tug from deep inside that's forcing me to keep going.

Try something different. What if the right guy is someone I already know? Someone I've missed. Hmm. After thirty-six years, it's time to do a stocktake.

I flick to Facebook, scroll through my Friends. There's Matt, who I'm pretty sure had a crush on me at school, Josh the music video director I worked with in my twenties and who definitely liked me, Stewart who I pashed once after too many vodkas backstage at a music festival. I click into their profiles. Matt is all doe-eyed, cuddling a newborn baby. Josh stands proudly next to his daughter on her first day of school (how did that happen?), and Stewart poses in a London nightclub with some blonde model. Definitely *not* husband material.

I check Messenger and two faces catch my attention: Sean from Bondi and Pierre the Stanford Professor from MaiTai. They've both sent messages and I've been too busy to reply.

> Sean: Hey Rebekah. Just checking in to see how you're going in the Big Smoke. How's business? Would be great to catch up.
>
> Pierre: Hi there RC. I'm in Boston and just found an excellent restaurant thanks to your Posse app. How's it going?

It's 6 p.m. Saturday here in New York, so it'll be 8 a.m. Sunday in Sydney. I text Sean.

Me: Hey, are you awake? Can you talk?

Sean: Just got back from a run. What's up?

Me: Calling you now.

'This is a voice I wasn't expecting to hear this morning,' he says cheerily. I imagine him in black running shorts, wiping his forehead with a towel. Probably about to drink some kind of healthy smoothie with protein powder mixed in.

'Hi. Yeah, sorry, it's been crazy over here,' I say. 'I just saw your Facebook message.'

'I've been reading your column,' he says. 'I love the article you wrote about managing engineers.' Our conversation is alive and flows like it always did. He asks if I've been dating.

'A bit. New York dating is more like a sport. I've had some fun but, you know, nothing serious.'

'I have news,' he says eagerly. 'I'm seeing a woman I met at university. We were good friends when I did my MBA then we lost contact for a while.'

The breath in my chest sinks like I just missed the last train home. 'That's great.'

There's a few beats of silence that are almost awkward. 'Listen,' I say, 'I've been meaning to ask you something.' I crouch in the corner of the room, under the window. 'With us, when we were dating, why didn't anything happen? I mean, we're a good match — you and me. We have loads in common. We like each other, don't we?'

Sean lets out a *pah* noise and pauses like he's looking for an answer. 'I just never got the sense you were interested. Women give clues in the way they relate to you, in their body language.'

I claw back through my memory. 'But you didn't ever try to

kiss me or anything. I thought you were going to, maybe on our second or third date. But it never happened.'

I'm aware that I sound desperate right now. The train has gone and no amount of reasoning will bring it back. Besides, he's right. I didn't give him any signals. I hadn't had that conversation with Jarrod about touch and flirtation. I didn't know.

'Another thing is, I remember asking if you wanted to catch up,' he says. 'I'd ring and say "Let's get coffee" but you were always busy. You'd say "I can't today but how about Thursday in two weeks' time" or something. There wasn't any immediacy. I mean, I figured if you wanted to see me, you would. That's the impression I got. After a while I moved on, in terms of my focus.'

After hanging up, I pour myself a cup of tea and message Pierre.

> Me: How are you? I'm coming back to San Francisco in August and would love to finally catch up!

He writes back immediately.

> Pierre: Hey there RC. How goes it? Would be great to see you. When are you in town?
>
> Me: August 12–20. Doing the investment rounds again. I'm actually living in New York these days.
>
> Pierre: I will be in NYC July 12–20 approx. Want to meet on July 13?

39. PIERRE

I stroll across 58th Street to meet Pierre. The humidity has frizzed my straightened hair and water droplets fall from an air conditioning unit attached to the building above. A smell like washing that's been left in the machine too long drifts past my nose and a truck spins hot dust from the gutter as it trundles past. *Gross. I hate this city.*

Pierre is waiting outside the restaurant. 'Hey,' he says, arms open to hug. 'You're looking great. Look at you.' He stands back.

I'm wearing a silk cream shirt, a long silver necklace that rests across my bust, tight jeans and my black heels. I wince at his compliment. I know he's trying to be nice; it's what men are supposed to say. I also know that I've put on five kilos since I saw him in Maui. So many nights alone in the apartment watching TV and eating frozen yoghurt from the shop downstairs. Pierre wraps one arm around my shoulder.

Quality Meats is an underground midtown steak restaurant that must have been built in the fifties. The tables are in nooks, the dark wooden walls are lined with wine bottles. A waiter in a white suit jacket shows us to our table.

'So, RC. Tell me what you've been up you?'

'Well,' I say, 'I've been trying to market Posse. Get more people using it, more stores signed up. And raise money of course. I've been meeting with investors.'

'Oh right. How's that going?'

I roll my eyes. 'I've closed four hundred K but I need a hundred more to reach the minimum for the round. There's this group who say they're in for two-hundred K but there's always another question, some new hurdle I have to jump through.' I shrug. 'You know what it's like.'

Pierre orders ribeye steak and a bottle of pinot noir from New Zealand. Three hours later we finish our second bottle. We've talked about politics, tech, what makes a successful entrepreneur. Our chat has flowed as easily as the wine. Pierre's skin is pale under his slicked-back hair and glasses. He is smart, yes, a pinch cockier than I would have ordered, but he challenges me.

Pierre links his arm in mine as we step outside and along to 5th Avenue to catch a cab. Cars and trucks roar into streaks of light.

'Hang on,' Pierre says. He darts behind me to my other side. 'Let me be a gentleman. Keep you safe from the traffic.'

Six nights later it's Friday and Pierre and I have been out five times, taking a break only yesterday when he had to speak at a robotics event for Google. Each morning after a date I'd notice the street seeming slightly lighter outside, like New York's dull buildings and parks had come back to life a little. *Could Pierre be the one? Our children would be clever.*

Tonight, Pierre has bought tickets to a show at the Blue Note Jazz Club in Greenwich Village. The week of dates feel like drawn-out foreplay. We've established that we like each other, he flies on to Boston tomorrow. Green shoots of anticipation spread though my veins. *Tonight is it.* I'm wearing my blue off-the-shoulder top again and tight leather pants. I spin in the full-length mirror on the front of my wardrobe and blow myself a kiss.

I'm running early so I swing past MAC on 22nd Street. A man with a shaved head and bright red lipstick greets me as I arrive. 'I love your top,' he says, flapping his hands.

'Thanks.' I smile. 'I've got a date tonight. Do you have time to do my eye makeup?'

I blast Madonna's 'Vogue' in my headphones and strut down 5th Avenue feeling like Sarah Jessica Parker: knee-high boots, eyes smoky blue, leather pants clinging to my skin.

I meet Pierre at Otto Enoteca, an old-school pizzeria with wooden tables and a giant open oven that roars with orange flames.

'I had a good look at Posse today,' he says, pulling his phone from his pocket.

'Great.' I nod. 'What do you think?'

'Look.' He narrows his eyes and flares his nostrils like he's smelled something. 'Do you want the truth?'

'Of course.' I sense he's about to be critical, but I need to know. I respect his brain and I'll use his feedback.

'I just don't get it. I mean, Yelp is already doing this. You've got a social twist, which is interesting. But I don't know, it's such a crowded space, yes?'

'Okay.' I'm trying to decipher the advice. 'How do you think it could be better? More different?'

He pushes out his bottom lip and scratches his chin. 'You've got all these fancy advisors around you: Lars, Bill Tai. What do they think?'

What's he asking? 'The numbers are good. Lots of people are using it.' I throw up one hand. 'They seem pretty happy with how it's going.'

He shakes his head. 'They're nice. They're sweet guys. They're not going to tell you it's bullshit.'

A slab of concrete drops from the ceiling and squashes me into a pancake of flesh, black leather and frozen yoghurt goop.

'I'm sorry, I shouldn't have said anything,' he says.

I peel my head up, just enough to speak. I muster every spark of strength that's left. 'Well I believe in it. It's not finished yet. I want to add payments so people can buy through it — that'll be different to all the other apps.'

He nods. 'You know what. I was wrong, I'm sorry.'

An hour later, we're watching a swing band at Blue Note. Musicians — drums, trumpet, saxophone, double bass and vocals — cram onto a tiny stage in front of red velvet curtains. We're dancing right at the front, bumping up against the crowd of all ages, sizes, colours. I try to thrust my body about in time with the music, but my shoulders keep hunching forward. I catch Pierre's eyes scanning my breasts, my stomach, my hips. I don't feel sexy anymore; I feel the opposite of sexy. *He thinks I'm fat. Fat and ridiculous.*

At midnight the band finishes their set. 'Wanna get out of here?' Pierre points to the door.

'Sure.'

There's no discussion about where we're going. It's unsaid and agreed: back to his hotel.

When we hop out of the cab hand-in-hand, a porter in a brown coat and a tweed hat swings open the door to reveal a grand foyer. I feel so small next to the big golden pillars, next to the tall smart professor. The voice in my head is back: *You and your stupid app. What a joke.*

We ride the lift to the twenty-second floor. Pierre swipes open the door to a room three times the size of my entire apartment, with a bed made up in the centre. Pierre rips open the thick cream curtains and the Brooklyn Bridge is lit up, just metres from the window. 'What do you think?' he says, grinning like a kid who knows he's made it. 'Pretty cool, huh?'

He wraps his arm around my waist and we kiss for the first time. We fall onto the bed and his hand is up my top. My mind is a mush of emotions. I'm still crushed, I guess from our conversation earlier but it's more than that. There is no Woman 1. *You are not smart or successful or sexy. Just a startup wannabe loser. Be grateful you're here.*

Pierre pulls my shirt over my head and I reach for the buckle on his jeans. We kiss and touch and kiss more. The voice is louder now, shouts swirling from every side: loser, old, ugly. I want Pierre to control me, to hold me down. Show me I'm worth something, even if just for the flesh.

Ten minutes pass and I'm still wearing my bra and undies. We stop kissing and pause like there's nowhere to go.

'Hey.' He reaches across me to the bedside table. 'Shall we see what's on TV?'

See, he doesn't want you. Not even for sex.

40. SUMMER IN THE HAMPTONS

Pierre's dark hair flaps over his Ray-Bans as he drives a black Jaguar SUV with the windows down. We met at JFK Airport this morning, where he hired a car to drive us to the Hamptons for the weekend. 'Can I get an upgrade, to impress my girl here?' he'd said to the man behind the counter.

'My girl'. That's nice.

I haven't dated anyone else since that night with Pierre two months ago. Not because we're exclusive; I've hardly spoken to him since he left that day for Boston. It's because the voice in my head won't stop chattering. It no longer makes right and left brain arguments; just a barking list of criticisms and instructions that leave me exhausted.

Back home in Sydney, two more team members have quit. I can tell they're all arriving in the office late, probably sitting around checking job sites. They know the money runs out soon. 'We're all okay,' Jen told me on the phone in her trademark chirp. But our customer growth has stalled, and the engineers have stopped releasing new features on the app. Every week, the New York investor group demands an update: What progress have you made? How many new customers? I want to tell them how difficult it is for me to inspire our team when I waste so many minutes answering their due diligence requests about financial projections, potential future competitors and patents. 'We'll definitely get there,' one of the investors said as she patted an encouraging hand on my shoulder one day. 'This is just a process we have to go through since we have so many members. Everyone has a question.'

Pierre invited me to the Hamptons over Facebook Messenger. I think he was coming to New York anyway and needed a plan for the long weekend. I needed a plan to escape Manhattan, a place whose constant crud, noise, pollution and bustle I just can't stand anymore. And if I squint my brain really hard, I can still see a future with Pierre.

Pierre reaches for the volume on the car stereo, cranking up 'Bullet the Blue Sky' by U2. 'You like this song?' he asks, and I nod.

We turn off the Long Island Expressway and it feels like another world. The road is framed by trees and perfectly trimmed hedges. Giant white farmhouses are spaced by flat green fields and vineyards.

'Let's see how the one per cent live,' says Pierre as we pull in to East Hampton Village. 'Where does Posse say we should go for dinner?'

I pull out my phone and search the app. 'There's a lot of recommendations for somewhere called 1770 House.'

'Great.' He looks up the number. 'I'll see if I can get a booking.'

We spend the afternoon driving up to the Montauk Lighthouse at the end of the island. We climb out of the car and up the grass mound next to the building. Below us is a rocky point and endless blue ocean. Pierre wraps his arm around my waist. 'If you squint your eyes really hard, you can see France from here,' he says.

I stretch my gaze into the horizon. 'Really?'

He turns, patting my back and laughing: 'Nah. It's three thousand miles or something. You can't see that far. It's the right direction though.'

At dinner we're seated in a romantic corner near the fireplace. The restaurant feels like an old inn, transformed into a decadent dining experience for wealthy New Yorkers here for the weekend. There are women wearing elegantly tied silk scarves around their necks. I order heirloom tomato salad for an appetiser, striped bass for mains, and we share a crème brûlée for dessert.

'Posse did well for us tonight,' says Pierre.

'See?' I shrug. 'It's gonna be big. I see it.'

The dinner costs close to $400. I don't offer to get half; it would wipe my weekly budget. With Pierre, I've never offered to pay. He has expensive taste and he enjoys treating me. At least, this is my interpretation of our unsaid agreement. *He knows I don't have any money.* This weekend he's organised the car, the Airbnb, snacks and all the meals.

It feels glamorous to be in the Hamptons, dining at one of the fanciest places in town. I wonder what Pierre expects from me. Back in New York he didn't seem interested in sex. But now we're away for the weekend, I wonder if it's rude to say 'no' after he's spent all this money.

I look at his smiling eyes. I like this guy. I want to sleep with him. *Or do I?* What if I don't want to, but I do anyway because I feel guilty that he's paid for everything? *What would that make me?* The crème brûlée in my stomach churns into a sickly gunge.

Back at our Airbnb, we eat Grain Waves on the couch.

'I'm really into *House of Cards* at the moment. Have you seen it?' I open my laptop to Netflix. We watch Zoe ring the doorbell at Kevin Spacey's house and Pierre is hooked. A couple of hours pass and I'm wondering what the plan is. 'I'm getting tired. I'm going to bed now.'

'Okay,' he replies. 'See you in the morning.'

At 6.30 a.m. Pierre knocks on the bedroom door wearing running shorts. 'I thought we could do a jog,' he says. 'I've got a conference call at nine. We could probably fit in a swim.'

I pull on my swimmers and shorts. 'I haven't run for a while,' I say. 'But a swim sounds good.'

Pierre parks the car at Main Beach. The morning sunlight is harsh on the beige sand and crashing waves. 'Let's run along this road, check out the houses,' he says.

We jog along a street parallel to the beach. The houses are white wooden manors with driveways and grand front yards the size of football fields. Pierre is running fast and my legs struggle to keep up. He gestures with his head that he wants to go faster still. A minute later he's gone.

I feel relieved to be back at my own pace. The blue of the ocean seems to dislodge the tension behind my eyes. The stunning wealth of the houses is like nothing I've seen. The road curves up away from the beach and joins another street. *Which direction did he go?*

I continue running as close to the beach as I can. The houses thin out and soon I'm in farmland, crossing a rickety bridge with tufts of green grass on either side. *Where's Pierre?* I try phoning him but there's no answer. I run further and I'm back in among the mansions, next to the beach. It's eerily quiet and I haven't seen a car or a person since Pierre left me an hour ago.

I step onto the sand: there's no one in either direction. *Should I try walking down the beach? But which way?* A whiteboard sticks out from the ground with scribbled information about today's temperature, tide times and water conditions. Behind it, the sky is clear against the rolling waves. I snap a selfie next to the sign, filter the image to clear up my skin and post to Facebook: 'Summer in the Hamptons'.

I hear a squawk. A giant hawk is circling overhead. *Are you here to show me the way?* The animal swoops down, its tail and wings spread in a perfectly symmetrical fan. It squawks again, narrowing, now shooting directly towards me. Its sharp claws reach at my head and I duck.

I turn to run, sprinting faster and faster, holding my hands up to shield, and the hawk is gone. I am lost and alone. I wish I hadn't watched all those true crime shows on cable. I imagine a man in a scratched pickup truck scooting towards me, not stopping. His truck hits me from behind, *smack* on the ground, and he piles my broken body into the boot. *If I scream out here, no one will come.*

A black Jaguar SUV pulls around the corner: it's Pierre. 'Where have you been? I've got that call in ten minutes. I'm going to be fucking late.'

Pierre blasts Bush and The Smashing Pumpkins as we drive the expressway back to Manhattan. I roll down the window for fresh air and traffic fumes hit my face. I still feel shaken, angry, confused about him and about me. About why I've become such a spineless flop of a woman.

There are two voices in my mind now, like I'm eavesdropping on someone else's conversation.

Angry: *You are an idiot to be out here with this guy. He was a jerk in Maui, then at the pizza restaurant, then this morning. Why aren't you standing up for yourself?*

Compassionate: *He's smart, interesting, confident, sexy. He visits jazz clubs and takes you jogging in the Hamptons. He wants a family. Come on, you're thirty-six years old.*

Angry: *You're ugly and that's why he isn't attracted to you. He'd take you more seriously if you were thinner.*

Compassionate: *You're lonely in New York and running a business is stressful. What percentage of startups fail? Come on, don't be so hard on yourself.*

Pierre turns down the volume. '*House of Cards* is good. Disorganised labour.' He mimes throwing a brick like in the story. 'Hey.' He chews the inside of his cheek, turning to catch my eye. 'What do you think about their relationship, Frank and Claire? I mean . . .'

Is he asking if I want a relationship like that? Where we sleep in separate rooms like Frank and Claire. A marriage of friendship, of convenience?

He puffs air out his cheeks, looks away and cranks the stereo again.

I slump into the car seat. No, that's not what I want. I want love. I stretch my mind out of my body again and picture myself from above. *Who is that woman now?* Hunched forward in yoga pants and a striped T-shirt. She's strong underneath. She's resilient. *Think about it.* She's built two companies from nothing. She's raised money. Posse is used by three hundred thousand people. Nineteen months ago she hadn't been on a date in ten years, and now she's been out with eighty-five different men. *Do I like her?* I'm not sure. I wish she had more faith in herself.

I remember the list in my book: smart, confident, fun. Pierre is all those things. I nibble my thumbnail and gaze out to the blurred lines of cars soaring across the freeway.

'Nice' or 'caring', that's what's missing. Someone who is a nice person and who cares about me. That's way more important than 'smart' or 'confident'. I picture my dad and I picture Steve: *caring* is what I love most about these men. *How did I miss that?*

My phone lights up with notifications from Facebook and Gmail. There's an email from Susan, the lead in the women's investment group.

> Hi Rebekah,
>
> Thanks for all your time answering our questions. It's been lovely getting to know you and learning more about Posse. Unfortunately, we've decided not to proceed with an investment at this time. Although we admire your energy and ambition for the business, we feel it's too risky for us to support the company before there is a proven revenue model.
>
> We wish you the best of luck.
>
> Susan

Argh! A red fireball scorches through my insides. They knew there wasn't revenue four months ago. All that time I could have spent growing the business, talking to other investors. I picture their group sitting round a boardroom table sipping coffee while they meet with another round of desperate entrepreneurs. *Rebekah, stop.* I take my face in both hands, mouth open in shock. *You've got eight weeks of money left.*

I look to Pierre, who seems lost in his own world mouthing the words to Billy Corgan's '1979'. I imagine reaching into my head and flicking a switch. *No more victim. Take control right now.* I make some mental scribbles. I'll write them in ink later.

Resolutions

1. Go back to Sydney. Do whatever it takes to raise $100K to close the round.
2. Exercise again. Re-join yoga, jog every day, eat healthy.
3. Only date men who are nice! Screen for 'caring' above every other attribute.

On my phone, I close the email and open Facebook:

> Ainsley Cullen and 157 others like your post: 'Summer in the Hamptons'.

41. THE ELEPHANT
IN THE ROOM

Tonight I'm meeting Mike at Rockpool Bar & Grill, an upmarket restaurant in the Sydney CBD owned by celebrity chef Neil Perry. Mike is a businessman from Manhattan who invests in startups for a living. He has white hair, a pink scalp and walks with his legs apart to accommodate his round belly. Tonight is a final 'getting to know you' dinner and I'm hoping he'll give me good news. *I really need good news.*

I first met Mike at the NY Tech Meetup, where he'd handed me a card. 'I can see there's a lot of people waiting to talk to you. Here's my number. Reach out if you're looking for investment.' I'd emailed him the next day but didn't hear back. In my final week in New York, I tried again.

'Rebekah!' he replied. 'I wondered what happened to you. I've been using Posse.'

We met at his one-room office near Central Park where a stack of framed sports posters lay propped up against the wall. I expected Mike to be slow, like his appearance suggested, so I was surprised at his sharp and thoughtful questions. He knew a lot about other Australian companies. 'Wow, you know the Canva guys. Can you introduce me?'

I asked how he likes to work with companies he's invested

in. 'I'm very hands off,' he said, reclining in his seat. 'I back people who I think are smart. Then it's up to them.'

'And what's your standard investment size?'

He swayed his head from side to side. 'A hundred K. Sometimes two hundred. It depends on the opportunity.'

'I've got four hundred already committed in the round,' I explained. 'I need one hundred more to close.'

'What's your monthly burn?'

'Seventy-eight. It mostly goes on wages. We've got a really strong tech team.'

'And how much have you got in the bank?'

'A hundred and ten.' I looked up, feeling my eyes drop open like I'm pleading for dinner.

He inhaled slowly through his teeth. 'You know what, I'm coming to Sydney in a few weeks. I've got some business to do down there. Let's meet again then. I'll visit your office.'

'Sure,' I said. *I'd rather you just say yes now.* 'That would be great.'

Yesterday I walked Mike through our Surry Hills office. I introduced him to Glen and the engineering team, to Jen and to our new graphic designer Anna. We'd sat at the Pieno café on Crown Street and I'd shown him the presentation again.

'This is exciting,' he'd said. 'I can see where you're going with this. Well done.'

I step into the grand dining room with marble pillars that look like the entrance to a courthouse. Mike arrives, leaning in to kiss my cheek, and a waiter shows us to our table. We pass an open kitchen where men and women in white shirts and chef hats toss food in frying pans and serve up plates on a clean steel bench under heat lights. My seat is on one side of a long bench. Mike is on a black chair opposite.

He examines the menu. 'Do you mind if I order for the table?'

'Of course, I just don't eat —'

'Seafood okay?'

'Great.' I smile.

He holds up a finger to the waiter, pointing to the wine list: 'We'll have a bottle of the 2005 Bollinger Grande Année Brut.' He smirks at the jaggedness of his French pronunciation. My eyes scan the list. $890! I could fly to New York for that.

His eyes crease as he sinks into the menu. The waiter returns, cracking open our champagne like it's no different to the $20 bottle I'd usually order and I imagine the faces of 890 children in Africa who could have eaten today.

'Cheers,' Mike says, raising his glass. 'Since we're celebrating.'

'Celebrating?'

'My investment in Posse.' He smiles. 'I'm in. Put me down for a hundred K. Send the paperwork tomorrow.'

Tiny balls of relief scatter around my body. 'Excellent!' I shake his hand. 'I'm looking forward to working with you. Next year I'm planning to add payment functionality. A revenue model should mean—'

He swats the air if he doesn't want to know. 'You've sold me on Posse. I'm backing *you* to pull it off.' He holds his finger up for the waiter again. 'My friend here only eats seafood,' he says. Then to me: 'Do you like caviar?'

I try to picture caviar in my head. 'I don't think I've had it before.'

He folds the menu. 'We'll get two of the caviar with the

toast, the crème fraîche, a dozen shucked oysters, and the grilled lobster for mains.'

He rests his arms on his stomach like a pillow, rocking back on his chair. 'Now, I want to learn more about Rebekah. Tell me, where did you grow up?'

We chat about New Zealand and my early attempts to start businesses. 'When I was nine years old, I used to look for lost golf balls and sell them back to the shop.' I ask about his business in New York: 'What got you interested in startups?'

'My father was in real estate. He made a lot of money doing apartment buildings in the eighties. My brother's still in the game. I just get more excited investing in people and ideas, you know?'

The caviar arrives and Mike takes my plate. 'Let me put this together for you.' He doles scoops of cream and black egg jam onto tiny pieces of toast. 'You're going to love it.'

I watch Mike as a guide for how to eat; he devours each piece of toast in single bites. I hold the toast in my mouth, consciously taking in the taste, which is fresh and strangely delicious. He coats the oysters in mignonette sauce and hands them to me one by one.

Our conversation is friendly and relaxed. I like Mike. This whole expensive dinner charade is bizarre, but he obviously thinks he's being impressive, treating me to fancy wine and food. I giggle inside at the strangeness of men. *A nice salad and a juice would have been fine.*

Next, two giant halves of lobster arrive on a plate, coated in garlic butter.

'Do you know how to eat this?' he asks.

I shake my head.

He takes the white napkin from his knee and stuffs it into

the top of his shirt like a bib. 'I'll break it up for us.' He grasps a lobster half. 'There's a psychology to this. A primal instinct sort of thing. You just rip into it.'

He twists the body slowly until it cracks; garlic butter and lobster juice coat the wiry grey hairs on his fingers in yellow. I gag a little and swallow my breath. 'There's meat in every nook and cranny of this lady,' he says, stacking chunks onto my plate.

As we eat, I notice sweat dripping down the sides of Mike's head. He uses his napkin to wipe his brow, the sweat oozing though his hair to create a gel-like effect. *He really shouldn't be eating all this rich food, drinking so much wine.* I picture him collapsing forward on the table, me calling an ambulance.

We continue to chat. Mike tells me about his grown-up daughter who's a fashion designer in London and his son who's studying law at Yale. 'I wanted him to go to Harvard, but his mother lives out there in Connecticut.' He presses his lips together. 'And what about you? Any children?'

I laugh. 'No.'

'Husband? Boyfriend?'

I glance over to the kitchen. 'Ha, no, not at the moment. I date sometimes, but I don't have a lot of time.'

He wipes his hands and face again, soaking his white napkin yellow. 'Starting a business is a big commitment. I know what it's like.'

It's getting late and I can feel my stomach struggling to process all the rich food. I've carefully sipped wine to give the impression that I've drunk more than I have. Mike polishes off the bottle and I've still got a full glass. Mike waves to the waiter. *Phew, he's going to ask for the bill. I've got to be up for yoga at 6.*

'Can we see the dessert menu?'

He orders a chocolate mousse cake to share. The plate arrives and he shifts to my side of the bench. He shovels a spoonful into his mouth and turns to catch my eyes straight on.

'Now.' He shuffles his hips on the seat. 'Can I address the elephant in the room here?'

I notice I've subconsciously crossed my arms. *Have I said something wrong?* 'Okay. I'm not aware of anything.'

'Oh, come on,' he says, mouth open so I can see the brown goo of the mousse strung together with spit between his teeth. 'Let's be honest. The elephant in the room is that you and me want to fuck each other.'

There's silence. My entire body turns to ice. I can't speak. Mike takes another spoonful of mousse and looks up, licking the side of his lip. 'We both know it. I'm just putting it out there.'

I scramble for a response. *Don't be rude, don't offend this guy. The company needs his investment.* But inside I'm screaming. *This is disgusting!* I'm angry with the world for putting me in this position, and I'm angry with myself for what I know will be a meek and polite response. I imagine my feminist superheroes swooping in, ready to swing. *I should tell him this is unacceptable, rude, verging on harassment.*

I clasp my hands together and force a smile. 'I'm really sorry if I've given you the wrong impression.'

'Come on.' He scowls, dropping a soft fist on the table. 'You've been flirting with me all night.'

Stay poised. Don't flinch. I play back the dinner in my head. The conversation had been nice, we'd shared our backgrounds, I'd asked questions. 'I was just—' *Don't be condescending.* 'I think that's just my personality. I wanted to get to know you, since you're investing in the business.'

He shovels in more mousse, not caring that he's eating all of it. 'We should go right now. Back to my hotel and fuck all night. It'll be amazing. We can order room service.' His eyes gleam with the thought of it. I'm imagining too, those lobster hands unbuttoning my shirt, sliding under my bra. Him perched on the side of a hotel bed, phone in hand as he orders more food, eats more food. The oysters, the fish eggs, the $890 wine, all back in my mouth. I hold back a retch.

'You know, I'm staying at the Wentworth Hotel,' he says, motioning towards the street. 'It's right around the corner. We'll be there in five minutes, no problem.'

This guy doesn't get it. He thinks proximity is a selling point. He thinks I'm going to say *'Oh, if you're just around the corner then that'll be fine.'*

I tell myself it's time to shut this down. I look directly into his eyes. 'I'm sorry, this isn't going to happen. I'm not a one-night-stand kind of person.'

He signs for me to stop. 'Look, it's your loss. It would've been fun. Forget it.' He sniffs, making a loud sucking sound like he's proud to be vulgar. Like he's reclaiming his dominance. *Is he still going to invest? Should I ask?* He holds his credit card in the air and signs the bill for $1800.

The next morning, I delete Mike's contact from my phone. I won't do 'anything' to raise the money. I step into Westpac on George Street and fill out a withdrawal slip: $160,000, almost all the money I have, save for the $11,000 I've put aside for egg freezing. It's enough to keep my team employed for another two months. Just till I can close the round. I imagine Sarah shaking her head. *'Don't put all your eggs in one basket.'* But what choice do I have?

42. PING

I googled 'Adam Theobald' this morning, so I know who to look for as I arrive at Di Bella Coffee House in Surry Hills. He's stands, spotting me first, and stretches out his hand with a wide smile.

Adam has bright chubby cheeks and dark hair that's thinning on top. We've been introduced by Ned, who started a rideshare company. 'Adam's the founder of Beat the Q,' he'd said. 'You know, the café payment app. You guys should work together.'

The barista at Di Bella is wearing a backwards baseball cap. Adam pulls his phone from his shoulder bag and looks up. 'What can I get you?' On the app, he orders a piccolo for himself and a peppermint tea for me; thirty seconds later there's a *ping* behind the counter.

The barista gives a thumbs-up. 'Got ya, Adam.'

'Impressive.' I smile. 'How did you start this thing?'

'Ah, well.' Adam fluffs out his thinning hair so it covers his whole head. 'I had a lot more of this when I started.' He laughs, pointing upwards. Adam tells me he got the idea for the app while waiting in line for a burger at a Jack Johnson concert. 'It took half an hour to get to the front. I was missing the show and I just thought "This should be easier."' He points to his phone on the table. 'We do everything on these things. I should be able to order, pay and get pinged when it's ready.'

I pick up his phone and navigate my way through the app. My first impression is that it's very blue and the buttons aren't where I expect them to be. I try ordering a piece of toast, enter my credit card details, and a white circle spins in the middle of the screen. 'Hang on, I don't think it's—'

Ping goes the iPad behind the counter, and the barista smiles.

'That's really cool,' I say, nodding my head. 'Our engineers have been looking at building pretty much the same thing.'

There's silence for a moment and our eyes lock, like two animals sizing each other up in the jungle. 'Tell me about your team,' I say.

'There's three of us. A mate from uni does the coding, and there's a young guy, Toby, who sells to cafés. I do everything else.'

We sip tea and coffee and chat. Adam shows me pictures of his baby daughter, who turned one in the weekend. I learn that Beat the Q is used by around a hundred cafés in Sydney and a few in Brisbane.

'How are you funding it? Have you tried raising capital?'

He wrinkles his nose. 'I raised a million to get started, mostly from friends. But honestly—'

'It's hard,' I interrupt.

'Investors want big growth numbers. They want global. Our business is small but it's solid. People who use it, love it.'

There's something about Adam that I like. He's got everything in just the right quantities: strength, conviction, work ethic, friendliness. *I could work with this guy. We'd make a good team.* He points to his phone. 'I really believe in this. It could be big, really big. The revenue model works. We've just got to figure out how to scale.'

'Okay.' I nod. 'Let's keep talking.'

43. CHRISTMAS DAY, AGAIN

There's a tissue box on the dressing table in my childhood bedroom. I remember the mirror behind when it was bordered with sticky-taped photographs of Kurt Cobain and Madonna. The surface is clear now like I'm a regular guest.

My iPhone reads 5.45 a.m. and the sky outside is red behind golden clouds. It's two years since I walked that street in Whangārei. *'If I meet a man by next Christmas.'* Two years, eighty-five first dates, Sydney, San Francisco, Maui, New York and back home to Wellington. I pull on a sweatshirt and shorts and grab the keys to Mum's car.

Adam and I had continued to meet most days in December. Cameron secured us a boardroom and we'd sketched the customer journey for our 'super app' on a whiteboard. We discussed the growth tactics that had worked for each of us and developed a plan for how we'd scale our new combined product.

I pull the car up next to Lyndhurst Park in Tawa, climb out and jog loosely down the hill. It's just on 6 a.m.; the houses behind the park are dark and quiet. The cool air smells of freshly cut grass and my sneakers crunch underfoot. A giant man in rugby shorts is running laps. He slows as he approaches like he's surprised I'm out so early. 'Happy Christmas,' he waves.

The long wooden stands still border the field like they did

eighteen years ago when I first sat with Steve. I perch on the bottom row with my knees to my chest and squeeze my eyes closed. I allow myself to dream. Steve stands on the bench above, his little poetry book in hand. Something hurts. I check myself. *My brain.* 'I miss talking to you. Learning from you.' I cross my arms against the morning breeze and think back through my eighty-five dates. All those shallow conversations. My brain feels numb with lack of exercise, millions of unused cells dying off with every passing year.

Lights in the houses behind the park are beginning to flick on. I imagine the children waking, sneaking through to the Christmas tree, those squeals of excitement.

A few hours later Dad is in the kitchen cooking salmon. Mum is chatting to one of her friends on the phone. I glide up the stairs to my bedroom and lie down. 'Steve. You're still with me, aren't you? I still need you.' I count the walls: one, two, three, four. There's no electric current up my back. Back then he'd only been gone a few months. Now it must be, what, twelve years?

44. THE PERFECT PARTNER

M el wears a flowing halterneck shift dress and looks like a model from a catalogue. She glances both ways before cautiously crossing Devonshire Street to The Book Kitchen. Mel moves in the same way that she runs her business: planned, precise and with conviction. Cliff flips up the back of a black skateboard with his foot, catching the end in one hand. Adam and I follow the genius kids like two old-timers in need of advice.

We take two couches in a corner surrounded by a wall of books.

'How's everything at Canva?' Adam asks.

Mel's lips are a flat line and she and Cliff smile at each other with their eyes. 'It's going pretty well. There's still a lot of work to do.'

Mel always strikes me as a mix of both confidence and humility. Like a cool cat with a ginormous brain. Their design platform still only has 500,000 users but it's clear their trajectory is straight up.

'We're raising capital at the moment,' says Cliff. 'We thought we were done, but —' he throws up an arm in frustration '— you know what it's like.'

I shuffle on the couch. 'I wanted to get us all together, firstly to introduce you to Adam. And to get some advice.' I pause.

'On business partnerships,' says Mel.

'Yeah.'

Last week we'd called a meeting of investors and shared the plan to merge our companies. Adam described how we'd combine the technology in the Beat the Q and Posse apps, and I explained how we'd market and sell the product. Everyone agreed that the strategy made sense and a few of the shareholders even asked if they could buy more equity.

'People keep saying that the biggest risk to our plan is me and Adam working together. We're both used to running our own thing,' I say.

'Isn't there some crazy stat on that?' says Cliff. 'Fifty per cent of business partnerships fail or something.'

I look to Adam. The situation feels a bit like an arranged marriage. We both have something the other wants. We like each other enough, and it'd be so nice to have a friend to share the highs and lows of running the business. I'm done with doing everything alone.

'I wanted to talk to you guys because you're the best example I know,' I say. 'You seem like a perfect partnership. What makes it work?'

Mel turns over her phone on the table. 'I made some notes.'

Of course she's made notes.

'The first thing is that we're both dreamers,' she says, holding up a finger. 'We're always talking about our vision for the business. We walk together every day, we have a lot of crazy conversations where we brainstorm ideas.' She looks to Cliff. 'What do you think?'

'Yeah, we talk about what the business will look like in five or ten years' time. We're both so clear on the goal that it makes every little decision easy. We don't have to ask each other.'

Mel nods, looking back to her phone. 'Another thing is that we never score points. Sometimes we'll disagree, but once a decision is made then it's a team decision. We don't ever talk about who wanted what or the process of how we made the decision.'

Adam leans in. 'So how do you argue?'

'Hmm.' Cliff scratches his nose. 'I wouldn't say we argue. We always focus on what's best for the company. Sometimes we have different ideas.' He tips his head both ways.

'The last thing is about trust.' Mel puts her phone away. 'This is going to be hard for you guys because you don't know each other yet.' She points to Cliff and back to herself. 'When we started our first company, we both did everything. After a while we worked out what we're each good at and we started dividing tasks. We know each other so well. We trust each other so—'

'So we can play to our strengths,' Cliff interjects, finishing her sentence like a second arm. 'It means we can get so much more done.' He fires us a hopeful look. 'You guys are going to need to trust each other, if it's going to work. It's a leap of faith.'

We finish up our cups of tea and chat about staff, how hard it is to find software developers, the plans for Canva's new office. 'We're building a commercial kitchen,' says Cliff. 'We're going to hire a chef so we can eat lunch together every day.'

Mel checks her watch. 'We better get back.'

Adam and I hang behind to unpack what we've just learnt and talk about how we'll work together as partners. I watch Mel and Cliff cross the road outside, speaking closely like they're planning a revolution.

45. CHARLIE

There's always a rush of new men on the dating sites in January. Kind of like the shops getting restocked after Christmas. Maybe guys feel the sting of a lonely holiday period too.

'Come on,' I whisper out loud. 'Let's see who's new on the shelf.' I key in eharmony.com. There are seven new messages in my inbox. Most are generic one-liners you would send to everyone; like me, they're just fishing. But there's one that's different.

> Hi Rebekah,
> Hope you're well and enjoying summer. I wanted to write because it looks like we have so much in common. I actually couldn't believe it when I read your profile.
> I'm halfway through season six of *The West Wing*. How good is it? So cool they got Alan Alda to play the Republican. I'm guessing you're watching *House of Cards* now too.
> I also see that you kitesurf. I live down at Botany Bay so I can get out in the mornings before work. Maybe we've seen each other down there?
> Anyway, you seem like an awesome person and I hope to hear from you soon.
> Charlie

My eyes dart from sentence to sentence, making sure I've read it right. *This is a real guy.* I click into his profile: 'Charlie P'. There are two photos: the first is a close-up of a guy in a white collared shirt, something you'd put on LinkedIn. In the second, he's wearing a blue patterned T-shirt over wetsuit shorts and standing next to a surfboard. His head is a mop of blond curls and freckles. *Adorable.*

I reply with some comments about season six of *The West Wing* and tales of my recent trip to New York. After an hour of messaging I ask if he wants to speak on the phone.

'Sure,' he replies, and shares his number.

This is it! I dial.

'Hi.'

'Hey Charlie, it's Rebekah.'

Our conversation rolls without gaps. I picture him lying in his Botany Bay flat near the beach. Charlie describes his place as 'basic but convenient for surfing'. He shares it with a friend while he saves for a unit of his own. His voice is soft and crackles a little like he just woke up. I notice my own voice mimic his. We agree to meet for dinner at The Winery on Friday. And for the next three days, two sides of my brain lock in a tug of war.

Left: *You can relax, this guy is perfect. You're thirty-six for a few more months. There's still time to make a family. You're going to scrape through.*

Right: *Don't get complacent. You haven't met him yet.*

Left: *Come on. This is the first time that everything seems to fit. He sounded lovely on the phone. Although, I don't love Botany Bay. Would he compromise to Bondi?*

Right: *Stop! You must shut down these imagined futures or you'll end up heartbroken again.*

I've spent the past four days getting ready: haircut, tick; nails, tick; eyebrows, tick; spray tan, tick. I'm wearing a cream silk dress I bought from Willow yesterday and cream heels from Shoes of Prey, whose office is a few doors along from ours.

Today is another Sydney scorcher. I check myself in the mirror one final time. The spray tan has clumped together in the crevasses of my neck wrinkles, it's streaking down my legs like lines of pulled pantyhose. *Damn.* It's too late for intervention. I clutch my black handbag and step around the corner to The Winery.

Charlie leans against the wall with a laptop bag over his shoulder. 'Hey,' he says, touching me lightly on the arm. He smiles like I might just be the one. 'I booked a table out on the balcony.'

We order wine, we chat about each other's day. I learn that Charlie works as a project manager in IT at the Commonwealth Bank. 'It's not my passion or anything, but it's okay. The people are nice.' He shrugs. 'And it pays really well. I take Mondays off to surf. It gives me a lifestyle.'

The sun is lower now and Charlie's skin is a shiny peach in the dimming light. His thick golden curls must look out of place at the Commonwealth Bank. *Is this my man?* I think he could be. I'm resting my chin on my knuckles. *Think, what was it Ruth said to ask?*

'Tell me about your family. What's your mum like?'

'Well I'm the only,' he says. 'I grew up with my mum, just the two of us. We're really close.'

'Is she in Sydney?'

'She's up the coast. But I go and see her every Saturday. She's getting on a bit now. She'll be eighty next month.'

Eighty. I calculate. *Eighty minus forty-three years.* She must have had him at thirty-seven. I'll be thirty-seven soon. *Fate!*

'What's she like?'

'She's a firecracker. Like you, actually. You two would get along. She's into every activist cause: climate change, refugees, save the wombats. You name it, she marches.' He laughs. 'It's inspiring really.'

At the end of our date Charlie hugs me like he doesn't want to let go. I reach up to adjust the pile of curls that are falling over one of his eyes. *This is a good man.*

'Hey, do you want to come kite-surfing on Sunday?' he asks. 'I've got a spare set-up.'

'Sure,' I say. 'Sounds fun.'

Two days later I stuff a towel into a beach bag and check my watch. Five minutes. Charlie is picking me up at 10. My spray tan has disintegrated into patches but it's still better than blinding white. I dig out a waterproof mascara and smear on a little foundation. Just enough to hide my blotches and still look like I'm not wearing any.

An orange panel van pulls up on Darlinghurst Road. Charlie jumps out, grinning. He runs to my side, opening my door like a chauffeur. 'My humble wagon.'

'Is it safe?' I joke, climbing inside.

The van is stacked to the roof with surfboards, wetsuits and kites. A tree-shaped air freshener wrestles with a decade's worth of damp clothes in the back seat. Charlie notices I've spotted the rusted hole at my feet and the road underneath. 'Ventilation,' he says.

We arrive at Botany Bay as an Emirates plane descends towards the airport. Our patch of sand is bordered by the runway on one side and a yard of cranes on the other. Charlie stands at the back of the van holding two hands up to the wind. 'It's blowin' today, my friend. What size kite are you used to?'

I pull my wetsuit up over my bikini and the wind smacks my hair in every direction. I gaze out to the choppy steel waves and brace myself. *Pretend to have fun, it'll be over soon.*

'I have to tell you something,' I say.

He looks up.

'On my eHarmony profile, I might have overstated my kitesurfing experience. I mean, I've done lessons.'

'How many?'

'Two.'

'Okay.' He reaches deep into the van and pulls out a giant green kite. 'I'll put you on a nine. It's for beginners.'

We step down to the beach, where Charlie pumps up the kite and lays out the strings just like my instructor had in Maui. 'I'll launch it and we can swap in the water.'

A few minutes later we're standing knee-deep in the choppy sea. Charlie clips the kite to my harness and it thrashes in the air like a wild horse.

'Now, you know to let go of the kite to depower it.'

My instructor in Maui had repeated this over and over. 'The most important thing to remember: don't hold onto your kite if it's out of control. That's how people fly away. That's how people die.'

'Got it.'

Charlie grips the loop on my harness and together we make a clunky boat dragging through the water. I concentrate hard to hold the kite steady.

'You've got this,' he shouts into the wind. 'Ready for me to let go?'

I don't think I am ready.

'Okay,' I yell. 'Let's do it.'

His fingers disconnect and I'm light, I'm gliding through the water, gybing from side to side. Charlie beams. He waves and his curls shrink into the distance as I sail downwind. *What an amazing guy. I knew that if I did enough dates . . .*

'Leggomite!' he shouts.

'What?' I'm imagining the cute face of our blond curly-haired son. *I hope he still visits me when I'm old, like Charlie does for his mum.*

'Let go of the kite!' Charlie is screaming now, and sprinting the beach.

A square rock cuts the surface right under my bum. 'Shit!' I let go of the bar. The kite collapses onto a pile of boulders next to the airport runway. *Is that noise a rip?* Adrenaline thumps through my chest. *What if I'd held on just one more second? Charlie is going to be mad. I've ruined his kite.*

He crashes into the water towards me — to me, not the kite — and wraps his arms around my back like I'm something precious. 'Are you okay?' He kisses the top of my head.

'Yes, I'm okay. I'm sorry, I got distracted. I'm sorry about your kite.'

He lets out a huge breath. 'Don't worry about the kite. It's nothing. I thought, I just. Jesus, I'm glad you're okay.'

46. SIXTEEN MISSED CALLS

'm still sweating from my morning run as I jump into the shower. My phone rings. *I'll call back later.* I feel a rush of anticipation for this morning's events. At 8.30, I'll meet Cameron and Adam for breakfast at Bills, a café in Surry Hills. We've almost finished the company merger and today we start to plan the next phase of the business.

The past month feels like reaching dry land after years of swimming alone in the ocean. Finally, I'm becoming secure. I've managed to raise $1.1 million from existing investors, the Russian billionaire and Cameron's friend in New York — enough to pay back my loan and fund the company though to December. And, finally, I'm shaping myself into some sort of order. I opened a term deposit like Sarah suggested and I've stuck to my diet. No sugar, no dairy, no processed anything. I'm not enjoying it, but I'm back to my regular weight.

My relationship with Charlie is developing at a steady pace. It isn't the overwhelming love affair I'd imagined. It feels calm and almost routine. On Valentine's Day he booked a fancy restaurant in the city and wore a tie covered in little silver ferns to impress me.

The phone rings again. *Should I get out to answer it?* The water is warm. It streams down my neck and across my torso. *Five more minutes.*

We haven't had sex yet, just long respectful kisses at the front door. Sometimes I wish he'd push open the door, just enough to show that there's an animal inside those Commonwealth Bank IT manager pants. Still, it feels so nice to know that I've found a man. In a few months we'll look for an apartment together and plan for making babies. I won't be alone again. No more splashing about hopelessly for the shore. I'm home now, I'm safe. My life is going to work out.

The phone rings again. I step out of the shower and wrap myself in a towel, still dripping. It's plugged in next to the TV.

Mum Mobile Text message 7.06 a.m.: Call me URGENT
Mum Mobile Missed call 7.06 a.m.
Mum Mobile Missed call 7.03 a.m.
Mum Mobile Missed call 7.01 a.m.

Far out, Mum. I roll my eyes. She never just calls once. Every random thought requires an 'urgent' response. I switch my phone to silent. I've still got to get dressed and put my makeup on. I'll call her back when I get in a cab.

My relationship with Adam is developing well too. I met his wife for dinner and she was equally enthusiastic about our joint venture. We've begun taking meetings together, as a team. I feel strangely joyful, sitting on the same side of the table as Adam. 'This is my business partner,' I say proudly, like it's some kind of validation.

Adam and Cameron have met several times now. I was nervous at first of how the dynamic might change. Would Cameron still mentor me with a male business partner involved? *Men can be funny like that.* But my fear was unwarranted.

If anything, Cameron seemed buoyed by the competition. Even more eager to impress. 'You must focus on hyper-local promotion,' he suggested. 'I'm friends with the CEO at Optus. I'll make an introduction.'

At our breakfast today we'll discuss who'll be on the board of directors for the new company. I'd like Cameron to be the chair and to include Gary, who has a lot of contacts in hospitality. Adam wants them on the board too. We just need to decide how they'll be paid.

I zip up my black boots and circle peach lipstick in the mirror. *Ready? Let's go.* I trot down the steps and across two blocks to hail a taxi that's driving in the direction of Surry Hills. Inside, I open my phone.

Mum Mobile 16 Missed calls

I feel two thumps in my chest. *A few missed calls is normal. Not sixteen.* I press to call.

'Rebekah. Where have you been? It's Dad. He's collapsed.' She's speaking so fast.

'What do you mean? Where is he?'

'He's in an ambulance. He's unconscious. Rebekah, you need to come home.'

'Hang on, hang on.' Victoria Street is a blur of lights and noise. 'Can you stop the car please? I need to get out.'

The driver tips his head. 'What?'

'Stop the car!' I shriek, chucking him a ten dollar note.

I crouch on the corner. Not Dad. I can't live without Dad. *Please God. Please.*

Ten minutes later I've stuffed a bag and I'm riding another

taxi to the airport. I call Mum again. 'Are you with him? Where is he now?'

'Just calm down, okay. Shouting isn't going to help. I'm on my way to the hospital. I've pulled over the car to talk to you.' Her voice is monotone.

'What happened?'

'I wasn't there. All I know is he was at the pool with his friend. One of the lifeguards spotted him floating in the water. He didn't have a heartbeat.' I'm silent. My head is going to burst. 'Rebekah, are you there?'

'Yes.'

'You need to prepare yourself.'

I hate my mother at this moment. I hate her for giving up. I hate her for being calm when she should have shattered into a million pieces. And I need her. My insides are falling, falling like they've just been dropped from the sky.

My fingers shake as I google 'Wellington Hospital'.

'Hi, I think my dad's been brought in. Robert Campbell?'

A woman taps computer keys in the background. 'No, no one of that name has been admitted today. If he's still in the ambulance, we wouldn't have—'

Click. I hang up.

The Qantas desk at the airport is crowded and my knees are weak. A man behind the counter spots my face soaked in tears, stretched in the shape of a scream. He waves me to the side.

'I've got to get to Wellington. My dad drowned, he's in an ambulance.'

The man moves with quiet purpose. He picks up the phone. 'QF161, can you reopen the gate? I've got an emergency passenger.' He listens and leans forward. 'Any bags?'

'No, just what I'm carrying.' I hand him my passport and credit card and he prints out a boarding pass. 'It's Gate 15. They're holding the plane for you. Good luck.'

I hold my breath for three hours. I spot Mum in Wellington on the other side of Customs and we collapse into each other. She grabs the sides of my head, looking into my eyes. 'He's awake. They managed to resuscitate him, but he was without oxygen for a long time. We don't know . . .'

I feel blood fill my veins and I fold into an airport chair in relief. 'Okay. He's alive. That's good.'

At the hospital, we follow the signs to intensive care. The corridors seem sterile and cold, a maze of cream linoleum lines. Mum speaks to a nurse who guides us into a room and behind a curtain.

'Dad.' I have to look twice. *Is that him?*

The nurse holds a finger to her lips. 'He's asleep. Here, take his hand.'

I pull a chair next to his bed and lift his floppy fingers into my own. He is white and still, his bones poke through sagging skin like raw chicken drumsticks. His face is covered in a giant plastic mask with blue vacuum cleaner tubes poking out the side. There's a wet towel on top of his head, tape from ear to ear and beeping machines everywhere.

I squeeze his palm and he opens his eyes. 'Dad,' I whisper. His fingers move in my hand just enough for me to know it's him. 'You gave me a big scare, you know.' He looks up again briefly and there's a tear on his cheek. He closes his eyes.

'Come on.' The nurse signals for us to leave. 'He needs to rest.'

Outside, I pace on a strip of grass next to the hospital carpark and zip up my puffer jacket to shelter from the wind. I check my phone and spot a missed call from Charlie. We'd been planning to meet after work. I should call.

I go to press the green button and hesitate. *Why don't I feel excited?* I must be exhausted by the day's events. But I *never* feel excited when he calls. *Oh, there's Charlie again,* I think when his number appears exactly as scheduled, when he returns every call within minutes. It's kind of annoying actually, so nice and dependable. There's no . . . What is it? I dial his number.

'Hey,' he answers.

'Sorry I missed your call before. I'm in Wellington.' I explain what's happened and Charlie speaks with the generous concern I expected.

'Just let me know if there's anything I can do. I'm here, okay. If you want me to come over.'

'It's alright. Thanks.' I feel myself smiling. *He's not annoying. Just caring.* 'We'll know more tomorrow. If everything's fine I'll probably fly back on Friday. I'm supposed to speak at this TEDx thing on Saturday. I haven't even started writing my talk.'

Mum sits across from me at a tiny table at Noble Rot Wine Bar, off Cuba Street in the centre of town. It's 5.30 and there's only a handful of customers in the place. I still feel jittery and hardly notice she's wearing a silk purple tracksuit, sneakers and socks pulled up over the bottom of her pants. A man in a red apron passes us each a menu.

'Let's get some dinner,' says Mum. 'They don't want us back at the hospital till seven.' She reaches across the table and covers my hands with hers. 'He's going to be alright. This time.' She glances down to our pile of hands and back up to me. 'We won't be here forever, you know.'

I imagine my heart ticking away in my chest, dishing out blood to all those delicate organs. It seems so fragile, the human body. If something stops, just for a moment . . . I look to Mum. Her heart could stop too, and what if it did? These people. These two strange people. They're all I've got.

'I've started seeing someone,' I say. 'This guy Charlie, I probably told you on the phone.'

'Yes, you mentioned.'

'He's really nice, Mum. I think, maybe this could be the one.'

I could lock this in right now. Charlie seems so keen. He's nice, likes the outdoors, watches *The West Wing*, wants a family. I picture us telling Mum and Dad that we're pregnant, how thrilled they'd be.

Mum's still squinting with concern. And a realisation spreads across my mind for the first time. I'd assumed she wanted me to find a partner so I could give her grandchildren, so she'd have cute pictures to show her friends. *It's not that at all.* She's thinking about me and my future and what happens when her and Dad aren't here. Who will love me? Who will I spend Christmas with?

'Why do you say "maybe"?' she asks.

'What?'

'Before, when you said he could be the one. You said "maybe". Why aren't you sure?'

I take a sip of wine. 'Did I? I didn't notice.'

She tilts her head to one side. 'How do you feel?'

She's jabbing at something in my chest and I need to defend myself. 'He's perfect. He's everything I ever wanted, so nice. He looks after me. He'll be a great dad.'

'But how do you feel? Are you falling in love with him?'

I'm plugging up the wound now, grabbing for anything I can. 'What does falling in love even feel like? It's been so long since, well.'

'Steve,' she says.

'Yes, Steve. It's not like that. It's not overwhelming. I don't think about him all the time. But when I remember he exists, I feel good. Isn't that what you want for me? Someone good, reliable?'

'Is that what *you* want?'

I'm so angry right now I could smash my fist through the table. *Don't remind me that you won't be here forever then dismiss my solution.*

'I just want you to be happy,' says Mum. 'Love is a wonderful thing, you know. Don't sell yourself short.'

47. MARINATED FISH

I hear two knocks. 'Hiya,' shouts Charlie. 'I've brought dinner.' I swing open the door and there he is, rosy cheeked and smiling from ear to ear. He steps inside, hugging me tight in both arms. 'I've missed you,' he says.

'I was only gone a few days.'

'I know, but.' He shrugs. 'I'm glad everything is okay.'

Dad had been awake when Mum and I went to see him after dinner. He kept asking why I'd come, then forgetting and asking again. By Thursday he'd started to improve.

'What happened?' I asked the doctors.

'We don't really know,' they'd said, shaking their heads. 'It might have been the change in his medication. He blacked out in the water. You're lucky the lifeguards got to him.'

I wrote my TEDx Talk on the plane this morning and fired off a brief to our graphic designer Anna to make up some slides. I now regret saying yes to the invitation to speak. TED is for people who've actually done something with their lives. I'd browsed through the list of other speakers: an environmentalist, a nineteen-year-old who's set up a charity to supply women in developing countries with sanitary products, that maths guy from Triple J. *They'll laugh at me and my pointless business ideas.* No, worse. They won't laugh, they'll cringe on the inside then clap and tell me it was great.

Charlie had insisted on coming over to help me with the talk. 'I really just need to practise,' I'd said.

'But I can help. I'll be your audience. I'll cook.'

Charlie slips open his leather satchel and pulls out three neatly packed Tupperware containers and a bottle of wine.

'What have you got?' I ask.

'This one is salmon.' He holds up a pink plastic box. 'This is just rice. And veges to steam. You do have a . . . ?'

'Ah, what do you need?'

He digs through my cupboard and pulls out a metal sieve. 'I can use this.'

I sit at the dining table, my back to the kitchen, reading through my notes. I flick through the slides trying to memorise the words. In the background, Charlie fries fish and whistles. I tap one finger over and over on my forehead. *Why is this so irritating?* The smell and smoke waft across the room and Charlie continues. My chest is tight. I've seized up so stiff that a limb might crack if anyone tried to touch me.

He passes me a plate that looks like it's been made in a restaurant. 'Do you want wine?' He unscrews a bottle.

'Not for me, but thanks.' I wave him off. 'I've got to focus on this talk.'

'Of course,' he says, pouring himself a glass.

I take my first bite. 'Wow, this salmon is delicious. What did you do? It doesn't taste like this when I cook.'

'I just marinated it,' he says. 'I did it at work, at lunchtime in the kitchen.'

Three hours later I'm alone in bed. I sent Charlie home early so I could get a decent sleep. 'Yes, good idea,' he'd said. 'You need to rest before your big talk.'

I imagine Charlie in the kitchenette at his office in the Commonwealth Bank. Colleagues in suits bustle past to pour tea and microwave their lunches. 'What are you doing, mate?' someone asks.

Charlie is alone in the corner with soy sauce and honey on the bench. He's coating pieces of salmon in little sandwich bags. 'I'm just marinating fish.' He blushes. 'It's for my girlfriend. I'm cooking dinner.'

My heart wants to kiss his freckled cheeks. *That's my man over there with the fish.* I also want to take two hands and push him as far away from me as possible. *What's wrong with me?*

I wake and check my phone: 2.12 a.m. *If only I could escape this talk today. I'm not ready.* The roof creaks. *A burglar?* Yes please, someone break in. That would be a good excuse.

I wake again at 3.56. Still too early. I step into the kitchen. The apartments across the courtyard are dark. I imagine Charlie standing behind me kissing the side of my face, making his way down my neck. His hands slide into my pyjamas — hold on. He'd never do that, at least not without asking first.

48. RELATIONSHIP STYLES

I slouch into the leather seat in Ruth's consultation room. She's holding the manila folder with my name on the front, waiting for me to speak.

'There's a few things,' I say, 'that I'd like your help with.'

'Shoot.'

'The dating.' I let out a sigh. 'You know that list I started with? What I wanted in a partner.'

She smiles and nods to her notes. 'I've got it here: smart, tall, fun. How did that go?'

'Ha. Not well. I found someone who is all those things. This guy Pierre in San Francisco. But he wasn't nice. He didn't seem to care about me.'

'Nice is important. There are a lot of narcissistic men around these days.'

'Yeah,' I reply. 'I think I've met a couple. No, more than a couple.' I laugh.

'I hear about them every day from women sitting in that chair.' She circles her finger in my direction. 'They meet these men, think they've found the one: charming, good looking, smart, they spend a lot of money. But there's no empathy. Remember you asked me once about couples I see, the ones that stay together and the ones that end up in all sorts of trouble.' She points her finger straight, like a schoolteacher.

'Nice goes a really long way. That's what women don't—'

'Okay,' I interject. 'I've got it. Nice is good.'

She shuffles back in her chair like she's glad the point is clear.

'Next issue,' I say. 'I've met this guy Charlie and he's really nice. He's *so* nice.'

She rolls her eyes. 'But you're not attracted to him.'

I look up apologetically. 'I don't know what's wrong with me. There's just no chemistry.'

'Look.' She crosses her ankles. 'I'm not going to tell you what to do. But I will say that this idea of "chemistry"—' she quotes the word with her fingers '— can be dangerous.'

'What is it then?' I ask.

'What you think is chemistry is usually just your relationship style.'

'But I don't have a relationship style. I haven't really had any relationships. Well, not for a long time.'

'You have a relationship with yourself, don't you?'

'I suppose.'

'And?'

'And what?'

'And, how do you treat yourself? Are you compassionate, generous? Do you love yourself, pamper yourself?'

How does this have anything to do with Charlie? She stares at me, waiting for an answer. I look down, remembering how I flogged myself running this morning. How I work in the office until my brain is flat with exhaustion. How hungry I am right now on this stupid diet.

'You might want to think about it,' she says. 'If you have a history of feeling like you don't deserve niceness, then you'll be uncomfortable when you meet someone who does things for you.'

'But this guy, Charlie,' I say, changing the subject. 'There's a few things that don't work.'

'Like?'

'He's really into surfing,' I say quietly, feeling pathetic. 'I don't surf.'

'You like the outdoors. That's something you have in common.'

'But our conversations. They're okay but they're not deep. They're not challenging.'

Ruth leans towards me. 'This might be news to you, but no one is perfect. People expect one partner to give them everything: emotional support, exciting sex, deep conversations, financial partnership, parenting skills. It's not realistic. In the old days we used to have a whole family, a community.'

'So you think I should stick with this guy then?'

She closes her folder of notes. 'When you told me you were going to do a date every week, the thing I liked is that you'd get a realistic view of the market. I see a lot of women who only date a handful of men. That's a very small sample and their expectations are way too high. They're looking for Barack Obama and he just isn't out there. You've met how many?'

'Eighty-six.'

'Right. You know the market. You know what men are available. You've got —' she rubs her fingers together '— comparative data. And if you find a good one, well.'

The room is quiet. The clock reads 1.40 p.m., still twenty minutes till the end of my appointment. I need another topic to pass the time. 'I spoke at TEDx Sydney on Saturday.'

'Did you?' Her voice inflects upwards. 'And how did it go?'

I bite my cheek. 'It was okay. People clapped and stuff, but I felt like I didn't have anything significant to say. The other speakers, they'd all done something incredible. Really made a contribution, you know?'

'And what would you have liked to say that you didn't?' she asks.

I pour myself a glass of water, taking the time to think. 'I guess I've been trying to work out the point of my life. I have this vision of being someone who's inspiring. Who gives myself when I think I can help people. I just haven't done anything yet. I need to get on with it.'

'Is this your impressive thing again?'

The minute hand on the clock circles again. *Is it?*

'This Charlie man, is he impressive?'

I picture Charlie at work in his plain white shirt and chino pants. 'I wouldn't say so, no. He's nice. Nice and normal.'

'And you need?'

My brain stretches and bends. It's like Ruth is probing close to where the answer is, but I still can't get to it. *I've almost got this.*

Charlie couldn't meet up yesterday because he had plans with his mum. 'We have a season pass to the Belvoir St Theatre. Mum catches the train down to Sydney for it. I can get another ticket. I'd love you to meet.'

I pull out a seat at a small table behind the piano at The Victoria Room. *My old haunt, I haven't missed you.* The bodybuilder behind the bar has been replaced by a young man with a neat shirt and shiny skin who looks like he only shaves to trim the fluff. In Gina's place, there's three women whispering to each other at the front desk.

In two months' time, I'll be thirty-seven years old. *Charlie is a good man.* I imagine us at age eighty, Charlie pushing me in a chair. He'd massage my feet, feed me frozen yoghurt.

Right brain: *You're thirty-seven, you've dated eighty-six men. There's no more time.*

Left: *Remember what Mum said. 'Love is a wonderful thing.'*

Right: *But what is love? Will it come later?*

Left: *You didn't come all this way, do all those dates just to . . .*

I wonder if life is a bit like musical chairs. We spend all these years dancing along, playing the game, and then all of a sudden the music stops. No. I still believe in magic. There should be magic.

Charlie bounds up the stairs, curls bouncing. He waves eagerly like an embarrassing dad picking me up from school.

'Can I get you a drink?' he asks.

I hold up my vodka lemonade.

He returns from the bar and takes a seat opposite me, reaching forward to hold my hand.

'I wanted to catch up,' I say. I retract my hand from under his and Charlie's eyes narrow. I gaze at his broad shoulders, the arms that wrapped me tight out kiteboarding, his soft lips that kissed my head. 'I'm not sure this is going to work.'

He flinches like someone punched him in the chest real slow. Our table is silent. I feel myself tremble. 'I'm sorry,' I say. 'It's not you. You're amazing. I'm just not feeling . . . I'm not feeling the way I should by now.'

He looks away, folding his arms. He's still and quiet.

'Is there anything you want to ask?'

He turns to me and there's a vein bursting from the side of

his head. His eyes are wet. He opens his palms. 'I don't really have anything to say. I'm surprised.' He rubs his red forehead. 'I thought we were good.'

I search for words. *We are good. That's why this is so ridiculous.* 'I'm really sorry. I wish I had a better explanation.' I find his hand to squeeze. 'You're going to make someone so happy.' I'm crying. I'm pushing everything I've ever wanted off the side of a cliff and I'm crying.

I walk home completely empty. I'm drifting again; there's no solid ground, no one who cares. No future to look forward to.

49. TINDER

The following Sunday, Sean contorts his face in amazement as we walk down the promenade at Bondi Beach. 'This guy sounds perfect. I don't understand.'

I fidget with the button on my denim jacket. 'I don't know. It didn't seem right.'

We order juices and perch on the hill overlooking the ocean. I let out a long groan. 'Back to eHarmony.'

Sean stops sipping and pulls the straw from his mouth. 'Give me your phone,' he says. 'No one uses eHarmony anymore. Not that I'm dating or anything, but all my mates—'

'Are on Tinder,' I interject.

'Yeah.' He clicks into the App Store. 'I'll set up your profile. It's easy.'

I reach for the phone. 'Wait. I haven't used Tinder because I don't want anyone from work knowing. I don't like the idea of people swiping me like a used car or something.'

'Oh, get over yourself. Everyone is on this. If you're serious . . .'

I remember Charlie and his thoughtful messages on eHarmony. 'But isn't it just for pickups?'

He places his hand on my shoulder. 'Trust me, eHarmony is for desperados. RSVP is a ghetto. Tinder is it.'

'Alright.' I hand him back my phone and Sean grins. A minute later he starts to swipe.

'Is that it?'

'Yep. It pulls your photos from Facebook. Look, you've already got two matches.'

Later at home I lie on the couch swiping faces: left for nope and right for like. When a guy that I like also swipes right on me, then Tinder says we're a match and we can start messaging. By 7 p.m. I've got a screen full of matches and messages ticking through like news updates. They don't stop.

> Tim, 39: Hey, what have you been up to this weekend?
> Dimitri, 44: Yes or no to pineapple on pizza?
> Hany, 38: Has anyone ever said you look like Jackie on House of Cards?

'Have you seen the new season of *House of Cards*?' Cameron asks from across a white meeting room table on the twenty-ninth floor. 'You look a lot like one of the characters.'

'Jackie,' says Gary. 'You do actually. She's ruthless.' He nods to Adam.

'I'm not ruthless. I'm actually very . . .'

'Oh she is, she is,' laughs Cameron. 'I've seen you in action. Anyway, you should watch it. You'll like Jackie.'

Adam opens a PowerPoint presentation and turns his laptop to face Cameron and Gary. There's a knock at the door and a young man with a trolley wheels in tea, coffee and biscuits. 'We'd like to run you through our plan for the rest of the year,' says Adam. 'Be great to get your feedback.' Adam and I flick through slides showing our teams working together in the new office.

'What are you going to call it, this super-app?' asks Gary.

'We're not sure yet,' I say.

'But it'll be something new,' says Adam. 'Not Posse and not Beat the Q.'

I pull up the budget and point to our plan to hire a sales team. 'We predict each salesperson will get four new stores per week. We earn an average of a hundred and twenty dollars per store per month, so it'll take just under four months for each shop to make us a profit. There'll be some churn of course, but —'

'Unit economics.' Cameron claps his hands. 'I taught you this.'

Our eyes meet and nostalgia draws us together.

Adam clears his throat. 'We wanted to talk to you about the board. We'd like you both to be directors, of course. We need to work out how to pay you.'

Cameron breaks my gaze and turns to Adam. 'Sure thing. I'll put some thoughts together.'

'We were thinking three per cent,' says Adam, the 'three per cent' trailing into a whisper.

Cameron pulls out his chair and stands behind me at the table, a hand on each of my shoulders. 'We love Rebekah. We've been there from the start.'

Outside, Adam and I pace up George Street towards the train station at Wynyard. We climb onto a carriage packed with afternoon commuters and I cling to a pole next to the door. Adam grips a handle on the roof. 'I have to ask,' he says, 'about you and Cameron.'

His words hit me like a punch of air. 'What do you mean?'

'I dunno.' He looks down the carriage like he's pondering one big question. 'I just picked up a vibe. Maybe it's nothing.'

'He's been incredible to me.' Inside, the punch twists into a strange knot in my stomach.

I swipe Tinder — left, left, right, right, left — like a bottomless deck of cards. There's a man in swim shorts with big tattoos across his shoulder, another holding hands with a toddler in a pink dress, standing awkwardly in front of the Harbour Bridge like a tourist, with a cute dog, hooking a giant fish, next to a red sportscar.

I wonder if any of these men are as nice as Charlie or as perfect as Steve. Left, right, left, right. So many options. I hover over a man with thick-rimmed glasses.

Date 87

'Do you know Neil Funn?' asks Simon, eyes gleaming behind his thick-rimmed glasses. It's 6 p.m. on Friday and we're sitting on wooden stools at an old pub in Paddington.

'You mean Finn?'

'Yeah, Funn,' he says, poking fun at my New Zealand accent.

Simon sips a giant mug of Guinness and there's a line of white froth on his top lip. We laugh and he tells me about a startup he's planning to launch which will help businesses with their social media advertising. Simon is funny, slightly annoying but endearing too. He's also funny to look at: short and round like he's been compressed lengthways. *He'll definitely call; I'm a great catch for him.*

I dawdle home wondering if Simon is it. *Two and a half years, eighty-seven dates.* I picture all the faces queued up on Tinder. I've got a date with Justin Doctor tomorrow, then Scott Oxfam next week. *Is Simon my best option?*

Two weeks later, I'm standing behind a podium at Google HQ in Sydney. A crowd of a hundred startup founders are here to learn how to raise venture capital. Every seat in the room is full. I pull back my shoulders, lift my chin high and click the right arrow on the remote to start my presentation.

Hang on. In the back of the room stands a short man in a buttoned-up jacket. He's squeezing himself into the corner like he doesn't want to be seen. *Is that? Yes.* Simon notices I've spotted him and smiles through gritted teeth.

I turn up my nose. *'What the? Why didn't you call?'* His lips make a crooked line and he shrugs. *'Shucks. You're nice, but someone better might be just around the corner.'*

Date 92

I'm pretty sure I can do better than the man with thick dark hair who's sitting opposite me at The Rusty Rabbit café in Darlinghurst. His name is Clint Campbell and yes, the convenience of not having to change my name if we marry has already registered. But this morning is our first date. We're getting breakfast.

'I'm in a band. We're kind of eighties hard rock with a female lead singer,' he says. 'Didn't you used to work in music?'

The following Wednesday night I wonder how close I can hold my hands to my ears without looking rude. I'm on a plastic chair in the echoey chamber of an empty Annandale pub. Clint's band is in full flight, the frontwoman screaming and thrashing her head about like a dying fish.

'What do you think?' he asks afterwards. 'Can you introduce us to some people?'

'What do you think?' I ask Cameron as I close my laptop.

Adam and I perch on the leather couch in his office. We've just finished showing Cameron and Gary pictures of our new app design.

'"Hey You,"' Cameron says out loud. 'It's a good name.' He rubs his finger up and down the ridge of his sharp nose, tapping. 'We've still got to finalise our deal. Remember, we talked about . . . ?'

'Of course.' I rush in. 'We've discussed it. We definitely want you on the board, and Gary too. We just have to work out terms.'

'It's going to be a lot of work, what you're looking to do,' says Cameron. 'I know you don't have money to pay consulting fees. It'll need to be equity.'

In the lift outside, Adam faces me. 'They're going to ask for something crazy. That's why he's priming us.'

I pinch my eyebrows together and shake my head. 'No way, I've known these guys forever. They'll be reasonable.'

Adam exhales in a long sigh and looks to the roof. 'We better get a deal done soon, before they do more work.'

Date 99

'For work?' says Bryce, responding to my question. 'Oh. I sell insurance at AMP. Professional indemnity. We protect the financial advisors, accountants, lawyers, that kind of thing.'

Bryce adjusts his sunglasses as we drive up Ocean Road towards Bondi in his convertible Jeep. 'Nice car,' I say.

He laughs. 'I bought it to piss off my dad. He's really into the environment and all that. It's one of the worst polluting cars you can get.'

I turn and cough at the smell coming from the exhaust.

I cough twice to remind the man opposite that I'm here. Adam and I are seated side by side in the café downstairs from our office. The man across the table is bald, with a tuft of hair under his mouth that I imagine him calling a 'flavour saver' to friends.

'Why do you want this job?' I ask. 'What makes you think you'll be a good salesperson for Hey You?'

The man replies directly to Adam. 'I've worked as a barista in Sydney for years. It's like a club — the owners, the baristas, they're my boys. They trust me.'

I ask more questions and the man continues to direct his answers to Adam. The experience is strange, like I'm invisible. I want to tip my head across the table. '*Hello!*'

'Whoa.' The man leans over as if he's about to whisper something to Adam. He indicates to the side with his head, widening his eyes in awe. A waitress in cut-off shorts with long flowing hair glides from table to table with a cloth. The man is frozen, tongue glued to the side of his mouth.

Date 100

Back at The Victoria Room, Craig's tongue is pressed up under his bottom lip like he's angry about something. He looks different to his photo on Tinder: his face is fatter, eyes smaller, ginger stubble longer. Not that looks count for anything, I remind myself.

'Oh god, what's that?' He points to the laptop in my handbag.

'Ah, I guess it's a Hillary Clinton campaign sticker. Is there a problem?'

He turns his face away like he's gagging. 'Am *I* on a date with a leftie feminist?'

I raise one eyebrow. 'What about you? Don't tell me you like Tony Abbott?'

A minute goes past and he gulps at his schooner of Victoria Bitter to finish up. Craig turns, his small eyes narrowed. 'This obviously isn't a thing, right?'

Why is he still talking?

'Can I give you a tip?' he adds with an impish smirk. 'For dating. You know, with other guys.'

'Sure, hit me with it.'

He points to my laptop again. 'The whole feminist thing. It's really unsexy. A huge turn-off.'

Back at home I lie on the couch with my phone in hand. 'Unmatch Craig, unmatch Bryce, unmatch Clint, unmatch Simon.' Two years ago, I might have wasted a minute pondering whether feminism is or isn't sexy. But not now. Not after a hundred dates.

'More than 100 comments.' My eyes blur. It's 6 a.m. and I've clicked into an email Loren sent me overnight.

> Your article about interviewing the male chauvinist in the café is going crazy. There's more than 100 comments already. Our moderators can't keep up!

I sit up in bed and open the *New York Times* website.

When Women Manage Men Who Don't Respect Women

by Rebekah Campbell

A few weeks ago, my business partner and I

interviewed a candidate for a senior sales role at our company. We met at a coffee shop and he seemed perfect: charming, smart and passionate about our business. He came to the interview prepared with suggestions relevant to our strategy. I was impressed. But a couple of things bugged me . . .

Under the headline: 325 comments. *Wow.* I begin reading: Kimberly from Abilene, Texas; KG from Vancouver Island; Kristin from Sweden; Nancy from Denver, Colorado; Judi from New York; Jean from Tucson, Arizona; Farah from Saudi Arabia. All women sharing similar experiences and counsel to steer clear of the sexist job candidate.

I roll in bed, wrapping myself in the blanket. There's something about sharing an experience with other women, knowing I'm not the only one. It makes me feel safe.

Date 103

I feel very unsafe as a passenger in Peter's blue VW Golf as he swerves left when I say 'right' on Liverpool Street at 10 p.m. *I shouldn't have got in the car with this guy. It's our first date.*

Peter is tall with neat brown hair and glasses, the type you'd get if you ordered 'stock-market trader' from a casting company. He's interested in American politics, speaks knowledgably about climate change, but there's something about the way he moves that unnerves me. Something is off.

'Do you want to go out again?' he asks, tongue circling the inside of his mouth. 'We could go for a walk on Sunday.'

Where are you driving me? I want out of this car. 'Sure.' I press my back against the car door. 'I think you missed the turn back there. Darlinghurst Road is that way.'

'I know,' he says, revving the accelerator. 'I want to keep you for longer, drive around the block.'

I force a smile.

'Shall we do the coastal walk at Rose Bay? We could get a drink after.'

'That sounds great.' *Whatever promise I need to make.* He zips through the tunnel at William Street. 'I can get out here, I'm just through the walkway.' *I'm not showing you where I live.*

At 6 a.m. the next morning my phone buzzes.

> Peter: Hope you had a good sleep.

At 6.30 the phone rings. 'Peter Trader'. I hit the red button. At 6.45 there's another text.

> Peter: Plan for tomorrow. I'll pick you up at 1?

He rings again at 7.10 a.m., and again at 9, 9.30, 9.40. 9.43. By midday I've had thirty-nine missed calls. Enough. *Be polite, but firm.* I text back:

> Me: Hi Peter. Nice to meet you last night and thanks for the ride home. I've done some thinking and I don't feel like there's enough of a connection to go out again. Best of luck with your search.

Twelve more missed calls.

> Peter: You said you wanted to go out again. You led me on.

I sleep with my phone on silent, the emergency services number already keyed so I don't waste time dialling if he bangs on the door. By 6 a.m. Sunday there are fifty-eight missed calls from an unknown number.

I imagine Peter stalking the streets outside. I need groceries but I'm scared he's going to see me. Another missed call. *Who can I ask for help?* I scroll through numbers on my phone, hovering over Charlie IT. *Should I?* No, I can't. Another missed call. I google 'Kings Cross Police Station' and dial the number.

'This guy I went on a date with, he keeps calling. I'm scared that he's stalking me. What can you do?'

They explain something called an apprehended violence order or 'AVO'.

'But that doesn't stop him if he wants to hurt me. Can't you guard my apartment?'

I message Peter. This time firm, not polite.

> Me: I've called the police and reported your behaviour. Don't ever call or message me again.

Finally, quiet.

I avoid the quiet streets as I walk to work on Monday. We've leased a full floor of a warehouse office building on Commonwealth Street and painted 'Hey You' in giant orange letters on a stand as you walk in. A screen mounted in the kitchen counts the number of people using the app every day. There are almost fifty desks, exposed brick walls, hanging plants and people in every direction.

Adam paces towards me clutching a newspaper. 'They

put us on the front page,' he says, holding open *The Australian Business Review*. 'Beat the Q and Posse Create E-commerce Heavyweight' reads the headline, with a photo of me and Adam smiling proudly. 'And did you see that email from Westpac?'

My phone buzzes. A message from Cameron.

> Cameron: Great story in the paper today. Will get that deal proposal to you soon.

I catch Adam's eye and wonder why I'm starting to feel nervous. 'It's Cameron. He says he's working on their proposal.'

'Good,' says Adam. 'It's taking way too long.'

I feel a stab of anxiety. 'It'll be fine. They're reasonable guys.' I check the TV screen for the metrics. 'We're going to have a record day today. More than two thousand transactions already.'

I switch on my TV at home and pick through a bowl of boiled vegetables and hummus on the couch. The news hums along: the Duke and Duchess of Cambridge parade through Sydney with their new baby. Tony Abbott defends his 'horror budget'.

'Residents of Surry Hills are in shock this evening as the remains of an eighty-seven-year-old woman have been found in an apartment, eight years after she died. Natalie Wood is being remembered as the woman Sydney forgot.' I hit + on the volume.

A female reporter stands outside a terraced flat just a few streets from our office. 'She died alone and forgotten on her bedroom floor. Her sister visited for a meal of boiled vegetables in 2003, and that was the last time anyone saw her alive.'

I look down to my bowl and shiver from the inside out. I google 'Natalie Wood Surry Hills' on my phone and read an article describing the scene: skeletal remains with gnawed bones still greasy and smelly, piles of instant coffee and cans of condensed milk years past their use-by date.

What would happen if I died in my sleep? How long would it take for someone to notice? I imagine my empty desk at work. Adam would try calling. My mobile would ring here on the coffee table until the battery ran flat. It'd be at least a few days, enough for the flies . . .

50. MY THIRTY-SEVENTH BIRTHDAY

'What are you after?' asks the waiter at The Rusty Rabbit.
'Scrambled eggs and feta please.'

'Anyone else joining?'

'No, just me.'

My mobile rings: it's Mum. 'What are your plans for today?' she asks. 'It's a public holiday over there, isn't it? Are you having a party?'

I feel myself slump over the table. 'No, Mum, I don't really like to celebrate birthdays.'

'Oh, come on. I wish I was still thirty-seven.'

Thirty-seven.

I pull open my Moleskine notebook, now frayed from riding in my handbag for two-and-a-half years. I glance through the goals I'd set for 2012, 2013, 2014, the note to self to 'FREEZE EGGS ON 37TH BIRTHDAY (if not in relationship)', the lists of guidelines and instructions to keep dating, lose weight, become successful. I close the cover and sip on a mug of green tea.

Outside the café, the streets of Darlinghurst are quiet. Most people are away for the long weekend. Inside, a coffee machine squeals, knives and forks drop together into trays, a baby cries and people chatter, but I can't make out any words. It's just one long drone of activity.

I'm thirty-seven and I'm exhausted. I want to drop this notebook into the little rubbish bin next to the door. But instead I begin to write.

What I'm giving up

1. Complaining about my appearance
   I accept my wide forehead, wonky eyebrow, the cellulite on the back of my thighs, my varicose vein and everything else that will grey, sag, fall out or whatever between now and age 100. This is me.
2. Being hungry
   No more dieting! I will eat healthy food most of the time and cake and frozen yoghurt when I feel like it. I will find my natural weight and quit believing I should fit into size 8 clothes like Barbie and those ridiculous twins from *Sweet Valley High*.
3. Dating
   109 dates is enough. I gave it a good shot.

I swallow the first two points whole but I'm having trouble chewing the third. *Should* I *give up dating?* I still want a family. But the thought of continuing to trudge along, night after night, waiting for calls back. *I can't.* Madeleine decided she was perfect 'with or without a relationship'. *Could that approach work for me? Am I perfect?* I wish I could just say yes and believe it.

I flick back to what I wrote after raising the round of capital in Maui. *'Every success is underpinned by a lot of effort.'*

What about Charlie? Is that solid ground still out there? I unlock my phone, key his name into Facebook. *Darn it.* Two cheeks pressed against each other. He and a woman with wet hair. They're at the beach with two kites. *Too late.* There is no solid ground. *I'm so, so tired.*

At school, I used to run cross country. I'd train every morning and every afternoon, run circuits around the neighbourhood and lift weights in the gym. I wasn't long-limbed like the other girls but I worked hard, I had willpower.

One race I remember vividly: the under-16s ten-kilometre road race from Lambton Quay. It was a dreary Saturday morning and I was one flick in a flock of a hundred girls striding down the central street, past Wellington Railway Station, around the bay and back. Nicole Keller was in front — tall, with legs like bamboo, taking one step for every two of mine. She always got first place. But not that day, I had decided.

We turned past the boatshed, the wooden planks of the wharf crashing underfoot. My legs started to slump and I gasped for breath. The other girls looked tired too and the pace of the group slowed. Every cell in my body wanted to stop. *I'm so tired. I should give up.*

And from some strange magical place my mind surged with determination: *I can still win this thing.* My legs started to fly faster and faster, past Nicole Keller and through that red ribbon, hands in the air.

It's 9 p.m. on Friday. I pick up my phone and notice a little 12 in a bubble next to the Tinder app. And from some strange magical place comes a surge of determination. *I can still win this thing.* I have one big sprint left in me. *Better review my strategy.*

First, I need a new tactic to filter on Tinder. There's only space to write 140 characters and most men don't write anything.

I need to use *my* 140 characters to scare off poor candidates.

Under 'Rebekah, 37', I write:

> Likes: Sunshine, Michael Jackson, Hillary Clinton, Trees, Books, Swimming in the ocean, Dancing to Michael Jackson. Dislikes: Pessimists, Tony Abbott

It's also time for a surge in quantity. My love may still be out there, so I'm going to uncover every available man in Sydney to find out. Five dates per week is my new goal, with a minimum requirement of three.

Dates 110–115

> Thursday: Mike Physicist at the Royal Albert Hotel (drink)
> Saturday: Bradley Army at The Rusty Rabbit (breakfast)
> Akio IT at the Turkish cake shop (afternoon tea)
> Cam Marketing at Darlo Bar (drink)
> Sunday: Luka Restaurant Owner at Bar Coluzzi (coffee)

The following weeks and months are a blur of faces, 'getting to know you' stories and awkward goodbyes. In early November, I count up the lines on my Google spreadsheet: 137. I have dated 137 different men. Is that a record?

51. THE HAMMER

'We've got ten minutes.' Adam and I are huddled at a small metal coffee table outside Ground Control Café at Circular Quay. The table legs wobble on the uneven footpath and our laptops slide together on the surface.

'We can't do this, Rebekah. I know you love these guys, but ten per cent is just way too much. They'd have more of the company than each of us. We've put our lives into this.'

Cameron didn't send his proposal the day that we were in the newspaper, or the week after or the week after that. We'd continued to meet every few days, the four of us in Cameron's office on the twenty-ninth floor. We planned the digital marketing strategy, who to hire, how much to spend, how much to raise. 'We need to finalise our deal with you guys,' I'd said after Cameron made a particularly brilliant suggestion to add a catering order function for corporate offices.

Gary swatted his hand like it didn't matter. 'We trust you. We'll work something out.'

Then yesterday, six months after Adam first whispered 'three per cent', the email dropped. The figure '10%' followed by '(ten per cent)' to make it clear the numbers weren't an error.

Adam leans in and accidentally tips the table, spilling the top of his piccolo. He wipes the coffee with a serviette. 'This is going to be a really hard meeting for you. I can tell them, if you want. You don't have to say a thing.'

'No.' I'm looking straight ahead, down the street towards Cameron's building. 'It's my relationship. I'll lead it.' I use my feet to kick off the pumps I'm wearing so I'm barefoot under the table. I tug on black Armani heels with a pointed front and stand, checking the back of my charcoal pencil skirt for sweat. In the middle of my cream shirt there's a diamond of dark and my bra feels damp. 'Let's go.'

Up on the twenty-ninth floor, we're shown along a carpeted corridor to a large conference room. I haven't been in this room before. The impressive board table is set for thirty or more. There's silver trays at one end with fruit and pastries that must have been left by a previous meeting.

I hover at the window while Adam takes a seat, leaning back, hands behind his head. 'We've got this — you and me. We don't need to give ten per cent to advisors, no matter how good they are.'

Down below, an enormous cruise ship makes its way into the clear blue harbour. I imagine myself next to the swimming pool, ordering cocktails. *Why do I put myself through this?*

Cameron and Gary burst through the double doors together. 'We weren't sure how many negotiators you'd bring,' Gary quips, tapping the table.

'We ran a workshop here this morning,' says Cameron, 'for Qantas.'

It registers for a second that I'm about to negotiate with two of the most sought-after business advisors in Sydney, probably Australia. And Cameron doesn't seem the type to drop his price. *How can I say no after all he's done?* I search my head for the words.

'Ten per cent is too much. You're not worth it.'

'Ten per cent is too much. You'd have more than me, more than Adam. It's not fair.'

'Ten per cent is too much.'

The cruise ship is approaching the docks. The railing is lined with tiny faces smiling and waving. *I wish I had a normal job, like those people. Why did I have to start a business?*

Cameron reaches to shake my hand. 'Hello Rebekah.' There's a strange formality to the way he's moving today that's unsettling. Adam stands for a handshake too, and pats his other hand on Cameron's back. 'How's it going, mate?' Cameron nods, looking nonplussed in his neat pink shirt buttoned to the top. He turns to me.

We shuffle into seats at the end of the table: Gary and Cameron on one side, Adam and I opposite. Out the window, the cruise ship has docked and a giant drawbridge is being lowered. I imagine the thrill inside each passenger as they disembark into the perfect — *Rebekah. Think!* I mentally slap myself. *How are you going to frame this conversation?*

The room is silent and still. They're waiting for me. Cameron has one eyebrow raised like he's curious how I'll perform. *'Three years of coaching. How's she going to handle this?'*

I place two hands on the thick white table and smile empathetically. 'Cameron, Gary. Before we start, I want to make sure you know how much I value and appreciate everything you've done for me and the business. There's no way we'd have achieved anything near the success we've had without your support.' Cameron cocks his head and pinches the skin on the bottom of his chin, still waiting. 'But the proposal you've . . .' Remember Cameron's coaching: never use 'but', always 'and'.

I breathe deeply and raise my head to deliver the blow. 'And the proposal you've sent us, while we recognise how important you are, there's just no way we'd be able to sell it to the other shareholders. The business is growing fast. All of the early investors who took a risk, we'd be diluting them by ten per cent just as it's all starting to work.'

Cameron is still. His eyebrows twist in a way that could indicate that he's intrigued, surprised or pissed off — I can't tell.

Can someone talk, please? I look to Adam. Gary looks to Cameron. Cameron's eyes fix on mine.

'You guys have been amazing, honestly,' says Adam.

Cameron bangs the table with his palms. 'Okay.' He pauses. 'I'm disappointed. I thought we were part of the team. I thought you valued us.'

'We do,' I interject. 'Honestly, you're vital to this.'

'Not vital,' says Gary. 'If we were vital, you'd pay us.'

In my mind I send runners to retrieve every piece of business knowledge I know. I scan through books, conversations with Cameron, courses I've taken online: 'Your body language may shape who you are', 'How to manage difficult conversations'. I square my shoulders. Cameron has placed his elbows on the table, hands clasped together over his mouth.

'We're all here,' I continue, 'because we're committed to working together. We want to find a solution.'

'But you're not really committed.' Cameron's eyes harden.

I catch myself. *Be calm, sit straight.* 'Of course we are. The company is worth twenty million now. What you're asking for is two million in stock. It's too much.'

'If it was just up to us—' Adam chimes in but Cameron signals with one hand for him to stop.

'We've put in so many hours already,' says Gary. 'You know what we charge per day?'

'Like I said, we value you both. We want you involved. We've just got to come up with an arrangement we can sell to the other shareholders.'

'I don't have any more time for this.' Gary lifts his bag from the floor and pushes out his chair to stand. 'Cameron?'

I remember the example in the 'How to manage difficult conversations' course but Cameron and Gary aren't responding like the woman in the video. I must be missing something. *What would he tell me to say?*

'You can sell it,' Cameron says, 'to the other shareholders. You can sell anything. I've seen you.'

I hold his gaze. I want to look strong, like he taught me. *He knows I can't cave to such an outrageous request.* But I can't blow this relationship either. Without Cameron, I'm lost. His eyes redden as he continues to stare at me.

'You know why people think the company's worth twenty mill?' says Gary. 'It's because Cameron backed you at the start. He got you in front of Launchpad Angels, introduced you to the guys in the States. And now this?' He shakes his head in disgust. 'Come on, mate.' He pats Cameron's shoulder.

'Guys,' I plead. *What the hell is going on?* I scan again for something, anything to say. My heart thumps fast and rough like a faulty clock. 'We want you in the business. We can't do this without you.'

'Yes, you do need us.' Cameron doesn't wipe the wet from his cheeks. He leans in so I can see the hurt on his face. 'There'll be a time, I tell you now. You'll need us and we won't be here.'

Five minutes later Adam and I are in the lift. My chest is

dropping faster than the twenty-nine floors and I clutch the rail wondering if I'll ever see the inside of this lift again. Ever be welcomed to the office, served tea and biscuits on the leather couch. Sweat pours from between my breasts and my shirt clings to my skin.

'What just happened?' I ask.

'I dunno. That was fucking weird.'

'Did I say something wrong?'

'You were totally reasonable.' The lift door dings open and Adam scuffs his foot as he exits. 'I think it's personal. I don't know. I don't get it.' He gives a tight smile as if to say he's sorry. 'Come on, let's get a drink.'

I'm upstairs at the Zeta Bar on George Street sipping vodka lemonade. Adam left half an hour ago but I'm not ready to move. The bar is backdropped by red velvet curtains and tall glass bottles. I watch the shapes of bodies moving about like I'm watching a film. Inside the screen, but not really here.

There's a couple perched together on a high table. They position themselves in cute awkwardness, obviously a first date. She's got a straight bob and giggles as she licks the salt from the edge of her margarita glass. He raises dark eyebrows and smiles flirtatiously. *They'll end up together, I can tell.*

At another table, a group of twenty-something women cluster around a bottle of champagne. A waiter in a black T-shirt and tight pants carries a tray. Everyone looks perfectly cast for the film. Not me: single, nearing forty, possibly the only person in history to date 137 different men and still not find a partner.

I sense something like a black empty bubble in my head. It grows to fill my skull before spreading to push nothingness right throughout my body. I've lost Cameron. I have no partner, few friends. I'm just a loser fluttering about in the backgrounds of other people's lives. I'm a shell. Nothing.

'Can I get you another?' The waiter has noticed me. I pat the sides of my chest, my back. *Am I here?* I feel dizzy. 'Are you waiting for someone?' I look up, wave my hand and turn to leave.

At the bottom of the elevator I stuff my heels into my handbag and pull on the pumps to walk home. The streets bustle with Friday evening merriment as I pace towards the Coca Cola sign at the top of the hill. People line up for underground bars and taxis crawl bumper to bumper, lighting the path in a yellow glow.

What happened in that meeting? Why did Cameron act so strange, after everything we've been through? Surely I can fix this.

I tap at my phone. Contacts, Cameron. I hit the green button.

'Hang on, hang on,' he answers. There's loud music in the background, voices and squeals like he's out somewhere in the city. The noise quietens. 'Sorry about that.'

'Can you talk. I really need to talk.' I'm quite certain at this moment that I should *not* be calling him. I should sleep and process everything that's happened. I should plan a calm and rational approach for next week. *But the emptiness is unbearable. I need to fix this. Make sure he's still there.*

'Sure, I can talk.'

I plop my bag on a bench under a bus shelter, curl into the corner of the seat and pull my knees up into a ball. There's no management course, no book with the template of what to say.

Heart: *Just apologise, do whatever it takes to win him back.*

Head: *But you didn't do anything wrong. You were straight, empathetic.*

Heart: *You need him.*

Head: *But ten per cent is too much. It's not right.*

'I don't know what happened today, but I'm really, really sorry that I offended you.'

Quiet.

'I can't lose you. We have something, don't you think?'

Quiet.

'I think, in life, sometimes we get sent people. Special connections.' I feel my lip tremble and I can't hold steady; it's making my voice all shaky. 'I love you. I really do. In a soul kind of way.' My jaw jolts, tears stream down my face.

An exhale on the other end of the phone. 'That's very nice of you to say. It really is.' Quiet again. I feel my emotion drain a little, a small cluster of brain cells fire back into action. 'Where do we go from here? We want you in the business. Maybe we make it a smaller time commitment? Just one meeting once a month instead of every week?'

Another long pause. 'Listen. What you're trying to do with Hey You; you'll need us every week or you won't get there. Whatever equity you give us, it won't be worth anything.'

The cluster of cells in my brain are standing now, dialling in support. They're marching, angry. We *can* do this. We want them involved; it'll definitely help. But we don't need them. Not enough to pay ten per cent.

'I can't come up with an answer now. We need to sit down, talk it through.'

I imagine him holding up his hand to stop me like he did earlier to Adam. 'It's clear that we have a cost. You aren't willing to pay that cost. End of story.'

It's not the end of *our* story. *What's he doing?*

'It's done.'

The emotion is back, tumbling cartwheels through my thoughts. *Save the relationship. You need the relationship.* 'The main thing I wanted to say is that I'm sorry about how I handled the meeting. I didn't want you to think I was a weak negotiator, after all that coaching.'

A party bus packed with women wearing sashes and hats screams past me, up the hill to Kings Cross.

'You were a hammer.'

'A what?'

'A hammer. It's the most ineffective of all leadership styles and you are particularly bad at using it.'

I let go of my legs and sit upright on the bench. *He's giving me advice. My old mentor is back.*

'Some people are natural hammers,' he continues. 'You have other, much better leadership styles to draw on.'

'Like what?'

'Like inspiration, like vulnerability. It's much harder to lead with inspiration and very few people can do it as well as you. Don't use a hammer.'

What he's saying does make sense. But did I use a hammer today? *'We're here to find a solution, we're committed to working together.'* I'm confused. I need Cameron. I trust that he's always right, but now I'm starting to wonder.

'Yeah, you're right,' I say. 'I hadn't thought of it like that before.'

The noise behind him builds like he's walking back in to the bar. 'Just be yourself. You'll get much further in life.'

This time I'm the one to pause. The emotion I feel right now
— hurt, love, vulnerability — it's so enticing. I love Cameron.

'That's good advice,' I say. 'Thank you. Is it still okay if we
catch up from time to time?'

He lets out a long, low sigh like the last fizz from a popped
can. 'It's not a good idea. We need to close this chapter, for lots
of reasons. You know what I mean.'

'But we're still friends. I mean, connections like ours.
They're so rare. You can't just—' The wave of emotion crashes
over my head. I can't think, breathe. I don't understand.

Five minutes later my phone buzzes. It's an email from
Cameron.

> Subject: Rebekah
> Email: She just called sobbing. Begged for forgiveness.
> Let's see what they come back with tomorrow.

He must have meant to send it to Gary.

52. A THOUSAND FLOWERS

It's 1.12 a.m. I wake on the couch, *West Wing* theme music still playing in the background, cushion soaked in tears. And it all comes charging back: the meeting, the phone call, the email. *What the fuck was that email?*

I mute the TV to think. I picture Cameron's face staring at me across the table today, his red eyes, his leaning in so I could see his hurt. *Was he really upset? Is he trying to manipulate me?* I wonder if he acted all upset so I'd give them ten per cent. But why? It's not like he needs the money.

And his words on the phone: 'Just be yourself.' *But who am I?*

I climb onto my knees and curl in a foetal position on the floorboards. My head throbs and in my ears there's a high-pitched ringing like crickets. *I am completely lost. I'm lost and empty. No one loves me.* I am nothing. This pain, this excruciating ache, is crippling. I need help.

Is this when you're supposed to call Lifeline or one of those services for people in distress? Is this the kind of situation they're there for? I imagine Steve next to me, ready to listen, but I also sense him fading. The shape of his face, his clothes. *Is that him?* Or am I making bits up as the passage of time blurs my memory?

Who can I call?

Mum and Dad? *They'd panic.*

Friends or Ruth? *Too late at night.*

Billy in New York. Yes. It'll be morning there. I dial his number. Two rings.

'Hey girl.'

'Hey Billy, can you talk? I really need to talk.'

'Of course. I just left for work, but I'll put you on in the car. There's no one else here.' The phone crackles for a second. 'What's up?'

'I had an awful falling-out with someone. A business mentor, he was really special.' I pause. 'I'm sorry, it's the middle of the night here and I'm on the floor. I didn't know what to do.'

'Okay, slow down. Who is this guy?'

'He's someone who helped me set up the business. He's been there right from the start, but it's more than that.'

A car horn blasts in the background. 'Sorry, I just have to get out of this traffic.' I picture his silver Tesla cruising onto the highway from Connecticut to Manhattan, his thick black hair bouncing on his shoulders as he checks his blind spot to change lanes. 'Okay, you've got me for the next hour. What happened?'

I explain yesterday's events, but as I hear the words fall out of my mouth I feel embarrassed, like my problem isn't serious enough for me to be this upset. 'The meeting just didn't go well. I don't know what I did wrong. He said I was a hammer.'

'A what?'

'A hammer. You know. Too direct. Forceful.'

Billy is quiet for a moment like he's thinking. 'That doesn't sound like you.'

I replay the meeting again in my head. It *wasn't* me. 'He was really upset. He cried. Now he doesn't want to know me at all.'

'Is this a boyfriend? Are you in love with him?'

'Yes, I'm in love but not like that. It's not a physical thing. It's like a soul thing. I can't explain it.'

'I get it. Like you and me.'

'Yes, exactly. But different, because he's not you. No one's like you.' I laugh. 'Do you think I could get him back? I mean, I can't lose him.' *I definitely sound pathetic now.*

'Look, sometimes special people come into your life, and sometimes they go.' He pauses. 'In my experience, if you really break something like that, then it's near impossible to get it back. Even if you can be friends again, it'll never be the same.'

I pull myself off the floor and begin pacing back and forth across my tiny living room. I know he's right.

'I'm sorry, sweetheart. This is going to hurt, but try to learn from it. Everyone in our orbit is here to teach us something and often not in the way we expect. Think about it.' I remember that Billy isn't just a great friend. He also runs a global business. I take three deep breaths.

'Now what else is going on, girl? What's happening with the men?'

I plop onto the couch and let out a snort. 'Nothing to report, I'm afraid.'

'What happened with that guy, what was his name again?'

'Charlie.' I'd called Billy when Dad was in hospital. 'I broke it off. It didn't seem like . . . ' I wish I had an explanation that made sense.

'Yeah, well, good that you didn't settle.'

'Really? I've dated a hundred and thirty-seven men now, Billy. Maybe I'm the one with the problem.'

'Whoa, a hundred and thirty-seven!' He laughs. I imagine him behind the steering wheel tipping his head back against the seat. 'There's nothing wrong with you. You're a gangster like me. That's why we do crazy things like start businesses. We keep going till we win.' He stops and for a moment I wonder if the phone connection is lost.

'Now Rebekah, listen to me. There is an amazing guy out there waiting for you to find him. The universe is conspiring.'

Somehow the topic seems lighter. Maybe I've accepted that my chances of finding love are so small that I've given up caring.

'Billy, I've been dating non-stop for three years. Something has to be wrong with me. I'm going to take a break.'

He cuts in. 'There is nothing wrong with you. You are perfect. I'm telling you, I can see this guy. And you're going to make him so happy, and —' he hesitates '— and you're going to make a family. I know it.'

I remember Billy's rambling house in the woods, his beautiful wife and their three children tearing across the furniture like a litter of pups. I crouch on the floor. 'Can I ask you something?' I don't wait for a response. 'Do you still think your first wife is with you? Even though she's dead, do you still love her? Do you still talk to her?'

I hear Billy take a huge breath and let the air out slowly. 'I think her presence is everywhere. But no. I don't think she's with me, not in an earthly way. Not in the way you mean.' He pauses. 'I loved her with everything when we were together and nothing will ever change what we had, but my life is with Gena now. She has my heart, a hundred per cent.' Inside me, a tornado of panic rushes into the empty space.

'So you don't think people stay with us after they die?'

'I don't know. Sometimes, maybe. But I don't think it helps to keep people around for longer than they need to be. I don't think they'd want us holding ourselves back. They'd want us to live.'

The tornado is a full-blown storm. 'I still talk to Steve every day. He's still with me.' Billy's smiley New York voice is shaky now. 'Oh, baby. He's gone. I'm sorry. You have to believe it.'

A howling smash. Every cell is battered. I flatten myself on the floorboards. 'I know.'

I wake just after 6. The bathroom is white. Above the clothes drier, tiny flecks of dust dance in the sunlight against the frosted window.

'Steve, are you still here?' I say to the flecks of dust. *Why would he be here, hanging about my clothes drier?*

Because you asked. You invited him.

'Are you still with me, Steve?'

There's no response. Just a beautiful stillness in the air. I see Steve driving down that long, flat New Zealand road, approaching the corner. *If only there hadn't been gravel on that exact spot. If only a car wasn't coming in the opposite direction at exactly the wrong time.* I picture the car spinning. *Did you end at that moment?*

I cover my mouth and nose with my hands, stretch my skin beneath my fingers and listen for the two sides of my brain to speak. But there's only one voice. *You are never going to know the answer.* Inside me is quiet.

'I'm letting you go now,' I whisper. My heart tugs and I want to hold on. 'Thanks for everything.'

Two hours later my running shoes pound up the steps and across the sun-bleached stone footpath between Tamarama and Bondi Beach. I've already done six kilometres and sweat pours from my skin like a tap.

I stop outside Icebergs Pool and lean against a pole to recover. The water is bright blue, the sky unusually high, and I'm in awe of how much space there is up there. I cross the grass towards the promenade, passing a couple pushing a pram, a man with a baby strapped to his front, a group of teenage skateboarders, four women laid out on their yoga mats. The outlines of the trees seem sharper than normal. *Is the light different today?*

I climb down to the beach and rip off my shoes and T-shirt. I sprint like a toy that's just been wound up, as fast as I can to the ocean. I'm light, flying across the sand. And I wonder if it's more than Steve I just let go of.

My head hits the water first. It's cold and it swallows my body in a single gulp. I dive deep and spin around on the bottom, opening my eyes underwater looking up. Rays of sunlight hit the surface and bend. *Magnificent.* My feet hit the sand and I leap through the waves, catching breaths as I go. I'm a baby discovering its alive in the world for the very first time.

Back up on the promenade, I carry shoes in dripping hands. I push my nose into my shoulder and my skin is wet and salty. It feels warm and soft against my cheek.

'I love you,' I whisper.

Hang on, wait. Who was I thinking about when I just said that? Cameron? Steve? A smile creeps across my face and my chest fills with a thousand flowers. *Oh.*

53. FRIDAY, 21 NOVEMBER 2014

1 p.m.

I peek out from behind a black curtain at ANZ Stadium at the faces of five thousand school-uniformed teenagers. Two screens frame the stage: National Careers Day 2014. I snap a photo of the crowd with my phone. A woman holding a notebook turns to check that I'm ready. 'It's my pleasure to welcome Rebekah Campbell, co-founder and co-CEO of Hey You, Australia's fastest-growing mobile app for cafés and restaurants. Rebekah started her entrepreneurial journey at age nine, collecting lost golf balls and selling them back to a shop. In her twenties she built a music management company which launched the careers of Evermore, Matt Corby . . . '

I pull back my shoulders, brush down my golden silk singlet and black leather skirt, adjust the clip on the microphone so it won't rub against my long necklace. I step up the stairs in sharp-heeled shoes and stride across the stage feeling the heat of three ginormous lights overhead. The faces in the crowd move, cheer and clap. I smile.

'Hello everyone, it's great to be here.' I stand behind the podium and a series of images appear on the screens: me at age nine carrying a sack of golf balls, at age twenty running a charity concert for youth suicide, at age twenty-five at the ARIA Music Awards with Evermore, and one from a few months ago, on the front page of the *Australian Business Review*. I share a story from each phase — how I failed, what I learnt.

Afterwards, a scattering of hands shoot up. I point to a girl in a pinstripe uniform. She's maybe fifteen, with long brown hair hanging loosely across her face. 'Yes, up on the balcony. What's your question?' A stagehand darts out of the shadow to hand her a microphone.

The girl stands. 'Do you think—' she stops, clasping at her arm like she wished she hadn't put it up. 'To be an entrepreneur, do you think it's harder for a girl?'

3 p.m.
I march across the office, hand outstretched.

'Brad Thompson,' says a tall man in a navy-blue suit and tie.

'Rebekah Campbell.' I feel clear and firm in myself, and look him straight in the eye.

We'd received a few emails from venture capital firms that day Adam and I were in the paper. One enquiry was from Jim, in the investment division of Westpac Bank.

> I just read about the merger of your companies. I'm a big fan of Posse and we use Beat the Q every day at our coffee shop downstairs. Are you looking for investment? Would be good to chat.

We'd met Jim the following week in a boardroom on the executive floor of Westpac's headquarters on Kent Street. Jim was short with grey hair and a lot more enthusiasm than I expected. 'Imagine if we put Hey You in our banking app,' he'd said. 'It would be great for our customers, a huge opportunity for you guys.'

Since then we'd traded daily emails with his team of business analysts. How many cafés do you have signed up? What do they pay? What's the market size? How secure is your technology? Then finally: 'The last step is for you to meet Brad. He's the boss.'

And now, here in our office is Brad Thompson with Jim eagerly tagging behind. Brad has cropped black hair, broad shoulders and walks with the certainty of someone who knows he's a ten in every category. In today's meeting he will decide the future of our company. Adam and I have worked all week on the presentation.

I show Brad and Jim through to our glass meeting room. My heels clack on the concrete floor. I glance down at the straight line of my leather skirt, the way that my necklace falls across the skin on my chest. There's power in the points of my shoes, elegance in the curve of my waist. I switch on the screen, connect my laptop and begin.

Afterwards, Adam and I shoot a '*We did it*' glance across the table. Jim rocks on his chair like he can't sit still. Brad is nodding. 'This is really good. I can imagine our customers benefitting from what you've got here.' He looks to Jim and smiles. 'Let's do it.'

We exchange well wishes for the weekend and Jim promises to send the paperwork through on Monday. My first instinct is to dial the person I always call when there's good news to share. '*You won't believe it!*' I imagine Cameron sound his trademark 'Boom!' down the line.

But we haven't spoken since that night two weeks ago. Every

time I've called, he's sent me to voicemail after one or two rings. I've replayed the meeting so many times in my head. *Was I a hammer? And what about that email?* Sometimes I feel like I could fold over and cry.

Tonight, however, I don't want to fold or cry. Tonight, I am wearing pointed heels and a leather skirt, and the company I started is about to become a household name. Tonight, I want to celebrate.

'We should get a drink,' says Adam, grinning.

I check my watch. 'I can't. I've got a date.'

54. SOUNDS A BIT LIKE 'PLOD'

I arranged to meet Rod at six because I knew I'd be exhausted from my talk earlier and the high-pressure meeting with Brad. We won't be staying for dinner. Just a quick drink at the bar and I'll be home in bed by 8.

I'd jumped back onto Tinder last Sunday after giving myself a week to recover from the breakup with Cameron. I am approaching another summer alone, which is fine. Next year, I'll turn thirty-eight. It's now far too late to get married and still make a family. But somehow, I'm no longer bothered. I am okay, with or without a relationship. Actually, I'm more than okay.

After a few minutes of left and right swiping, I'd connected with two men — Rod and Francis — and set up calls with both of them. Francis is in advertising. We were supposed to meet last night but he texted me twenty minutes beforehand saying he had to work late, so we rescheduled to Saturday. Rod is an academic in something, but I can't remember what. I've given up taking notes.

I arrive at The Winery early, at 5.55 p.m. I should go to the bathroom, check my makeup and apply a coat of lipstick, but it seems like such an effort to climb up all those stairs. Besides, this date is going to be quick.

Inside is a throng of men and women clinking glasses and shouting over 'Uptown Funk' by Bruno Mars. There's a bicycle hanging from the ceiling and four giant moose heads staring down from the rafters. *Now, who is this date again? Rod, that's right. I don't really like the name 'Rod', it sounds a bit like 'Plod'. Why did I swipe Rod?* I pull out my phone to check his Tinder profile and I scan the bar for bald heads like the one in his picture.

I spot what looks like the top of a prickly bowling ball at the bar. He's holding a jug of beer, stumbling forward over an enormous belly. I let out a sigh. *Oh well.*

My mobile rings. 'Hi, it's Rod. I'm outside.'

'Oh, hi, hang on.' The guy with the belly isn't on the phone. 'I'll meet you out front.'

I head back out down the path of hanging plants to a trellised archway of purple flowers. There's a man underneath holding his phone. He looks up and his eyebrows arch in recognition. *That's why I swiped.* Those eyes, clear blue and crinkled at the edges.

For a fraction of a second everything around me seems suspended. From way out there in the universe, the light from a star that's been burning since the beginning of time strikes earth for the very first time. It's so bright. Waiters freeze like statues, diners hold forks and glasses halfway up to their mouths, and the music whirs to a silence.

'I'm Rod.' He holds open his arms for a hug.

'Hi.'

He feels warm and familiar as I wrap my arms around his back. The commotion of The Winery resumes, and he smiles at me as he approaches the counter. 'I've got a dinner reservation.' The maître d' leads us to a table half on the balcony, half inside. 'This is perfect, thanks.' He pulls out a seat for me.

Rod has a shaved head, neat stubble and wears a maroon button-up shirt. I picture him ironing it in preparation for our date and feel my heart squish to soft dough inside my chest.

Our eyes meet across the table and I notice I'm biting my lip.

'So Rebekah, tell me about your day.'

'Ah, I had a huge day actually.' *And I'm quite sure it's just getting started.* 'I gave a talk to five thousand Year 10 students at ANZ Stadium. It was a career's day thing. I had to tell them about my job, what lessons I've learnt, you know.' I pull out my phone and show the photo I'd taken from behind the curtain. I tell him about the student who asked if being an entrepreneur was harder for a girl. 'I mean, where would a fifteen-year-old get a crazy idea like that? Of course, I told her it's a massive advantage.'

Rod chuckles. 'Of course.'

A waitress appears. 'Are you ready to order?'

Rod and I look to each other. 'Sorry, we haven't looked at the menu yet,' he says. 'But we'll get drinks.'

'I'll have a glass of rosé, please. The house one is fine.'

'Me too. Just give us a couple more minutes for dinner,' says Rod.

The waitress smiles and taps her iPad.

I continue describing my day. I tell Rod about the meeting with Brad from Westpac. 'He said they want to invest. Can you believe it? A few years ago, it was just me and a crazy idea. Now we've built this whole business and thousands of people use it every day.'

'What's the name of the app again?' Rod asks, pulling out his phone.

'Hey You. You use it to find cafés, order and pay instead of lining up.'

'I've seen this,' he says. 'You've got the orange logo, right? My coffee shop at the uni has it.' He searches the map for Macquarie University. 'Here it is,' he says. 'This is awesome. I'll use it.'

A notification pops up on my iPhone: 'Less than 10% battery remaining.' 'Would you mind if I put my laptop on the table to charge my phone?' I pause, and there's a faint left–right brain struggle still carrying on, as if I'd be bothered to listen.

Right: *Are you crazy? He'll think you're work-obsessed.*

Left: *But I need my phone. I need to be contactable in case something happens with the app.*

Right: *You need to downplay your work. Not stick it on the table!*

And I smile as I dig into my handbag, the two voices drifting away to nothingness.

'Let me help you.' Rod moves our water jug so there's space on the table. I open my laptop to plug in the USB charger just as the waitress appears with two glasses of wine on a tray. She stops short of our table, noticing the lack of space. 'Um.'

'Oh, sorry. I'll take them,' I say, placing our glasses on the chair between us. 'Thanks.'

'Ready to order?'

'We still haven't had a chance. But let's do it,' says Rod, opening the menu.

'You choose,' I prompt. 'I'm a vege plus fish. Get meat for yourself if you want, but I won't eat it.'

'Sure.' He scans the page. 'Okay. The calamari starter, the salmon, the gnocchi and something green. Broccolini.' He folds the menus.

Rod points to the Hillary 2016 sticker on my laptop. 'I didn't know she was running?'

'She hasn't announced yet,' I say. 'I just found someone selling these stickers online. I think they're fundraising in the hope she'll run.'

'That's really cool,' he says. 'What is it about her that you like?'

'I love that she's such a fighter, that she never gives up.' I feel my eyes burn with passion. 'She's had so much thrown at her, people trying to bring her down. She just keeps getting up, fighting for what she believes in — universal healthcare, children's rights, women's rights. And can you imagine how incredible it'll be for a little girl to see the most powerful person in the world on television, and for that person to be a woman? We might stop getting questions like the one I got today.'

Rod sits back in his seat, eyes beaming like I'm the one who just made history.

'I'm sorry, I've been talking too much,' I say, realising I'm breaking every rule in my notebook. 'Tell me what you've been up to. What is it that you lecture in again?'

'Education,' he says. 'I teach teachers.'

'Oh, wow. Why did you decide to become a teacher of teachers?'

'That is a long story.' He pauses while the waitress delivers our food. 'I struggled at school. I wasn't good at maths or anything, so I was pretty naughty. The teachers, they just wrote me off. Then in Year Ten, this one geography teacher took an interest in me, she told me I had talent. I started working hard. I got great marks. I wanted to give other kids what she gave me. Self-belief, I guess. So when I finished school, I trained to become a teacher.'

'What did you teach?'

'Geography, of course.' He laughs. 'I taught geography for ten years. Then I worked out I could impact even more kids by training teachers. I did a PhD and became a lecturer.'

I scan the heads at tables across the balcony. There are heads with black hair and heads with blonde hair, there are heads with scarves and glasses and hooped earrings. But the head opposite me feels different to all the others. This stubbly face with bright blue eyes and wrinkles in the pattern of a smile. It's like it was made exactly for me, a match.

'So, Rod,' I say reaching forward to squeeze lemon on our plate of sizzling calamari. 'Tell me, what is it that makes a great teacher?' I hook a piece of the sizzling crumbed squid on my fork.

'Easy,' he replies. 'It's about personal relationship and expectations. For a teacher to impact a student, the kid has to feel like you're interested in them personally, that you care. Then you have to tell them you can see their talent and that you're going to help bring it out.'

'What about the teacher's knowledge of their subject?' I ask. 'Or how they present it?'

'Yes, that all matters, of course. That's most of what we teach them at uni.' He stops to take a sip from his glass. 'Think about it though. You must have done well at school. Who were your best teachers?'

I cock my head to one side; and feel the flowers in my chest again as I remember two names. 'Mr Harries taught me in Year 6 at primary and Ms Godfrey, my Year 11 English teacher.'

'And what did they teach you? Do you remember any of the subject matter?'

I scan my brain. *I must have learnt something in English.* 'Ahh, no, I can't remember.'

'So why were they great teachers?'

The flowers are in full bloom now. 'I remember the way they made me feel, like I was special.'

'Exactly,' he says. 'And to give that experience to every kid in a class of thirty; that's what makes a teacher great.'

The waitress appears again. 'Another of the same?' Rod points to our near-empty wine glasses.

'Sure, thanks.'

I sit back and watch Rod for a moment. *It took a really long time to find you.*

'Tell me about your family,' I say. 'Any brothers and sisters?'

'I've got an older brother in Sydney and a younger sister in Newcastle. They've got two kids each. We spend a lot of time together.'

'Your mum and dad? What are they like?'

'They're still in Lane Cove, the same house I grew up in. Mum and I are very similar.'

'In what way?'

'We're both sensitive. My bro says we wear our hearts on our sleeves.' He chuckles. 'Dad and the others are different. They're really practical. Dad built our family house himself, by hand. He did all the wiring, the plumbing. That kind of thing.'

'Are you close?'

'We are now, but it took a long time. He's so conservative, really tight with money. When I left school he wanted me to live at home, save for a deposit on a house. I wanted to move to Newtown, play guitar.'

Rod rests his hands on the table. I notice the creases on his knuckles, the dark brown hairs on the top of his fingers. I feel like I've known these hands forever, like they've travelled the world, touched all these different things, but they were always mine. Our eyes catch. *Is he feeling what I'm feeling?*

'What happened, with your dad?' I'm taking a risk now, but it feels right to go deeper.

'We fought. We fought for years and Mum acted like a

bridge. But over time, things changed — we both changed. He chilled and started to accept me. And I realised that I'm a lot more like him than I thought. Lots of his qualities are pretty useful, actually.'

'Like what?' That hand looks so lonely on the table, trembling a little. I want to reach out and hold it.

'Like being organised, like not wasting things, not spending more than you need to.' His mouth tightens with pride. 'He's super fit too. Rides a hundred K through the national park every weekend. He'll be off with his mates at eight tomorrow.'

I decide to absorb this moment so I can write it down later. How do I feel right now with Rod? Why is this different to the other 137 dates? Is it him? Is it me? We both sip from our glasses, gaze locked, I don't count the seconds.

'What about your family?' asks Rod.

'I'm the only child. Mum and Dad live in New Zealand. Mum is kind of . . .' I remember a photo she texted me last week. She was onstage in a black university cap being handed a giant scroll, her pale skin flushed pink with excitement. 'She just finished her Master's, graduated on Wednesday.'

'Wow.'

I hold the image in my mind, Mum's proud face, and I feel two little hands reach out from inside my heart and applaud. 'Yeah, it's pretty cool actually. She worked for years. I mean, she's in her sixties now and still studying.'

Rod brushes the top of my arm with his hand and I feel the hairs on my skin shimmer like sequins. 'Shall we go out somewhere else?'

'Yes,' I say. 'Let's go dancing.'

Upstairs at Sticky Bar, the three-piece band is belting out an Arrested Development cover from the corner of the room.

'Have you been here before?' shouts Rod, casting his eyes around the tiny packed club. Three women dance freestyle on a tabletop, others jump on secondhand couches, streamers fall from the roof, a man in a top hat pours champagne from a giant bottle into open mouths, and strobe lights flash like it's all a dream.

'I had my birthday here, a couple of years ago.' I remember myself hunched on that seat, checking the news on my phone while other people danced. How rigid and self-conscious I'd felt.

I twirl, lifting my hands over my head like Madonna. Rod grooves, smile stretched across his face, eyes fixed on me like I'm someone spectacular.

55. THE CHOICE

I wake on Saturday morning feeling like my whole body is resting in a warm bath. I replay last night in my mind: Rod dancing, the way he squeezed my hand when I kissed him on the cheek as the taxi dropped me home. Could it have been so perfect?

My phone buzzes.

> Rod: Hi Rebekah. Lucky I'm not a chauvinist.

What? I'm still half asleep.

> Rod: Loved your article about the guy at the job interview. What a creep!

Rod must be Googling me. He's reading my *New York Times* column. I sit up in bed and tuck my hair behind my ears. *He's awake and he's still thinking about me.*

> Me: I'm glad you like it ☺

I make my way to brunch at Bills on Liverpool Street. Madeleine is sitting wide-legged next to the window, her pink skin shining like the sun. 'Oh my, you're—'

'I'm pregnant!' I embrace her in a giant hug.

We order breakfast and I lean in, both hands flat on the table. 'I have news too.' I describe Rod, our incredible date, how I put my laptop on the table, danced with my arms in the air. 'This is it. I just know it, he's the one.'

She places her hands over mine. 'I do have to say, the way you're speaking right now, how you're holding yourself, your eyes — it's like you're lit up. I've never seen you so happy.'

'There is something I have to ask you. That night at your flat. You said there was something else, a mistake women make once they've found the guy. What is it?'

She squints. 'Yes, that's right. The mistake is to question. Women keep asking themselves, "Is he the one? Could I find someone better?"' She points at me with one finger. 'Don't do that. You have to choose him.'

'What do you mean "choose"?' I pull my hands out from under hers. 'I'm pretty sure he's the one.'

She presses my hands back to the table so there's nothing in between us. 'I'm saying there isn't one magic person out there who makes everything perfect. It's whoever you choose. If you say he's it then he's it. Simple as that. I see women spend their whole lives looking for "the one". Then they meet someone, they get excited, but after a while . . .'

'They find something wrong.'

'Exactly. Everyone has something that'll annoy you. If you look for evidence that he's a jerk, then you'll find it. If you dump him, then the next guy will have something different.'

I nod.

'Tell me three things,' she says. 'Does he make you laugh?'

I recall my conversation with Rod. 'He's not a joker, but I'm not either. He's happy, I felt happy with him.'

'Okay, so he's positive.'

'Yes, definitely. His face, it just *looks* like a smile. It *is* a smile. The whole thing,' I say, noticing my own smile as I remember his.

'Great,' she says. 'And does he make you feel bigger than you know yourself to be, or smaller?'

I replay how impressed he was when I showed him that photo of the crowd, how he downloaded my app, 'loved' my *New York Times* article. 'Bigger. Much bigger.'

'And finally, are your core values aligned?'

I close my eyes as Rod's story about why he became a teacher comes gushing back. 'Yes, one hundred per cent.'

'Well. He's the one. Hallelujah.'

Our breakfasts arrive. Madeleine licks her bottom lip and I grind pepper onto my eggs. 'Is that what you and Joe did, chose each other? You said after your weekend away together that you could've got married right then.'

'Yes, we had a conversation about it. We decided we were forever and we wouldn't put any energy into questioning it. We put all our energy into making it work.'

I shake my head in disbelief. 'You don't ever argue?'

'Of course he annoys me sometimes. I get frustrated, but in the moment I stop.' Her eyes sharpen. 'I never let myself think: *Are we compatible? Is this the right relationship?* No. I honour my commitment. I've chosen, remember?'

'And so . . .' I wave for her to continue.

'We focus on making each other happy. Creating the most amazing relationship in history.'

I rub my chin as I imagine a new set of challenges. I want to make that commitment to Rod. But how will I make sure it sticks?

56. A DEAL, IF YOU LIKE

It's 1 p.m. Sunday and there's been no further messages from Rod. *I thought he'd want to see me today. Why hasn't he called again?* Our date was amazing. *Wasn't it?*

I'd messaged Francis (my date for last night) after I got home from breakfast with Madeleine.

> Me: Hi Francis. Wanted to let you know that I met someone last night and it's already serious. I need to cancel our date.
> Francis: OK but do you want to meet anyway, just in case it doesn't work out? You seem really nice and it looks like we have a lot in common.
> Me: Sorry but no. I'm very sure about this person.

I sniggered for a moment that Francis, who was blasé about rescheduling our date so he could work on Thursday, seemed so much keener once he knew I was taken.

I plop onto the couch and place my phone face-up on the coffee table. I wait. I get up and make a cup of tea. I check the phone to make sure I haven't accidently left it on silent. No. I turn on the television. I check the phone again. It's now 4 p.m., thirty-one hours since Rod's last text message.

Stuff it, I'll call him.

I dial. Ring, ring, ring, ring, ring.

'Hi, this is Rod speaking. Sorry I can't take your call right now. Please leave a message.'

'Hi Rod, it's Rebekah. Just wanted to check in and see how your weekend's going. I'm going for a walk to the park if you'd like to catch up?'

Did he see my name flash up on his phone? That warm bath feeling inside is draining like someone pulled out the plug.

That evening, the pain of waiting is so fierce that I almost can't bear it. I look at my phone on the table — it could give me an answer if I only press the buttons. *Should I try again?* No. Remember what Ruth said about chasing. Sit tight.

Just then, my phone buzzes.

> Rod: Hi Rebekah, I got your message and sorry for not replying earlier. My dad passed away yesterday. I'm going to be busy with my family this week but please do stay in touch. Rod xx

What? I read the message again and again. It takes me ten minutes to construct a reply.

> Me: Oh Rod, I'm so sorry to hear that. Thinking of you and your family at this time. Please let me know if there's anything I can do. I'll reach out again in a week or so. Lots and lots of love, Rebekah xx

I pace from wall to wall in my tiny apartment. My heart lurches up, down, sideways. *What happened to Rod's dad?* Didn't he say something about cycling yesterday? *What does this mean for our relationship?* I hope he doesn't forget about me.

He won't forget. I know it.

I sit with my head in my hands to take it all in. I imagine Rod with his family right now. I try to picture his dad. He'd look like Rod, those gorgeous eyes with more wrinkles around the edges. *Did I just lose my father-in-law?*

I'm struck by a sense of grief for something that never was. I remember how Rod's hand trembled when he described their relationship. Rod's dad, *my* father-in-law. I cast my gaze up. My mind stills.

'Are you still here?' I ask out loud. 'I'm sorry we didn't get to meet.'

Am I crazy, talking to dead people like this? I don't even *know* Rod's dad. We've only been on one date. But somehow, it seems right.

'Look, I don't know if you can hear me.' I wait for a sign, a dusting of sprinkles across my shoulders, a creak in the roof perhaps. Nothing.

'I'm going to speak to you just in case you are there and you can hear me.' I pause. 'Okay?' More silence. I sit on the coffee table and cross my legs.

'You don't know me and you're probably wondering why I'm talking to you. Well, I think I love your son. And I'm pretty sure you're supposed to be my father-in-law.' I get up to pace again. *Is there something I wanted to say here?* I reach inside myself for the words.

'I don't know your name, but I want to propose something — a deal, if you like.' My head is clear. 'If Rod is who I think he is—' I stop to rephrase. 'I'm very sure that Rod is who I think he is.' I picture my sweet man from Friday night, his passion for teaching, the way he looked at me on the dancefloor. 'Please let me have him. If you let me have him then I promise to make him very happy.' My voice is strong and assured. 'He is *it*. And I'll spend every day for the rest of my life making our relationship the most amazing relationship in history. It'll be my number one priority. I promise. Every. Single. Day.'

I feel tears streaming down my cheeks and I collapse forward. *I want this so badly.* 'I promise,' I cry out again. 'Please let me have him. Please, please.'

57. WHERE THERE IS
A BEGINNING, THERE
IS ALSO AN END

Rod is smiling as he crosses Crown Street. He's thinner than he was two weeks ago, there's a dark pink line under each of his eyes. But there's still positivity at his core, radiating from the inside.

We'd spoken on the phone last weekend. 'I'm at Mum's house,' he'd said. 'There's a million people here — relatives from London, friends from school. Right now I'm in her bedroom with my back against the door.'

I heard a knock in the background. 'Hang on.' There was rustling and muffled speech. 'Sorry, that was my sister just checking I'm okay.'

There was a moment's pause while I searched for something to say. *Do I ask what happened? Will it upset him?*

'He was out cycling,' Rod began, as if he sensed my unease. 'In the national park with his friends. This seventeen-year-old kid. He was chasing another car.'

'Oh Rod.' The needlessness, the unfairness, the sudden stop. I wanted to send my heart down the wires.

Out on the street, I open my arms and we hold each other. Taxis, buses, pedestrians and bikes all whizz past, oblivious to the feelings that are passing between us. 'Come on,' he says, pushing open the door of the Chinese restaurant. 'Let's get dinner.'

We sit out in the back alley drinking lychee cocktails, talking, laughing, sharing songs from our phones and holding hands across the table. His cheeks and eyes seem cast solid in that wonderful smile.

I check my phone: 11 p.m. 'Sticky Bar?'

Four hours later Rod kisses me goodbye and my apartment door clicks shut. It wasn't our first kiss. That was on the dancefloor surrounded by partygoers on tabletops, girls in bright lipsticks and feather hats, open mouths downing shots of tequila and our favourite band in the corner. Rod spun me around and pulled me into his chest. I wrapped my wrists behind his neck.

We kissed more in my apartment: on the couch, against the dining table. Until I said, 'I think we should slow down. Not mess this up, you know?'

He'd replied with an agreeing but disappointed mumble.

And now he is on his way home. And everything is different. I glance around my empty apartment. I'd booked an Airtasker to clean it this afternoon. The floor is unusually tidy and smells like flowery products. The cushions on the couch are piled on the coffee table so they wouldn't get in the way of our fumbling.

Inside, that warm bath feeling is back. My heart isn't lurching; it's calm and secure. It knows I've found my man. The rest of my life from here on in will be different. And as I drift, grinning, towards my bedroom, as I lie back on my pillow knowing this, I have an unexpected realisation. Where there is a beginning, there is also an end. I will miss my old life.

I won't miss Tinder or filling my weekend with useless chores to avoid the onset of loneliness. I won't miss lying alone in bed listening for a rapist at the window or ticking 'single' on the health insurance form or being squeezed onto the end of the table at dinner parties. I won't miss visiting the fertility specialist alone or holidaying alone or ducking out of the movie cinema early in case anyone sees me — alone.

But I *will* miss my identity as a single professional woman in Sydney. I will miss being the kind of woman Brad Thompson could date. I will miss the possibility of Cameron in New York, the coy smiles in meetings, the mild flirtations across the table. All that stops now. I have a new identity. I'm someone's partner.

I remember Ruth said once that the Latin 'cide' in 'decide' is the same as in 'homocide'. It means to kill off. 'Every time you make a decision,' she'd said. 'You kill off the other options. That's just the way it works.' Am I ready? Is this what I really want? Like Madeleine said, I have to choose.

58. A CONFESSION

I lift my head from the tartan picnic blanket I'm lying on. I peer down my chest, across at the miles of golden Byron Bay sand and out to the bright blue ocean rippling in perfect lines of froth. Sunlight pours through bunches of long leaves in the pine tree overhead.

It strikes me as strange, the crispness I'd noticed that morning on Bondi Beach hasn't passed. I'd assumed there was something different in the light that day, or perhaps before then there'd been an unusually high level of dust in the air. And that morning a strong gust of wind must have cleared it. But surprisingly, the dust cloud hasn't returned. As I lie at the end of the beach, everything is sharp in focus: the cliff face is more jagged than I remember, the colour of the sky more vivid, the edges of the leaves more detailed, the hills more beautiful, the faces of children playing on the sand more joyful. And I'm beginning to wonder if what's changed isn't in the dust or the light. I'm beginning to wonder if what's cleared is the inside of my head.

Most stunning of all is the man emerging from the water in boardshorts. He's just swum along the beach and back, bobbing way out behind the surfers and the breaking waves. I'd checked once every minute for sharks. 'I'm not losing you,' I'd said. 'Not after . . . never mind.'

Rod picks up a towel and I silently admire his broad chest, covered in dark hairs and water droplets. It's been six weeks since I'd first spotted him under the purple flowered arch at The Winery. Six weeks of dates: dinner dates, coffee dates, early morning swim dates. Today is our first holiday date, and tonight will be our first overnight together.

I spread out the blanket for Rod and hand him a bottle of cider.

'That was awesome,' he says, twisting the top. 'There's dolphins out there. It's so clean.'

I wriggle awkwardly, feeling a twist of anxiety inside. I don't want to ruin this perfect moment, but— 'There's something I have to tell you,' I say.

'That sounds ominous.'

I grit my teeth.

'You're married,' he says. 'You have a child?'

I cover my face in my hands and peep through. 'No, nothing like that. Just something I should have said.'

He touches the inside of my knee. 'What is it?'

'It's just. With sex.' My heart thumps. Do I really have to say this? *Yes.* 'It's just that I'm not that experienced. I don't go away with lots of men or anything. There's only been . . . I just don't want you to think, you know, with expectations. You might think that a woman like me. And I might not be . . .'

He is completely still, eyes quizzical like he's watching a family of tiny monkeys climb from my ear and dance flamenco across the side of my face.

'Well, you know. That was awkward. I just wanted to tell you. We should talk about these things. Don't you think?'

He places a hand on each of my shoulders and presses

the crown of his head to mine. 'Listen,' he says. 'It's not a performance. Sex is about intimacy. It's about connecting with each other, deepening our relationship.'

'Oh.'

He holds his lips together like he's trying not to smile.

'Yes, okay. That makes sense.'

The next morning, I wake naked in Rod's arms, pressed against his soft skin. Last night we cuddled and talked and kissed and touched and, yes, we had sex. It was wonderful and loving, and not at all scary or embarrassing. I feel my body tingle with happiness. I belong here. I roll to snuggle my cheek against his stubble.

'Hey,' he says, smiling.

'Hey.' I sit, pulling his head onto my lap. I pause, trying to phrase the question I've had in my mind since our first date. 'Did you know? That night at The Winery. Did you feel it?' I want to describe the light from the star that'd been burning since the beginning of time, the way everything in the restaurant seemed to freeze. 'Did you know at our first date? That this was really something. That we were, you know, done.'

He lets out a long, slow exhale and reaches to stroke my face. 'This is going really well, you and me. Let's not rush.'

'But . . .' I want to shake him by the shoulders. *He must know how special this is. He must feel it.* I breathe in. I breathe out. 'Okay.'

He arches his neck up to kiss my chin. 'Let's just keep getting to know each other. See what happens.'

59. CHANGES

I silently mouth the words of my presentation as I flick through my PowerPoint. I'm at a table surrounded by five men in expensive suits drinking coffee, chatting, leaning back in their seats. Another man with grey hair walks into the room and there's a series of waves and hellos as he passes our table.

'That's David McLean,' says Brad. 'He's CEO of the New Zealand bank. I'll introduce you afterwards.'

A woman in glasses and a navy blouse appears from behind two heavy doors carrying a clipboard. 'We're forty minutes behind,' she says. 'I'll let you know if there are any other changes.'

'Tea?' Jim pours me another cup. 'You know, this is a strange phenomenon. You've got all the top managers in the bank, just sitting. They have to wait till they're called.'

Behind the heavy doors is the Westpac board meeting. Eleven directors along with other key executives are locked in discussion, making important decisions. In twenty minutes' time — actually an hour, now they're running late — I'll enter that room with Brad.

It's Friday 5 June 2015, four days before my thirty-eighth birthday. Hey You has continued to outstrip everyone's expectations since we signed our deal with Westpac. Last week we processed more than seventy thousand transactions thanks to some clever partnerships led by Adam and a red-hot sales team led by me and our sales manager, Paul. We've begun work on an integration with the Westpac banking app, which we hope will explode our customer numbers when it launches in September.

In the past six months, my relationship with Rod has continued to grow exponentially too. I said goodbye to my Darlinghurst apartment in April and moved into Rod's Coogee flat. 'This is just probation,' he'd said, nervous at the speed of our progress.

I'd giggled, pointing to an elderly couple sitting outside the bottom floor of our building. 'That'll be me one day, pushing you in a chair. And you'll still be talking probation.' He smiled cautiously.

We'd organised a lunch with his mum, Dianne, his brother, Vaughn, and sister, Natalie. I felt nervous at first. *Will they like me?* 'Don't worry,' said Rod. 'They'll love you because, well, you love me.'

I nuzzled into his chest. 'And I do. I love you so much.'

It's funny, really. After all this build-up, falling in love isn't what I expected. I'd imagined huge surges of emotion, that my heart would soar like a swinging trapeze. I wouldn't want to eat or sleep. We'd need each other and miss each other every moment we were apart.

But actually, it's strangely calm. Rod's slow and steady approach does irritate me, but it's also somehow reassuring. I know that when we wake in the morning Rod will smile, he'll roll to his side, tell me he loves me, we'll both eat breakfast, bus to work, bus home. On Saturdays, we'll get coffee at the corner café, swim at the beach, watch Netflix at night.

The warm water feeling is always there, like a rising tide of joy that gets higher every week we spend together. Inside my chest, my heart is expanding. I didn't know it had so much capacity.

'Shall we start trying?' I'd said, just last week at the café. We'd had the 'Let's make a family one day' conversation a while ago. 'You'll be the most incredible father.'

Rod put down his newspaper, simultaneously grinning and biting his lip. 'Sure.'

The group waiting outside the Westpac board meeting has changed; people have stepped inside, then left, and new people have arrived and joined the waiting table. There's now a woman in a checked suit and cream heels. 'Anyone got plans for the weekend?' she says, like she wants to ignite small talk.

'Just hanging with the family. My eldest has soccer,' says Jim.

Brad looks up. 'How old are your kids?'

'Nine, six and four. Two boys, then a girl.'

Brad swivels in my direction. 'You have children?'

I picture my gorgeous Rod, out teaching the teachers right now. And I glance at my phone, which just pinged with a notification from the ovulation tracker app I installed last week. 'No. Not yet, anyway.' I flip over my phone. 'You?'

He shakes his head. 'People keep telling me to put it—'

'Put it off for as long as you can.' Jim finishes his sentence, laughing with his open mouth open.

'And my partner, well,' Brad pinches his lips together like he wouldn't normally disclose such personal information. 'Well, she's much . . .'

Much younger, I finish his sentence inside my head. *Of course she is.* And any last fragment of grief for my old life, for the mild flirting and possibilities that existed when I was single, seem to evaporate to dust and smudge into the carpet. Never to be thought of again.

60. THE UNIVERSE

Rod is side-skipping on the street, waving at my bus. Tonight, we're meeting his mum at the pub for dinner. Tonight, we have big news to share.

The ovulation app predicted that, at thirty-seven, I'd have a one in ten chance of getting pregnant each month. I'd mentally set aside a year, so I didn't think much of it three weeks later when I started to feel dizzy out jogging. *Hang on, what's the date again?* I sat on the toilet, staring at those two pink lines like they were a mirage. I checked the stick from every direction, rereading the instructions to make sure I hadn't misinterpreted anything.

Rod had been out with a friend at the time. When he arrived home, I told him to sit.

'You're pregnant,' he said, his smile stretching so wide it could have snapped.

I wrapped my arms around him, and we held each other on the bed.

Rod's face stilled. 'Hang on though, let's not get too excited. It's just the first step. You know, at our age. We should wait till we really know this is happening.'

'I know, I know,' I said as girls' and boys' names floated through my head like angels.

Two weeks later we held hands as a woman rubbed a gel-covered wand across my stomach. And there it was. A stagnant tadpole with a tiny heartbeat. 'It's our baby,' I gasped, turning to Rod. He stood still, jaw on the floor, eyes streaming with tears.

Since then there's been more scans and blood tests — every check you can buy, we've done it. And on 18 February 2016, we are expecting the arrival of a darling baby girl. Almost like the universe conspired.

Rod holds my hand as we enter the pub to meet Dianne. She's sitting at one end of a bench wearing a lavender scarf over a thin white shirt. Her blonde hair is neatly bobbed, her blue eyes are so clear and beautiful, like the sea. Rod is a head, shoulders and half a chest taller than his mum. He holds her in a long hug and kisses the top of her head. 'Great to see you.'

We order food and chat about incidental things. Dianne speaks softly in the pensive tone of someone who has recently experienced loss. I wait for an appropriate gap in the conversation. After the food, Rod gets another round of ginger ale. *How will she take this news?* She already has four grandchildren, but this is the first from Rod. And this is the first new life since . . .

Her hands quiver a bit on the bench. I reach across to hold them and look directly into her eyes. 'We have some news to share.' I squeeze.

'Yes.'

'We're having a baby.'

'Oh.' She looks to Rod and back to me. A few seconds pass and then wow. Her entire being seems to explode like a water fountain. Emotion everywhere. 'You're having a baby?' She's crying, and so am I.

'Yes,' says Rod, reaching for the print-out of the scan.

We hug and cry and laugh, and talk about the strange wonder of life.

She takes my hand under hers. 'You know, when we lost Dennis that day of the accident, in the afternoon. We went to the morgue together — me, Rod, Vaughn and Natalie. We had to identify the . . .'

I think back to last November, to the day after we met. I'd have been sitting on the couch in Darlinghurst, my phone on the coffee table, watching and waiting for Rod to call.

'You know he went back in — Rod.' She glances at her son. 'We'd all come out. Rod wanted to go back. Tell his dad something.' Dianne squeezes my wrists. 'He wanted to tell him about you. Said he'd met the most amazing woman.'

Rod's face is in his hands, eyes closed. 'Did you?' I ask. 'We'd only been on one date.' He opens his eyes, they're wet.

Light from that star is streaming between us.

Sparks shoot through my body like a meteor shower. *You knew it too. Right from that first night.*

EPILOGUE

Christmas Day, 2020

I wake cocooned between sheets and a warm chest. 'Mummy.' The voice of a small person is somewhere near my face. 'Mummy!' A tiny finger is poking at my chin. I open one eye, peeking. A small boy with a curly brown mop of hair is puffing against my ear.

'Bobby.' I smile reaching for my two-year-old son. He dives into the covers, plonking his head on the pillow between me and Rod, and falls back to sleep in an instant, snoring.

I check my iPhone, face-down on the bedside table: 4.03 a.m. We are lying under Mum and Dad's roof in Wellington, where we are staying for the summer holiday. It's the same roof I lay under in 2002, begging Steve's ghost to return. The same white walls I woke to just a few Christmases ago when I doubted I'd ever find love. When I'd fretted about Pierre and Matthew and all the other dates that seemed like a giant waste of time.

I wake again with two small feet across my neck, the bottom of a nappy hard-pressed against my cheek. 'Mummy.' The voice of another small person is somewhere near the door. 'Mummy, Daddy. It's Christmas!' I gently rearrange Bobby's limbs so he's under the covers, and pull myself to sit. 'Come on. Santa!' Our daughter Eve is jumping up and down, thumping the floor with all the might of her four-year-old legs.

I check my phone again: 5.27 a.m. 'Okay.' I roll to Rod. 'Let's do this.'

Eve scoots down the carpeted stairs on her bum like she's riding a slide at the park. I hold Bobby's hand as his short, chubby legs cautiously take one step at a time. At the bottom they both run through the kitchen, into the lounge. I flick the light on. Rod boils the kettle.

'That's *huge*,' gasps Eve, standing back to take in the packed Christmas stockings and pile of wrapped presents that had magically appeared as she slept. Bobby kneels under the tree, rattling a box.

———

At the start of this book I told you that, even though the journey would be treacherous, I'd still tell myself to go for it. And I want to describe here exactly what it is that's out there at the end. But it's difficult to put into words. Love, family and belonging aren't like a movie that's simple to recommend. There are parts that challenge me, there are parts that are exhausting.

The parts that I was thinking of when I said *'What's out there at the end is so much more than I imagined'* are the moments. Like when two-year-old Bobby burrows his head into my shoulder, when he wraps his whole hand around my index finger as we walk on a bush track. When Eve looks directly into my eyes as she tells me a secret, and when Rod whispers how much he loves me after he thinks I've fallen asleep. It's these moments that my heart erupts in joy. They are so euphoric that I would happily relive every year of pain, trudgery and bad dates if only to experience one of them.

I hope that you enjoyed my story. I have written as accurately as I can. I've tried to be honest everywhere — except, well, I'll admit it here. I did buy that porn DVD at the adult shop. I was too embarrassed to tell you when I wrote that chapter. I watched it for ten seconds before ripping it out of the player and slamming it into the bin. I did *not* try to become the woman on the stool!

Later in this epilogue, I have tried my best to unpick and summarise the key take-aways from my journey and to clarify some points that might have left you confused. I enlisted the help of experts, including a leading professor in dating psychology, my business coach and, of course, Ruth. But first, I want to update you on the progress of some friends.

Madeleine and Joe Lobsey continue to build the most amazing relationship in history. They have three gorgeous children (Lucia, Elliott and Mariella), who fill their house with board games and dancing and an endless supply of recycled cardboard craft. Madeleine works as a communications and sponsorship manager at a non-profit, runs her own business as a marriage celebrant, teaches ethics at the kids' school, and continues to run the leadership training programme at Landmark Worldwide. I feel incredibly blessed to have her in my life.

Melanie Perkins and Cliff Obrecht married in January 2021. At time of writing, Canva.com is valued at $19 billion, used by more than 50 million customers in 190 countries and is definitely on-track to beat Microsoft! Mel and Cliff have established a foundation and plan to use their wealth and influence to be a force for good in the world. Yes, they both really are as thoughtful and generous as they appear in this story.

In 2014, Bill Tai launched the Extreme Tech Challenge, the world's largest startup competition for entrepreneurs tackling global challenges. He continues to kiteboard obsessively and in 2020 had a 'great year' as the first investor in Zoom.

Lars Rasmussen recently relocated to Greece with his wife, Elomida, and their four-year-old daughter, Neneli. He left Facebook to pursue his next entrepreneurial idea (after Google Maps), Weav.io – a platform which adapts music to human movement.

Sarah Hawley (*née* Riegelhuth) sold her share in Wealth Enhancers in 2018 and two years later launched Growmotely. com — a tech platform for remote workers and for businesses looking to hire. Sarah met Joe Hawley in March 2020, and quickly fell in love when they quarantined together during Covid. They married in October 2020, and recently welcomed the arrival of baby Luka. How quickly life can change!

Sean Nunan is still with his partner and moved to Melbourne in 2018. His book *Big Time* is available on Apple and Amazon.

Billy and Gena Mann recently celebrated 20 happy years together, and now have four wonderful children (Jasper, Felix, Lulu and Indie). Billy runs a music and media company, fundraises for progressive political movements, and still writes songs with artists including Pink. He is co-founder and a board member of the Rema Hort Mann Foundation in memory of his late wife. Gena founded an app called Wolf+Friends, a global community bringing together mums of children with special needs. They insist that their six-year-old daughter Indie is the boss of their house.

Westpac promoted Hey You in its mobile banking app in 2015, sky-rocketing our customer growth. The Hey You app has been downloaded by more than a million Australians to find cafés, order, pay and get rewards. It is profitable (hooray!) and employs a team of smart and passionate individuals in the Sydney CBD.

Adam Theobald spotted an opportunity to build an app to help café owners streamline orders with their suppliers. He decided to pursue this venture fulltime in 2016, and his business 'Ordermentum' is now used by 26,000 hospitality venues across Australia. He lives in Sydney with his wife, Fabienne, and their two children, Harrison and Emily.

Jennifer Lyne, my Irish sunflower, still works as Hey You's business development manager and is a delight to everyone who meets her. She recently became single and is in the process of getting out there to meet a partner. This book is dedicated to her and every other woman on this journey.

———

I've cooked Christmas lunch today. It's prawn-cocktail stuffed avocados to start, followed by teriyaki salmon, mashed potatoes and broccolini, then pavlova and ice cream for dessert.

'Champers, anyone?' Mum trots into the kitchen wearing a purple tasselled dress and a reindeer antler headband. If she'd asked my opinion . . .

Dad is in the backyard monitoring Eve and Bobby on the trampoline. 'Grandpa, watch me!' Eve shouts, leaping into what I'm sure in her head is a soaring ballerina pose, but in reality looks more like the jump of a clumsy giraffe.

'That is incredible,' says Dad. 'Can you do it like this?' He lifts his arms with pointed fingers.

Inside, Rod is setting the table. 'I've put you here,' says

Mum, pointing to a dining chair facing the lounge, tassels shimmying on her chest. Rod places his beer on the coaster and then hesitates. He looks to me, pleadingly.

'What?' I whisper.

He nods in the direction of the lounge, to the sparkling bronze statue of Mum's breasts on the mantlepiece and directly in his line of sight. 'Can we . . . ?'

'Sure.' I swap his beer with my champagne glass. 'Let's put Rod here,' I call to Mum, 'so he can see out the window.' From the corner of my eye I spot Mum smirking at the squeamishness of our exchange. And there's a tiny part of me that's proud.

———

I cried and laughed many times filling these pages. Retelling my thoughts from the past has been an odd and confronting experience. There were times I wanted to shake myself, hug myself and warn myself of the stupid mistakes I was about to make. Mistakes that seem so obvious in retrospect, but they weren't obvious at the time. But from every mistake comes a lesson learned. These are the ones I feel most compelled to share.

1. Personal growth is a process and a practice

I've read a ton of self-help books. I've nodded and smiled, thinking, *Yes, I've got it.* But in the real world, my actions didn't change.

As I wrote about myself dating Matthew, stuffing lamb into my purse and hiding my opinions, I wanted to yell down the keyboard 'What about Madeleine!' At that point she'd already told me the story about deciding she was perfect, with or without a relationship. I should have known not to change myself.

Ruth's explanation for this is that old habits die hard: 'When you've had a certain thought pattern for a long time, then it's not going to change in an instant. You don't become a great runner by reading about how to run, or by getting advice on how to run. You have to practise.'

This is definitely true for my journey. I was able to comprehend who I needed to be and what I should look for in a partner much earlier than I was able to apply the knowledge in real life. While I hope that my story will have led you to some personal insights, please know that knowing, while helpful, won't make the difference. Growth is a journey and you have to stick at it.

2. The voices can be banished

I asked Ruth why I spoke so harshly to myself, particularly when I felt down. '*Loser.*' Where do these voices come from and could I have been more proactive in quietening them?

'As children, we experience distress – someone won't play with us, we make a mistake at school, we don't get invited to a birthday party – and we don't have the software or the wisdom to step back and look at the big picture,' she explains. 'We come up with explanations based on the only thing we can control: ourselves. "There must be something wrong with me." You create a tape that plays over and over inside your head. "I'm not good enough. I'm not clever enough. I'm not naturally likeable." It becomes a habit.'

'What about my judging and being jealous of others?'

I asked. I hated the voice that had criticised Madeleine. And somehow, as I grew to accept myself, the voice dissolved.

'Judgement is simply a process of analysing how safe you are,' says Ruth. 'When you meet someone new, you'll scan what they say, how they look and how you perceive them interacting with you. If you expect to be rejected, you'll create a story about them to defend against it.

'I suggest looking up acceptance and commitment theory (ACT),' Ruth continues. 'Particularly the work of Russ Harris at www.actmindfully.com.au. Recognise that the tapes you're running in your head are very old narratives. Try to step back and use your wise adult mind to look at reality. Remember, too, that you're only responsible for your half in every interaction. Practise self-compassion and create new stories.'

3. What happened with Cameron?

Before I explain this one, I want to be clear that Cameron and Gary are made-up people. Every scenario and interaction that I described with Cameron was based on real life — just with different men at different times. There was one particular business mentor whom I loved dearly and with whom I had a terrible falling-out at a meeting. He cut me out of his life, which left me devastated and questioning the meaning of someone being 'gone'. Everything I wrote about that night — lying on the lounge floor, the midnight phone call with Billy, saying goodbye to Steve, and my experience at Bondi Beach the following morning — is a hundred per cent real. I met Rod two weeks later. My relationship with the mentor never recovered.

Victoria Mills is one of Australia's best-known business

coaches. She has a particular focus on supporting female business leaders. Once, over lunch, I asked her 'What is it that you get asked most? What's one problem that women business owners come to you with more than anything else?'

Her response surprised me: 'Male mentor breakups.'

I had assumed that I was the only one.

'It's common for women to seek out mentors to help them grow, and mentors are very often male,' she said. 'There's a power imbalance to be aware of. In a healthy mentor–mentee relationship, both people will learn through the experience. But if the mentee just needs help and the mentee is a woman, the mentor a man, then it's easy for the relationship to slide into a father–daughter dynamic. And things get personal.'

I told Victoria about my breakup with the Cameron character and how he didn't want to see me again. 'That is quite typical,' she said. 'Your business was starting to evolve. You had new people around you: a cofounder, new investors. To do a deal, you needed to negotiate as equals. Your relationship wasn't structured to cope with that shift.'

4. Why did I break up with Steve?

This is a question I asked myself over and over as I wrote those chapters. I'm sure that Ken doll was partially to blame. I'd formed a distorted and superficial picture of what a perfect husband looks like. But I've concluded that the main reason was that in childhood I also developed a deep-seated belief that I was different and not enough to be liked by being myself. My strategy for dealing with this was to become impressive and, then, perfect. *If I was perfect, then others would like me.* Of course, perfection is impossible. I had unrealistic expectations of myself and unrealistic expectations of others. If I had to be perfect, then my partner would also have to be perfect.

This is why I pushed Steve away. Even though he was a spectacular person, while I had this limiting self-belief, I wasn't able to say, 'You're enough, you're it.'

When he tragically died, I realised the magnitude of my mistake. I became consumed with grief and regret, and then used him as an excuse. In death, he was perfect. I'd never find anyone as perfect as him.

Now that I'm able to reflect on this journey, I am more convinced than ever that in order to find peace in our lives and love with our whole hearts, we must first be able to accept ourselves as enough. But, back to my first point, it doesn't work just to say 'I'm perfect. I am enough,' and try to believe it. Thought patterns are entrenched. You have to go through a process. Which, for me, was 138 dates.

If any of this resonates for you, then I recommend reading *The Gifts of Imperfection* by Brené Brown. It's a great guide for whole-hearted living and beautifully articulates the beliefs that hold us back.

5. Grief and breakups

I wish we knew what happened to people when they die. But we don't, and so how we relate to those who have passed is based on our personal beliefs — not on facts. I do not know if Steve was ever with me, if he heard me talking as I imagined his ghost on the bed. If he was lying next to me all those years that I imagined him there or if he ended that day of the accident.

But I know that I can choose what I believe. For a while, I took great comfort in believing he was with me. And then one day, I realised this belief wasn't helping me anymore. With a great amount of pain, I chose to believe that he was somewhere else.

Dr Geoff MacDonald is a professor of psychology at the University of Toronto and is a world-leading researcher in singlehood, dating psychology and intimate relationships. I shared my story with him, and he elaborated on the process of what we go through when we lose a relationship.

'It all comes back to attachment theory and attachment hierarchy,' says Geoff. 'Different people will solve different needs in your life. You might have a friend that you play tennis with, another that makes you laugh. The top of the hierarchy is a romantic partner because they fill so many needs: emotional support, sexual gratification, companionship, financial stability, a partner in parenting. And there's symbolic needs, too, that person can represent the foundation of your identity.'

'And when you lose someone?' I ask.

'Well, then you have to restructure your attachment hierarchy. You have to outsource those needs to other people. This is why the initial stages of grief are difficult.'

'Is it the same for breakups?' I ask. 'When the person hasn't died, they just don't want you anymore?'

'Yes, there's a sudden sense of loss and your body releases opioids. That's why you feel physical pain for a while. Then you try to get the person back. Eventually, you realise they're not coming back, you reorganise your hierarchy and you start to feel better.'

I remember how I felt when Matthew wouldn't return my calls. How I couldn't eat, couldn't sleep. He had fulfilled my need for status. When Madeleine pointed this out, I rearranged my hierarchy in my head; I no longer needed status and I no longer needed Matthew. The pain dissolved.

'What I hear in your story,' continues Geoff, 'is that you hung on to Steve for a long time. You continued to try and fill your needs with him at a symbolic level. When you let him go, you opened a space in your attachment hierarchy and someone else was able to come in and fill that space.'

6. What to look for in a partner

I recently caught up with Jen for dinner and she asked me what to look for in a date. I'll repeat here what I told her over a glass of rosé. This list is a mash-up of my own experience and the advice of others. It is not definitive and not ordered by priority, but I think it is a good list.

Nice is essential. If someone speaks fondly of their family and indicates that they've cared for people who've needed them, then this is a very good sign.

Positivity and optimism. This is different to 'fun'. Life is sometimes going to be difficult. You will lose people you love; you will struggle — everyone does — and these moments are often when relationships break. Optimism has been proven as key to resilience. If both people in a relationship have a positive and optimistic outlook, then I think you'll generally have a happier time together and it's more likely that your relationship will withstand challenges over time.

Makes you bigger than you know yourself to be. I believe that personal growth is central to fulfilment and happiness. It's important to be in a relationship with someone who is proud of your achievements and supportive of your journey to evolve as a person.

Aligned values. There are many ways to determine if someone's values align with your own. You could discuss the news or politics; you could watch how they treat the waiter in a restaurant. The best diagnostic tool I've found is to ask the question 'Why do you do what you do for a living?' A person's answer to this question tells a lot. What excites them? Is it helping people? Making money? Perhaps they work in technology and want to contribute towards solving climate change. Perhaps they're a lawyer because they saw some injustice when they were a kid and wanted to make things fair. Or perhaps all their friends at school did finance but they didn't like maths (remember Henry?). A person's answer to this question will also tell you how much they value themselves and their time. Have they even thought about why they do what they do? This brings me to my next point.

The ability to self-reflect. On our first date, Rod described his relationship with his dad. He said that he grew up pushing back against his dad's conservative values. But that over time, he realised he was more similar to his dad than he thought and that, actually, a lot of his dad's characteristics were useful. This signalled that Rod is self-reflective. He is able to recognise that he might not always be right, then he can step back, imagine another perspective and reach a new conclusion. What this means for our relationship is that when we clash, we both naturally step back, imagine the other's perspective and come to a compromise position. Your partner needs to be able to self-reflect or you will end up surrendering in every argument — and over time this will squash you.

Steady Neddy. See below.

7. What to look for in the start of a relationship.

'We've spent a lot of time evaluating the personality traits of people who have successful long-term relationships,' says Geoff, the professor of psychology. 'The trait that is most predictive is conscientiousness. It's not sexy, but Steady Neddy is who you're looking for.'

I remember those first few months with Rod — how he always called when he said he would, there was never any panic. And how I questioned if that slow-rising, warm-water feeling was what falling in love was supposed to feel like.

'Yes,' says Geoff. 'The problem is that people confuse chemistry with uncertainty. When someone is unreliable, you'll question whether they like you or not. And when they turn up, you get a huge rush, which you think of as passion. But it's actually just relief. The first few months of a relationship should be a steady period of getting to know each other. Feelings deepen as you build a shared reality over time.'

8. What about the magic?

When I repeat my story of 138 dates to friends, the question they most often ask is 'What did it feel like, that moment you first met Rod? Was it magic? Did you know?' When I picture him standing under that flowered arch at The Winery, I see his warm eyes. They seemed familiar, like he'd always been there. In in my mind, the world stopped turning.

But I wonder if that moment really *was* magic or if my memory has reconstructed it like that because I now know what happened next. I can tell you that my first date with Rod felt different to my first date with Charlie or Sean or Dan, or any of the other nice men I met. One part is that I felt we existed in the same psychological space, and another part of it I just can't explain.

Although I have done my best in this book to describe how I fell in love, I'm also sure that there is something indescribable that happens between two people when they connect. It is magic. We aren't meant to understand it.

I do remember, however, the moment when I knew Rod was the one. It was that first night at The Winery, in the middle of munching down gnocchi and sipping rosé, when I saw him light up as he talked about becoming a teacher. I can recall exactly what happened in my brain. It was a decision. *'This man is it.'* There was still uncertainty about who he was and how it would all go. But it wasn't an all-knowing 'yes' spoken to me by God. It was an active decision made by me.

9. Making relationships work

As I read back over my description of the first few months of the relationship with Rod, I'm aware that it sounds too perfect. Perfect isn't realistic (see point four). We did argue, and we still argue — usually over small things like him working too late or me talking too long on the phone.

But as I wrote the chapter on Mel and Cliff's advice for business partnerships, I realised that the same principles apply to romantic relationships. Rod and I talk a lot about vision: what's important to each of us: Where do we want to be in five years' time — both as individuals and as a family. We set goals together at the beginning of every year. This keeps us aligned and we never end up disagreeing on big decisions. We also trust each other. When we bought a house, he did the negotiation. When we sold the house, I arranged everything. We know what each other is good at and we don't micromanage. When someone makes a mistake, we own it as a team — there's no point-scoring.

When he annoys me (which is often), I don't ever allow myself to question if he is the right relationship. I've chosen forever, and that's it. I made a pact with his dad; I promised to spend the rest of my life making our relationship the most amazing in history. I promised that it would be my number one priority. And I always remind myself what I said at the end of that promise: 'Every. Single. Day.' So, one day recently I told him off for looking at his mobile phone when he should have been more actively engaging with the kids. He got frustrated, and I got frustrated. But I remembered the pact, and I caught myself. Not *most days* or *overall*, but *today, now.*

This brings me to my number one tip. I started this process looking for what I could get from a partner: 'smart, tall, fun'. I learnt that relationships are about what you give. As soon as I promised to give Rod an incredible life, giving became my focus. And I discovered that giving is much more fulfilling than getting. Becoming vulnerable, letting a partner contribute to you — that is a gift as well, the gift of enabling someone else to experience the delight in giving.

I asked Geoff and Ruth what parting pieces of advice they would like to share with anyone looking for a relationship.

Geoff: 'Don't underestimate how much you contribute to your relationship outcomes. A lot of people tell me they want to give up on online dating because everyone they meet is a loser. And my response is to ask: "What is the one constant on all those dates?" It's you. I'll give you an example. I have a colleague who is super warm and extroverted. We go to conferences together and I'll be chatting to someone at the table and when my colleague arrives the other person lights up. My colleague doesn't realise it's her. It's just how she experiences the world; she thinks everyone is like that. So, if you experience the world as being full of glum losers, well . . .

'If you want to meet the right person, then first focus on becoming the right person. My favourite hobby is to tell people to go to therapy. You need to invest in yourself if you want to become better at relationships. The first thing to learn is emotional regulation. Become aware of your emotions with your therapist, practise sitting with negative and positive emotion. People go squirelly in their relationships when they aren't effective at managing their emotions.

'The next is to learn basic relationship skills. You can't just expect to be good at relationships. There are a lot of simple principles you can learn. Like if your partner is upset, then don't try to jump in and solve the problem. Listen, ask questions. That kind of thing. I recommend reading *Intimate Relationships* by Rowland Miller. It's the textbook of do's and don'ts I use in my course at the University of Toronto.'

Ruth: 'My practice is full of lonely men and women who want love, but they avoid putting themselves out there. They use every excuse: no one's any good, I'll do it once I'm thinner, I'm too busy with work. But really, they're afraid of getting rejected.

'That's part of your story too. You were working so hard to be perfect. You were afraid that if you tried dating then you might get rejected and discover that you're not perfect after all. It's a big risk, terrifying. You spent ten years focussing on what you're good at — your career. You used busyness as a smokescreen. And then you reached a crisis point at thirty-four-and-a-half. You were about to miss out on having a family. That big ticking clock pushed you out of your comfort zone.

I'm convinced that success in relationships is seventy-five per cent determination. The only thing that doesn't need hard work is failure. My advice is for people to try exposure therapy. Just go for it, experience the possibility of rejection. It won't kill you, it's where you'll find your growth.'

And before we end the story there's a few points I'd like to clarify.

Sex and business

Much has been on the news about sexual harassment and inappropriate behaviour in business and politics. I'm conscious that my story touched on these themes at times without always resolving a firm position. My priority was to write honestly and describe my real feelings as I had them. Sometimes these feelings were confusing and my actions not as strong as I'd have wished.

I became close to an unmarried male mentor and some of our interactions were described in the 'Cameron' character. I wondered if sexual chemistry had developed between us, I canvassed flirtations in my head. And this was where it stopped. There is nothing wrong with admitting that I developed feelings. But I made a decision not to blur business and sex, and I'm grateful that I did.

What happened with creepy investor Mike in the restaurant

was very different and not OK. He tried to use his position of power to convince me to have sex with him. There was never any question – the answer was 'no'.

But I wish I had responded with more outrage. At the time, I wrote a high-profile column and I should have shared my experience. I kept quiet because I felt ashamed. I wondered if, by going to a restaurant at night and engaging in friendly conversation, that I'd led him on. I hadn't.

To any woman has had a similar experience, I apologise for not writing about this earlier. We must call out obnoxious behaviour, even when it isn't criminal. We must share our stories and arm each other with the knowledge and insight to respond powerfully in the moment.

Thoughts on IVF

I do not want this book to leave you with the impression that there is any shame in egg freezing or that, because I was able to have children in my late thirties, that it is easy for everyone. At almost 38, I was lucky to fall pregnant quickly. When we tried for a second, two years later, it was less straight-forward. We went through a cycle of IVF, which was successful and gave us our baby boy.

As I sat back in the fertility specialist's room, this time Rod next to me, the doctor showed us a chart. Our chances of conceiving would have been much greater if I'd frozen some eggs at age 35. Knowing how much I wanted to be a mother and how important my children are to me now; I wouldn't take any chances if I had my time again.

IVF is an incredible scientific advancement for women and families. If you are considering egg freezing or IVF treatment, then I recommend researching the success rates of different clinics and shop around for pricing. Egg freezing doesn't have to cost all your savings.

Building a business

I exited Hey You as an employee in 2017 and stepped off the board in 2018. I am proud of everything that I achieved as Founder CEO of Posse and later as co-founder co-CEO with Adam.

I want to state clearly that I've simplified my depiction of starting a technology company in order to write an engaging story. Pitching for capital and kitesurfing in Maui were significant events — and good milestones to demonstrate the emotional highs and lows of my experience as a startup founder.

But the reality of leading Posse and Hey You was mostly hard unglamourous work — budgeting, hustling for customers, fixing broken software code, organising insurance, apologising to angry customers, learning that most of my assumptions were wrong and trying new tactics. If you are building a business or if you are thinking about launching something, then, yes, it can be exhilarating, and the rewards can be huge. But please don't expect your experience to mirror what I've written in this story.

Choices

I chose to leave Hey You a year after transitioning to a new CEO. My choice was a result of intense personal reflection; identifying my innate talents and linking them with my vision for what I wanted to contribute in life.

I was initially surprised by the impact of my blog posts, newspaper columns and in person talks. I received hundreds of emails and LinkedIn messages from people saying they could relate to a story I'd shared, and they'd learnt something they planned to use in their relationships or business. Part of my vision is to 'give myself when I think I can help others'. I've therefore chosen to build a career in writing, speaking and teaching. If you'd like to follow my adventures further, find me at rebekahcampbell.com.

I said at the start of this book that 'woman should voice what they want in life without fear of judgement.' My choice was to find love and make a family. This may not be your choice. It is up to every woman to determine her own priorities, be that love, career, art, travel, contribution or something else.

The message I'd like you to take from this book is to choose your direction powerfully and go after it with two feet. Don't dilly dally in fear or hope or self-defeating narratives about not being enough. Every day is too precious for that.

———

It's 11.02 p.m. and I just stepped out of the shower. Dad's snore is rattling down the corridor. Eve and Bobby are snuggled under their blankets. Rod is in bed, probably wondering why I'm taking so long. It is Christmas, after all.

I turn to the mirror and remember Michelle, the nurse from the Botox clinic. If she were here now, I'm sure she wouldn't describe my naked body as perfect. I turn to the side, noticing the arc of my back. You know, after forty-three years, it looks pretty good. My arms are long and pale. I love the way my hair hangs over my collarbone.

I lean closer, examining my wrinkles. Every line is a year of learning, a year of challenges, a year of experiencing beauty in the world — another year that not everyone gets to have. To age is a privilege. I am so grateful for my lines.

And for all those things that I used to hate about myself — my droopy eyebrows, my scrawny knees. I was so sure that my genes were defective. Well, the two most magnificent children ever created came from my genes. When I look at their faces, I still sometimes can't believe it.

I am happy to report that I have given up trying to be perfect or impressive. My relationship isn't perfect, my parenting isn't perfect, I am not perfect. I am quite ordinary. And there is nothing more extraordinary and perfect than an ordinary imperfect life.

SPECIAL
ACKNOWLEDGEMENT

In the time between our break-up and his accident in 2001, Steve Pengelly met and fell in love with Wellington artist Emma Chamberlain. They had eloped one year earlier and on that Saturday in October, were driving from Auckland to Wellington to meet with both sets parents and plan a romantic celebration of their marriage for family and friends.

Steve had graduated from Victoria University with a double major in English and Women's Studies (now known as Gender Studies) and a Masters with First Class Honours from Auckland University. He was passionate about equality for all and was one of the first men to major in Women's Studies in Wellington. Steve had continued to write both personally and professionally and had begun to build a business in this field.

Steve was every bit as unique, talented and precious as I have described him. His loss is tragic, not just to those who knew and loved him, but to all those who didn't get the opportunity to meet him and experience his enthusiasm for life and his brilliant creativity and poetry, which no doubt would have been published.

My deepest thanks to his Mum Chris van Vugt, Dad Mike Pengelly and sister Rachael Martin, for their support in my writing this manuscript and for helping me to accurately reflect Steve's life in the years post our relationship.

THANK YOU

A huge thanks to my darling Rod Lane for supporting me in every imaginable way as I wrote this book. I love you, Bobby and Eve more than everything. You are *everything*.

Thanks to my Mum, Jacqui, for being exactly who you are and for allowing me to publish this! And to Dad, Rob, for encouraging me to write and for always being my first editor (except for this book which you aren't allowed to read so you won't see this acknowledgement).

To Dianne Lane, thank you for being a kind generous mother in law, Nana to Eve and Bobby and for raising such a wonderful son. To Rod's siblings Natalie Patterson and Vaughn Lane, thanks for your love and for welcoming me to your family.

To Melanie Perkins and Cliff Obrecht, Madeleine and Joe Lobsey, Billy and Gena Mann, Ruth Osborne, Bill Tai, Lars Rasmussen, Jennifer Lyne, Sean Nunan, Loren Feldman, Adam Theobald and Sarah Hawley. Thank you for your friendship and for trusting me to share our stories.

Madeleine Lobsey would like it acknowledged that much of her self-confidence and wise advice stems from teachings at Landmark Worldwide. She feels privileged to have participated in and led Landmark programs for more than 18 years.

To all the people whose interactions with me contributed to the 'Cameron' and 'Gary' characters. You know who you are! Thank you for your mentorship.

And to Andy Morris, the best publicist in New York, who sadly passed away in 2019. I miss your humour, optimism and sharp mind. I wish we could have worked on this book together.

Much gratitude to the team at Allen and Unwin New Zealand and Australia especially Jenny Hellen who hunted me down after reading an unrelated article that I'd written online. I appreciate your enthusiasm for this story more than you know. To Leonie Freeman, thanks for your care for this manuscript and for calmly accommodating all my last-minute changes.

To Holly Hunter, the best editor I could have hoped for. Thanks for always being the reader's champion and for slicing my work into something more punchy than 120K words with no chapters.

To Professor Geoff MacDonald at the University of Toronto Department of Psychology, thanks for helping me to make sense of my journey and for your contribution of points in the Epilogue.

Thanks to everyone at the Australian Writers Centre for your wonderful courses (I did many). Especially to Pamela Freeman, I would have written a different book without your insightful feedback. And my class in the 6-month 'Write Your Novel' program 2019.

Thanks to my writer group buddies for being willing to read the drafts over and over and for always being positive as well as helpful: Tiina Sepulveda, Emily Harris, Mia Wagg, Alan Noble, Anneline Padayachee.

Special thanks to Fleur Brown for your mentorship throughout this process. I learn something from you every time we speak.

Thanks to these inspiring women, many of whom were among the first to read this book and were so generous with feedback and ideas: Naomi Simson, Emma Isaacs, Lauren Miller, Jodie Fox, Jess Scully, Jane Lu, Deborah Claxton, Michelle Duval, Victoria Mills, Jaquie Brown, Alison Deans, Amber Jones, Katie Noonan and Lisa Mitchell.

Thanks to all the mentors, backers and friends who have supported my life and career journey thus far. There are way too many to list. I believe that the universe conspires to bring us the right people at the right time and I am grateful to have found all of you.

To my forever best friend Liz Cameron, thank-you for being my rock, my 'cool' barometer and my biggest cheerleader since age 14. Thanks for your encouragement and for always being at the end of the phone. You are the sister I always wanted.

I wrote much of this book in cafes and libraries. Special thanks to Brick Lane Espresso in West Pymble for allowing me to sit on one cup of green tea each day for months, and to Eseta and Matty at Café Kaizen in Porirua for asking about the book every morning and for not noticing while I laughed and cried out loud to my keyboard.